WYNDHAM LEWIS

was born in 1884 on a yacht off the coast of Canada. He was educated in England, and, in 1909, after his return from an extended sojourn in Paris, his first stories appeared in *The English Review,* under the editorship of Ford Madox Ford; two years later, his paintings had their first public showing. In the years that followed, he was associated with such men as Ezra Pound, T. S. Eliot, Ford Madox Ford and James Joyce in exerting a major influence on the course of modern literature. After service in World War I, however, Lewis became an increasingly solitary figure, following his own path as a writer, painter, and subtle and original critic of art, society, life and politics. Always blunt and outspoken, his works of fiction and criticism were shunned by the ruling members of the Establishment. He came to America during World War II, and returned to England in 1945, where he lived until his death in 1957. His writings include *Tarr, The Revenge for Love, Self-Condemned, Time and Western Man, Men Without Art,* and many other works of fiction and nonfiction.

WYNDHAM LEWIS

A SOLDIER OF HUMOR
And Selected Writings

Edited, with an Introduction, by
RAYMOND ROSENTHAL

A SIGNET CLASSIC

PUBLISHED BY THE NEW AMERICAN LIBRARY, NEW YORK AND TORONTO
THE NEW ENGLISH LIBRARY LIMITED, LONDON

Library of Congress Catolog Card Number: 66–28095

ACKNOWLEDGMENTS AND COPYRIGHT NOTICES

The editor wishes to thank the following for permission to reprint from the books listed:

Doubleday & Company, Inc., New York, for selections from *America and Cosmic Man* by Wyndham Lewis. Copyright 1948 by Wyndham Lewis.

Harcourt, Brace & World, Inc., New York, for selections from *The Wild Body* by Wyndham Lewis. Copyright 1928 by Harcourt, Brace & World, Inc.; © 1956 by Wyndham Lewis.

The Hutchinson Publishing Group, London, for selections from *Rude Assignment* by Wyndham Lewis. Copyright 1950 by Wyndham Lewis.

Methuen & Co. Ltd., London, and Mrs. Anne Wyndham Lewis, for selections from *Blasting and Bombardiering, The Caliph's Design, Wyndham Lewis the Artist, Men Without Art, The Writer and the Absolute, Filibusters in Barbary;* and for "Cantleman's Spring Mate," "The Ideal Giant," and *The Enemy of the Stars.*

Henry Regnery Company, Publishers, Chicago, for selections from *Rotting Hill* by Wyndham Lewis. Copyright 1952 by Wyndham Lewis.

SIGNET CLASSICS are published by
The New American Library, Inc.
1301 Avenue of the Americas, New York, New York 10019

Table of Contents

Introduction

WYNDHAM LEWIS was part of that astonishing group of
writers that gathered in London around 1914 and, as a
result of their activities there, set in motion what we now
call modern English and American literature. I state this at
the outset, since only a few years ago critical opinion was
inclined to disregard or even overlook Lewis' right to belong
to that crucial circle of creators. Today, however, the fact is
widely accepted, and one can encounter Lewis' name as a
matter of course in any respectable survey of modern writing. Therefore "the men of 1914," as Lewis himself dubbed
them, meaning by that phrase T. S. Eliot, Ezra Pound, T. E.
Hulme, and a later recruit, James Joyce, had Lewis as an
important charter member. It is with this idea that the present anthology has been collected—to show what T. S. Eliot
meant when, in 1918, he described Lewis as "the only writer
among my contemporaries to create a new, an original prose
style" and called him "the most fascinating personality of our
time." In the process, this selection will provide a roughly
chronological and representative sample of Lewis' writings
from more than fifty years of work and from ten of the
forty-odd books and pamphlets he produced during his lifetime.

It is in fact above all as a personality that Lewis commands our attention. Esthetically this is both his great charm
and his great limitation. Whereas the "personalities" of the
other figures in that formidable artistic grouping tend, with
almost classical reticence, to disappear into their greatest
works, Lewis or his surrogate is always at the center of the
stage, announced by an indelible stylistic flourish and surrounded by a throng of embattled opinions. This is seen not
only in his critical and autobiographical writings but also
in his plays, short stories and novels. In that first exploratory
article, T. S. Eliot tried to isolate the elements of this pre-
potent personality, and his main points are worth remembering: "impressively deliberate and frigid"; "intelligence . . .
united with a vigorous physical organism which interests itself directly in sensation for its own sake"; "humor . . . as
the instinctive attempt of a sensitive mind to protect beauty

9

against ugliness; and to protect itself against stupidity"; and, finally, the unique combination of "the thought of the modern and the energy of the caveman."

Although each of these descriptive phrases is extremely pertinent and can be applied to the whole of Lewis' developing work, the reader will notice that they are hardly the attributes one usually associates with the accepted idea of the personality. The *costume* of personality, with its cozily familiar trappings of race, national trait, and individual idiosyncrasy, is totally absent. In contrast to Joyce, with his fondness for sentimental opera and the humorous gab of Dublin pubs—or Pound, with his crackpot interest in cranky financial theories and esoteric, buried cultures—Lewis seems, as Hugh Kenner in his brilliant study of him claims, truly a "man from nowhere," an impersonal person composed of "pure" ideas and emotions subordinated to a strict intellectual method, with none of the endearing frailties that help to make all men kin. "The place of honor is . . . outside," Lewis declared in one of his last critical books, and the pride and courage, the radicalism, of that declaration still does not conceal its pathos.

Lewis' role as "outsider" came to him, so to speak, naturally—by birth. The son of an American father and an English mother, he was born on a ship in the Bay of Fundy on November 18, 1884, went to school in England and spent his youth roaming the European continent, trying, as he put it, "to overcome the effects of an English education." He seemed to be successful, for in the very first story in this collection and one of the first he published, "A Soldier of Humor," we meet the quirky, severe, aloof, energetic personage, exemplar of a long line of such "alter egos" or "showmen," whom Lewis concocted out of his sense of difference and uprootedness: "My body is large, white and savage. But all the fierceness has been transformed into *laughter* . . . I move on a more primitive level than most men, I expose the essential me quite coolly, and all men shy a little. This forked, strange-scented, blond-skinned gutbag, with its two bright rolling marbles with which it sees, bull's-eyes full of mockery and madness, is my stalking horse. I hang somewhere in its midst operating it with detachment."

Ker-Orr, the showman, is a "laughing machine," a "Soldier of Humor," "disposed to forget that people are real— that they are, that is, subjective patterns belonging specifically to me, in the course of this joke life, which indeed has for its very principle a denial of the accepted actual." Yet this brash approach to experience is not merely stylistic swagger. It is based on an intricate yet systematic conception of the relations that exist between society and the individual, the body and the spirit, the "gut-bag" and the "subjective patterns" of this "joke-life." At the inception of his career, in his poetic essay, "Inferior Religions," and his play *The Enemy of the Stars,* Lewis illustrated his special standpoint with a density and allusiveness that have been the delight and despair of the critics, who usually find it easier to quote than to encompass and explain him.

To put it briefly: the body is an absurd machine, the Self or personality is wrested from the Not-Self or the natural, material world by the molding, creative force of the intellect, yet, inevitably "the process and condition of life . . . is a grotesque degradation and 'souillure,' [1] of the original solitude of the soul." "Self, sacred act of violence, is like murder on my hands. The stain won't come out," Lewis says in his play *The Enemy of the Stars.* "It is the one piece of property all communities have agreed it is illegal to possess. . . . Self is the ancient race, the rest are the new one. Self is the race that lost."

The rigor of these categories resembles in a startling way the bleak, unearthly terminology of a Manichean or a modern religious mystic, not only because of the position of evident inferiority in which the body is placed, but also because of the strict separation of spheres and powers, the careful allotment of qualities, the mapping of the grounds of spiritual conflict. Yet Lewis, though obsessed by such patterns throughout his artistic career, was a determined agnostic. For him, the body was not a sacred vessel but a prison that could be brightened and civilized only by the vigorous play of the intellect. His satiric, sardonic humor, which is another way of saying his art, was his sole means of escape from the cage of implacable antinomies that he himself had erected, having first discovered them in reality. This is the ground-bass —this insistence on the tragically comic disparities inherent in human existence—and it confers depth, resonance and excitement on almost everything that Lewis wrote.

An unremitting, dazzling consciousness, which sometimes can degenerate into mere self-consciousness, distinguishes Lewis' prose. Lewis is not a writer who eases you into experi-

---

[1] dirtying

ence, enticing you by a beguiling, unaccentuated flow in which his ideas are unobtrusively inserted. He hustles you into it, abruptly, peremptorily, almost brutally. He is of the school of brilliance, which depends wholly for its effects on "epithetic sparkle," clear, aggressive ideas, a bravura finish, and whose exponents are so numerous in French and so few in English literature. Neither Swift nor Smollett, despite their similarity to him as satirists and historians of morals and manners, can stand as models in this lonely field. Only Ben Jonson and Thomas Nashe, the "snarling satirists" of the Elizabethan age, with their gusto, eloquence and "offhand, generous abundance," their curiously external approach to life, skin-deep and determinedly fixed on the surface look and feel of men and things, give us the proper literary antecedents for Lewis' peculiar stance.

There was, however, a strikingly modern depth to Lewis' "surface," for he had discovered and described the absurd, the anguish of being caught between being and the void, long before these ideas reached us as an intellectual fashion elaborated in Paris on the framework of the latest German metaphysics. Characteristically, though, he saw them through the magnifying, unromantic lens of laughter. "It is comparatively easy," he says in his early essay, "The Meaning of the Wild Body," "to see that another man, as an animal, is absurd; but it is far more difficult to observe oneself in that hard and exquisite light. But no man has ever continued to live who has observed himself in that manner for longer than a flash. Such consciousness must be of the nature of a thunderbolt. Laughter is only summer lightning. But it occasionally takes on the dangerous form of absolute revelation."

Strangely, rather appallingly, Lewis lived, at least as an artist, in precisely that "difficult" manner for all the rest of his days. As a consequence, there are many times in his fiction when the sheer sensation of animal triviality overwhelms him, when the incessant, thudding movement of his style becomes a fatiguing diversion to conceal from himself the terror of "absolute revelation." This is especially evident in such an overornate, overloaded and finally meretricious novel as *The Apes of God;* yet the continuing struggle with the self-imposed limits of his own vision opens out at last, in his later years, into the rich, hard-won, fully achieved humanity of his finest novels, *The Revenge for Love* and *Self Condemned.* If "laughter is the mind sneezing . . . the brain-body's snort of exultation," as Lewis had said, some explosive yet vastly relieving operation of this kind permitted him to see not only his neighbor but also himself through the focus of his grimly amused categories. His unsparing realism about the "sad human amalgam" often induced paranoia, that satirist's occupational ailment from which Lewis suffered as other people suffer from athlete's foot—a slight, irritating, insidious disease that can never be completely cured. But in 1951, when the artist who personified the Eye and its riches announced that he could no longer see and so must discontinue his work as art critic for *The Listener,* the style that had been honed on a horde of puppets was turned playfully, relentlessly, heroically on himself: "It amuses me to collide with a walking belly; I quite enjoy being treated as a lay-figure, seized by the elbows and heaved up in the air as I approach a curb, or flung into a car. I relish the absurdity of gossiping with someone the other side of the partition. I am not allowed to see them. I am like a prisoner condemned to invisibility, although permitted an unrestricted number of visitors. . . . Pushed into an unlighted room, the door banged and locked forever, I shall then have to light a lamp of aggressive voltage in my mind to keep at bay the night."

Some critics have ascribed the rage that so obviously boils beneath the sculptured surface of Lewis' prose to an embittered nostalgia for a lost golden age, located in the Italian Renaissance of Michelangelo and Leonardo da Vinci and affording him a comfortable vantage point from which the turmoil and mess of modern times could be safely scorned. While there is some warrant for this in Lewis' exaltation of the wholeness and sanity of art and science in the Renaissance compared with their frantic vulgarization today, I can see nothing comfortable or nostalgically self-delusive in his rage, which arose more from his stark perception of the nature of human life and his constant effort to square this essentially ascetic view with the far from ascetic demands of an artist's activity. For Lewis, the mind and its transforming gift rescues all of reality from chaos and insignificance. ". . . The material world must . . . be imaginary," he asserts in *Time and Western Man,* "and the very effrontery of its superb solidness and the bland assurance with which it is camped before us, should actually help us to realize that. . . . On a still day consider the trees in a forest or in a park, or an immobile castle reflected in a glassy river: they are perfect illustrations of our static dream; and what in a sense could be more 'unreal' than they? That is the external, objective, material world (made by our 'spatializing' sense) to which we are referring. It is to that world that hellenic sculpture . . . belongs, and all the Pharoahs and Buddhas. . . ."

Yet this shining, sounding universe could become dead, gray, and inert whenever the mind went astray or abdicated its function and "the sleep of the machine" supervened. This active, shaping attitude was, if anything, intensified by the fact that Lewis was also a painter who approached life from a predominantly plastic, visual standpoint. Thus, in novel after novel, from *Tarr* to *Snooty Baronet* to *Childermass,* Lewis seems intent on exposing both the solidity and delusiveness of external appearances. His characters are all mannerisms, tics, visual idiosyncracies. They chug like extremely mobile mechanisms through their cavernous, flashy milieus, charged by the explosive ideological manias of an increasingly ideological age. Opposed to the main direction taken by his great contemporaries, his art wished to be a public art, both in the sense of speaking to an entire educated society and of refusing to descend into some private, dimly lit corner of privileged consciousness.

"Out of its [modern art's] very limitations and frustrations," Lewis said in his autobiography, *Rude Assignment,* "it has created something. Its little dark and stony desert has flowered. Like a prison art, or the introspection of the recluse, or the strange genius of the demented, it will survive in some form, as an integral part of our cultural expression. . . . [But] Art of the first order must be lost in this cul-de-sac. A whole society, not an unrepresentative fragment, is demanded by great gifts of speech and great interests in public affairs such as Dante and Milton possessed, for instance. The public stage, with live actors—in contrast to the private Mystery, staged in a rich patron's cellar, for an audience of cognoscenti of shadow pictures of an obscure emotional underworld—is what now stands empty. With his architectonic appetites, requiring air-filled spaces, for Buonarroti there would be no place today, nor would there be for most of the so-called 'great masters' of the past."

Here we have Lewis looking rather benignly back on almost a quarter of a century of his own destructive criticism. For Lewis' modernism soon took the form of opposing what he regarded as the dissolving, disintegrating tendencies of the Zeitgeist. He believed that the modern world was in a permanent revolutionary crisis and transition, engineered by the conjunction of science and technology and variously but, in essence, docilely reflected by its prime interpreters in the sensitive areas of "advanced" art and philosophy. The inevitable by-product of this revolution, he contended, would be the destruction of the individual, source of all value and beauty, and the dissolution of "our public material paradise." Machinery had taken the place of nature, and the men who were in charge of the machinery oppressed the mass of men just as nature had oppressed them in the past. Moreover, he saw the "technical dissolvent" working like a potent chemical, fomenting a dark and feverish "mental world" in such disparate yet curiously related places as the philosophies of Alfred North Whitehead and Bertrand Russell and the novelistic schemas of Proust, Joyce, and Gertrude Stein. Rather arrogantly, he appointed himself esthetic, philosophic, scientific and political adviser to, and castigator of, the chief exponents of experiment in the field of modern art, whom he considered excellent craftsmen but inadequate critics. Art was too serious an affair to be left in the hands of even the best of the modern artists. "My conception of the role of the creative artist is not merely to be a medium for ideas supplied him wholesale from elsewhere, which he incarnates automatically in a technique which (alone) it is his business to perfect. It is equally his business to know enough of the sources of his ideas, and ideology, to take steps to keep these ideas out, except such as he may require for his work."

Modern life, he asserted, was in its essence a chaos of good and bad; it could not be wholeheartedly endorsed, particularly by the writer and artist. "The extreme complexity and intermixture of the good and bad, in the sense of what is good for people in general and what is bad for them, make this task a very difficult one. It is the supreme task for the sociologist or philosopher today. [For] almost anything that has been praised or advocated has been put to some disgusting use." With this as his program and convinced that "in the West, through the agency of Science, all our standards of existence have been discredited," "that an immense and radical translation from a free public life . . . to a powerless, unsatisfying, circumscribed private life" was in progress, that "in the arts of formal expression, a 'dark night of the soul' is settling down," he wrote a series of polemical books, *Time and Western Man, The Art of Being Ruled, Pale Face, The Doom of Youth, The Diabolical Principle and the Dithyrambic Spectator,* that took their stand on the side of an ancient common sense. His position was against romanticism in all its guises and for the classical, which he described as "anything which is nobly defined and exact."

We are now living in the thick of that benumbed, rampaging transition that Lewis considered his particular province as a critic and creative writer. It is therefore more difficult to remember how elated and optimistic the first great modern writers and artists were, how decisive a part an inspiriting sense of a future that was there to be created played in the production of the works which now form the foundations for the well-established and essentially unadventurous modernist academy. Today the struggle to transform and enhance the raw materials afforded by everyday life has become an outmoded, even despised occupation, and the typical "highbrow" artist, such as Samuel Beckett or William Burroughs, is content to huddle into his dark private corner and passively mirror the horror and confusion of existence, leaving to others the task of evaluation and interpretation. That "inferno of moronic idiocy and decay" Lewis saw in the wake of the modernist revolution has come into its own, and the artists have settled down with relative comfort on their quaint reservations, devoting themselves to strange rites and magics incomprehensible to the broad society. Indeed, the cynical acceptance of a majority that lives in a perpetual sentimental and sadistically sexual daydream created by the engines of the mass media seems to provide the unexpressed postulate and background for most of these artists' activities. That public realm, brilliant, architectonic, and life-enhancing, that Lewis desired has shrunk considerably, for although there is a larger audience today for "advanced" art, it is an audience that unthinkingly accepts and even battens on these conditions of enforced segregation. At the same time, the tendencies toward greater unreality and vulgarity, toward a general state of mass somnambulism, are being vastly magnified and empowered by the enormous development of the mass entertainment industries.

A vulgarized adaptation of the scientific attitude of "wait-and-see" has seeped into quarters one would have imagined immune to such inhibiting disciplines. In truth, the world has been turned into a vast laboratory and all of us are the objects of an experiment whose outcome the experts are not quite sure of. Some people are exhilarated by the prospect; others are wary; still others are frightened to death. It all depends on what your estimate of man happens to be. Lewis' estimate was both very low and very high. What made man like a God—his intellectual and creative power—was, in his eyes, matched on the other end of the scale by the men who were living "the sleep of the machine" and who asked for nothing better than a rule, a convention, a uniform, to rid them of the burden of freedom and responsibility. Throughout his work, that heavy human mass, always ready to be galvanized into violent life by some apocalyptic political creed, hovers about him as a constant threat. Like many of the artists and writers of his generation, who imagined that the breakthrough symbolized by modernism had given them the means to construct an entirely new world, manipulating people as they manipulated paint or words, Lewis tended toward an authoritarian solution of political problems which, he thought, were simply annoying disturbances invading the orderly calm of the artist's workshop. The First World War introduced him to violence and the machine, in both of which crucial contemporary phenomena he soon became the most detached and percipient of "experts," but the Second World War was a much more drastic experience, for it convinced him that the rigid esthetic and intellectual patterns evolved by the writer in his study could not be applied to political life without great destructiveness and suffering.

This anthology is a record of Lewis' struggle with himself and his chief concerns, ideas and obsessions. It is also a record of the manias and delusions that Lewis found in the modern world and tried to understand and explicate. Although he can be labeled, roughly, as a rationalist in thought, a classicist in art, and an authoritarian in politics, his mind was too closely engaged with the problems of contemporary existence to opt for an easy solution in any of these fields. There is a prophetic quality to all of Lewis' writing, though it is not a prophecy that can be formulated and used as a recipe against the chaos and unpredictability at the heart of the contemporary situation.

Once, when discussing this very chaos and unpredictability, Paul Valéry declared that "We are all backing into the Future." What he meant was that no matter how adventurous, daring and "advanced" a scientist or artist was, his mind and sensibility were conservative structures, based on habits, beliefs and methods that were precious inheritances from a rapidly receding past. Propelled forward by a blind mechanical force, he had to look back, for to consent to the destruction of these inheritances would be tantamount to destroying the ancient premises on which civilization had been built and has managed to survive up until now.

It is precisely as a mediator between that Future and that Past, sometimes as a defender of the Past against the inhuman encroachments of the Future, sometimes as a proponent of the Future against the subjugation of the Past, that Wyndham Lewis assumes his value and importance today.

RAYMOND ROSENTHAL

A Note on the Text

The text of this edition follows Wyndham Lewis' eccentric systems of capitalization and punctuation, as well as his use of italics.

PART I

short stories and plays

A Soldier of Humor" and "The Death of the Ankou" both come from Lewis' first volume of short stories, *The Wild Body*, in which the expository essay, "Inferior Religions," was also included to set forth, by means of a sequence of brilliant paradoxes, the method used in writing the stories themselves. Perhaps no modern writer, save for Thomas Mann, has been so elaborately explicit about his method and ideas as Wyndham Lewis. Yet there are dark patches which call for the commentator. The central paradox in "Inferior Religions" is Lewis' belief that human reality rests on an absurdity, a void, which only the writer's poetic consciousness can seize and represent. "Things acquire a kind of realness," he was to say, "only when the mind has worked them over." Yet the mind itself, since it has its habitation in the body and is part of the "madness of nature," produces hallucinations, distortions, fixed, rigid patterns that convert living beings into mechanical monsters. Over and over again these puppet-like monsters are the objects of Lewis' "grotesque realism," his search for the revealing "stylistic anomaly" in the surface world of action and thought, "that vortex of burlesque and strenuous encounters."

"A Soldier of Humor" is a prophetic farce—prophetic of the waves of Americanization which, some decades later, were to inundate Europe—a farce about the shreds and tatters of nationalistic feeling floating through the world and in this case fastening obsessively on a wayward Frenchman. It is also a rich anecdote that provides Lewis with a leisurely opportunity to be gay, ornate, comically expansive about the routine mishaps and adventures of foreign travel. "The Death of the Ankou" is a tight, objective tale which describes the effects of a pagan, superstitious image of death as it reverberates through two minds—the sophisticated mind of the narrator, Kerr-Orr, and the half-literate, peasant mind of the blind beggar, Ludo. As restrained and precise in the telling as a story by Flaubert, its effect is achieved by a stern reticence that makes this brief story take on the homely grandeur of a folk tale.

The Enemy of the Stars was written in 1914 and published in Lewis' avant-garde, Vorticist magazine, Blast. It is a dream play that tries to attain the geometric severity and "abstraction" of Cubist art. Its two protagonists—the intellectual, Arghol, and the sensual, ordinary man, Hanp—are forerunners of a whole series of such intimately linked but antagonistic duos—from Joyce's Daedalus and Bloom in Ulysses to Beckett's Pozzo and Lucky in Waiting for Godot. Here, however, violence is the predominant atmosphere, in the thoughts and fantasies of the characters, the nature of the scene—Northern, inclement and harsh—and the final resolution of the action. Hanp, the ordinary man, is a threatening figure, a presage of the time when mediocrity, aware of itself and desperate, would be armed with technology and become not simply an attitude but an entire social environment.

"Cantleman's Spring Mate" and The Ideal Giant are war pieces, having been published in 1917 and 1918, when Lewis was already in the army, yet they differ from most creative work about the war since they deal with war's emotional and ideological underpinnings and motivations rather than realistically depicting its boredom, horror and drudgery. In both, the protagonist's mistaken evaluation of reality leads to his humiliation at reality's hands. Cantleman thinks that he can outwit nature by imitating it, but, as Lewis comments, "he had no adequate realization of the extent to which, evidently, the death of a Hun was to the advantage of the animal world." Kemp, the artist and intellectual, in the play The Ideal Giant, has a complicated theory of action. Rose Godd, however, proves how simple, indecent and mysterious an action can be, how remote from all theories. The subjects they explore—one in a richly sensuous key, the other in a fireworks of effervescent talk—were to become central concerns to all of modern literature.

The last two stories, "The Bishop's Fool" and "My Disciple" are from the book entitled *Rotting Hill* and represent Lewis' sardonic response to two aspects of romantic, sentimental extremism—the first in politics and the second in the plastic arts. Coming at the close of his career, they can be regarded as a kind of fictional summing up, adroit, playful, unusually amiable, of Lewis' own lifelong struggle with, and attraction to, extremism.

A Soldier of Humor

PART I

SPAIN is an overflow of somberness. "Africa commences at the Pyrenees." Spain is a checkboard of Black and Goth, on which primitive gallic chivalry played its most brilliant games. At the gates of Spain the landscape gradually becomes historic with Roland. His fame dies as difficultly as the flourish of the cor de chasse.[1] It lives like a superfine antelope in the gorges of the Pyrenees, becoming more and more ethereal and gentle. Charlemagne moves Knights and Queens beneath that tree; there is something eternal and rembrandtesque about his proceedings. A stormy and threatening tide of history meets you at the frontier.

Several summers ago I was cast by fate for a fierce and prolonged little comedy—an essentially spanish comedy. It appropriately began at Bayonne, where Spain, not Africa, begins.

I am a large blond clown, ever so vaguely reminiscent (in person) of William Blake, and some great american boxer whose name I forget. I have large strong teeth which I gnash and flash when I laugh. But usually a look of settled and aggressive naïveté rests on my face. I know much more about myself than people generally do. For instance I am aware that I am a barbarian. By rights I should be paddling about in a coracle. My body is large, white and savage. But all the fierceness has become transformed into *laughter*. It still looks like a visi-gothic fighting machine, but it is in reality a *laughing* machine. As I have remarked, when I laugh I gnash my teeth, which is another brutal survival and a thing laughter has taken over from war. Everywhere where formerly I would fly at throats, I now howl with .... That is me.

So I have never forgotten that I am really a barbarian. I have clung coldly to this consciousness. I realize, similarly, the uncivilized nature of my laughter. It does not easily climb into the neat japanese box, which is the *cosa salada* [2] of the Spaniard, or become french *esprit*. [3] It sprawls into everything. It has become my life. The result is that I am *never* serious about anything. I simply cannot help converting everything into burlesque patterns. And I admit that I am disposed to forget that people are real—that they are, that is, not subjective patterns belonging specifically to me, in the course of this joke life, which indeed has for its very principle a denial of the accepted actual.

My father is a family doctor on the Clyde. The Ker-Orrs have been doctors usually. I have not seen him for some time: my mother, who is separated from him, lives with a noted hungarian physician. She gives me money that she gets from the physician, and it is she that I recognize as my principal parent. It is owing to this conjunction of circumstances that I am able to move about so much, and to feed the beast of humor that is within me with such a variety of dishes.

My mother is short and dark: it is from my father that I have my stature, and this strange northern appearance.

Vom Vater hab' ich die Statur . . . [4]

It must be from my mother that I get the *Lust zu fabulieren*. [5] I experience no embarrassment in following the promptings of my fine physique. My sense of humor in its mature phase has arisen in this very acute consciousness of what is *me*. In playing that off against another hostile *me*, that does not like the smell of mine, probably finds my large teeth, height and so forth abominable, I am in a sense working off my alarm at myself. So I move on a more primitive level than most men, I expose my essential *me* quite coolly, and all men shy a little. This forked, strange-scented, blond-skinned gut-bag, with its two bright rolling marbles with which it sees, bull's-eyes full of mockery and madness, is my stalking-horse. I hang somewhere in its midst operating it with detachment.

[2] salty or bitter humor
[3] wit
[4] I get my height from my father
[5] the delight in telling stories

I snatch this great body out of their reach when they grow dangerously enraged at the sight of it, and laugh at them. And what I would insist upon is that at the bottom of the chemistry of my sense of humor is some philosopher's stone. A primitive unity is there, to which, with my laughter, I am appealing. Freud explains everything by *sex:* I explain everything by *laughter.* So in these accounts of my adventures there is no sex interest at all: only over and over again what is perhaps the natural enemy of sex: so I must apologize. "Sex" makes me yawn my head off; but my eye sparkles at once if I catch sight of some stylistic anomaly that will provide me with a new pattern for my grotesque realism. The sex specialist or the sex snob hates what I like, and calls his occupation the only *real* one. No compromise, I fear, is possible between him and me, and people will continue to call "real" what interests them most. I boldly pit my major interest against the sex appeal, which will restrict me to a masculine audience, but I shall not complain whatever happens.

I am quite sure that many of the soldiers and adventurers of the Middle Ages were really *Soldiers of Humor,* unrecognized and unclassified. I know that many a duel has been fought in this solemn cause. A man of this temper and category will, perhaps, carefully cherish a wide circle of accessible enemies, that his sword may not rust. Any other quarrel may be patched up. But what can be described as a *quarrel of humor* divides men for ever. That is my english creed.

I could fill pages with descriptions of myself and my ways. But such abstractions from the life lived are apt to be misleading, because most men do not easily detach the principle from the living thing in that manner, and so when handed the abstraction alone do not know what to do with it, or they apply it wrongly. I exist with an equal ease in the abstract world of principle and in the concrete world of fact. As I can express myself equally well in either, I will stick to the latter here, as then I am more likely to be understood. So I will show you myself in action, maneuvering in the heart of the reality. But before proceeding, this qualification of the above account of myself is necessary: owing to protracted foreign travel at an early age, following my mother's change of husbands, I have known french very well since boyhood. Most other Western languages I am fairly familiar with. This has a considerable bearing on the reception accorded to me by the general run of people in the countries where these scenes are laid.

There is some local genius or god of adventure haunting the soil of Spain, of an especially active and resourceful type. I have seen people that have personified him. In Spain it is safer to seek adventures than to avoid them. That is at least the sensation you will have if you are sensitive to this national principle, which is impregnated with *burla,* or burlesque excitants. It certainly requires *horseplay,* and it is even safer not to attempt to evade it. Should you refrain from charging the windmills, they are capable of charging you, you come to understand: in short, you will in the end wonder less at Don Quixote's behavior. But the deity of this volcanic soil has become civilized. My analysis of myself would serve equally well for him in this respect. Your life is no longer one of the materials he asks for to supply you with constant entertainment, as the conjurer asks for the gentleman's silk hat. Not your life,—but a rib or two, your comfort, or a five-pound note, are all he politely begs or rudely snatches. With these he juggles and conjures from morning till night, keeping you perpetually amused and on the qui vive.[6]

It might have been a friend, but as it happened it was the most implacable enemy I have ever had that Providence provided me with, as her agent and representative for this journey. The comedy I took part in was a spanish one, then, at once piquant and elemental. But a Frenchman filled the principal role. When I add that this Frenchman was convinced the great part of the time that he was taking part in a tragedy, and was perpetually on the point of transplanting my adventure bodily into that other category, and that although his actions drew their vehemence from the virgin source of a racial hatred, yet it was not as a Frenchman or a Spaniard that he acted, then you will conceive what extremely complex and unmanageable forces were about to be set in motion for my edification.

What I have said about my barbarism and my laughter is a key to the militant figure chosen at the head of this account. In those modifications of the primitive such another extravagant warrior as Don Quixote is produced, existing in a vortex of strenuous and burlesque encounters. Mystical and

6 alert

humorous, astonished at everything at bottom (the settled naïveté I have noted) he inclines to worship and deride, to pursue like a riotous moth the comic and unconscious luminary he discovers; to make war on it and to cherish it like a lover, at once.

PART II

IT was about eleven o'clock at night when I reached Bayonne. I had started from Paris the evening before. In the market square adjoining the station the traveler is immediately solicited by a row of rather obscene little hotels, crudely painted. Each frail structure shines and sparkles with a hard, livid and disreputable electricity, every floor illuminated. The blazonry of cheap ice cream wells, under a striped umbrella, is what they suggest: and as I stepped into this place all that was not a small, sparkling, competitive universe, inviting the stranger to pass into it, was spangled with the vivid spanish stars. "Fonda del Universo," "Fonda del Mundo": Universal Inn and World Inn, two of these places were called, I noticed. I was tired and not particular as to which universe I entered. They all looked the same. To keep up a show of discrimination I chose the second, not the first. I advanced along a narrow passageway and found myself suddenly in the heart of the Fonda del Mundo. On the left lay the dining room in which sat two travelers. I was standing in the kitchen: this was a large courtyard, the rest of the hotel and several houses at the back were built round it. It had a glass roof on a level with the house proper, which was of two storys only.

A half-dozen stoves with sinks, each managed by a separate crew of grim, oily workers, formed a semicircle. Hands were as cheap, and every bit as dirty, as dirt; you felt that the lowest scullery maid could afford a servant to do the roughest of her work, and that girl in turn another. The abundance of cheap beings was of the same meridional order as the wine and food. Instead of buying a wheelbarrow, would not you attach a man to your business; instead of hiring a removing van, engage a gang of carriers? In every way that man could replace the implement that here would be done. An air of leisurely but continual activity pervaded this precinct. Cooking on the grand scale was going forward. Later on I learned that this was a preparation for the market on the following day. But to enter at eleven in the evening this large and apparently empty building, as far as customers went, and find a methodically busy population in its midst, cooking a nameless feast, was impressive. A broad staircase was the only avenue in this building to the sleeping apartments; a shining cut-glass door beneath it seemed the direction I ought to take when I should have made up my mind to advance. This door, the stairs, the bread given you at the table d'hôte, all had the same unsubstantial pretentiously new appearance.

So I stood unnoticed in an indifferent enigmatical universe, to which yet I had no clue, my rug on my arm. I certainly had reached immediately the most intimate center of it, without ceremony. Perhaps there were other entrances, which I had not observed? I was turning back when the hostess appeared through the glass door—a very stout woman in a garment like a dressing gown. She had that air of sinking into herself as if into a hot, enervating bath, with the sleepy, leaden intensity of expression belonging to many Spaniards. Her face was so still and impassible, that the ready and apt answers coming to your questions were startling, her *si señors* and *como nons*.[7] However, I knew this kind of patronne; and the air of dull resentment would mean nothing except that I was indifferent to her. I was one of those troublesome people she only had to see twice when they arrived, and when they came to pay at the end of their stay.

She turned to the busy scene at our right and poured out a few guttural remarks (it was a spanish staff), all having some bearing on my fate, some connected with my supper, the others with my sleeping accommodation or luggage. They fell on the crowd of leisurely workers without ruffling the surface. Gradually they reached their destination, however. First, I noticed a significant stir and a dull flare rose in the murky atmosphere, a stove lid had been slid back; great copper pans were disturbed, their covers wrenched up: some morsel was to be fished out for me, swimming in oil. Elsewhere a slim, handsome young witch left her caldron and passed me, going into the dining room. I followed her, and the hostess went back through the cut-glass door. It was behind that that she lived.

The dining room was compact with hard light. Nothing in its glare could escape detection, so it symbolized *honesty*

7 yes, sir's; indeed's

on the one hand, and *newness* on the other. There was nothing at all you could not *see,* and scrutinize, only too well. Everything within sight was totally unconscious of its cheapness or of any limitation at all. Inspect me! Inspect me!—exclaimed the coarse white linen upon the table, the Condy's fluid in the decanter, the paper bread, the hideous moldings on the wall.—I am the goods!

I took my seat at the long table. Of the two diners, only one was left. I poured myself out a glass of the wine *rosé* of Nowhere, set it to my lips, drank and shuddered. Two spoonfuls of a nameless soup, and the edge of my appetite was, it seemed, forever blunted. Bacallao, or cod, that nightmare of the Spaniard of the Atlantic seaboard, followed. Its white and tasteless leather remained on my plate, with the markings of my white teeth all over it, like a cast of a dentist. I was really hungry and the stew that came next found its way inside me in gluttonous drafts. The preserved fruit in a syrup was eaten too. Heladas came next, no doubt frozen up from stinking water. Then I fell back in my chair, my coffee in front of me, and stared round at the other occupant of the dining room. He stared blankly back at me. When I had turned my head away, as though the words had been mechanically released in response to my wish, he exclaimed:

"Il fait beau ce soir!"

I took no notice: but after a few moments I turned in his direction again. He was staring at me without anything more than a little surprise. Immediately his lips opened again, and he exclaimed dogmatically, loudly (was I deaf, he had no doubt thought):

"Il fait beau ce soir!"

"Not at all. It's by no means a fine night. It's cold, and what's more it's going to rain."

I cannot say why I contradicted him in this fashion. Perhaps the insolent and mystical gage of drollery his appearance generally flung down was the cause. I had no reason for supposing that the weather at Bayonne was anything but fine and settled.

I had made my rejoinder as though I were a Frenchman, and I concluded my neighbor would take me for that.

He accepted my response quite stolidly. This initial rudeness of mine would probably have had no effect whatever on him, had not a revelation made shortly afterwards at once changed our relative positions, and caused him to regard me with changed eyes. He then went back, remembered this first incivility of mine, and took it, retrospectively, in a different spirit to that shown contemporaneously. He now merely enquired:

"You have come far?"

"From Paris," I answered, my eyes fixed on a piece of cheese which the high voltage of the electricity revealed in all its instability. I reflected how bad the food was here compared to its spanish counterpart, and wondered if I should have time to go into the town before my train left. I then looked at my neighbor, and wondered what sort of stomach he could have. He showed every sign of the extremest hardiness. He lay back in his chair, his hat on the back of his head, finishing a bottle of wine with bravado. His waistcoat was open, and this was the only thing about him that did not denote the most facile of victories. This, equivalent to rolling up the sleeves, might be accepted as showing that he respected his enemy.

His straw hat served rather as a heavy coffee-colored nimbus—such as some browningesque florentine painter, the worse for drink, might have placed behind the head of his saint. Above his veined and redly sunburned forehead gushed a ragged volute of dry black hair. His face had the vexed wolfish look of the grimy commercial Midi. It was full of character, certainly, but it had been niggled at and worked all over, at once minutely and loosely, by a hundred little blows and chiselings of fretful passion. His beard did not sprout with any shape or symmetry. Yet in an odd and baffling way there was a breadth, a look of possible largeness somewhere. You were forced at length to attribute it to just that *blankness* of expression I have mentioned. This sort of blank intensity spoke of a possibility of real passion, of the sublime. (It was this sublime quality that I was about to waken, and was going to have an excellent opportunity of studying.)

He was dressed with sombre floridity. In his dark purple-slate suit with thin crimson lines, in his dark red hat band, in his rose-buff tie, swarming with cerulean fireflies, in his stormily flowered waistcoat, you felt that his taste for the violent and sumptuous had everywhere struggled to assert itself, and everywhere been overcome. But by what? That was the important secret of this man's entire machine, a secret unfolded by his subsequent conduct. Had I been of a superior penetration the cut of his clothes in their awkward amplitude, with their unorthodox shoulders and belling hams, might have given me the key. He was not a commercial traveler. I was sure of that. For me, he issued from a void. I rejected in turn his claim, on the strength of his appearance, to be a small vineyard owner, a man in the automobile business and a *rentier*.[8] He was part of the mystery of this hotel; his loneliness, his aplomb, his hardy appetite.

In the meantime his small sunken eyes were fixed on me imperturbably, with the blankness of two metal discs.

"I was in Paris last week," he suddenly announced. "I don't like Paris. Why should I?" I thought he was working up for something now. He had had a good think. He took me for a Parisian, I supposed. "They think they are up-to-date. Go and get a parcel sent you from abroad, then go and try and get it at the Station Depôt. Only see how many hours you will pass there trotting from one bureau clerk to another before they give it you! Then go to a café and ask for a drink!—Are you Parisian?" He asked this in the same tone, the blankness slightly deepening.

"No, I'm English," I answered.

He looked at me steadfastly. This evidently at first seemed to him untrue. Then he suddenly appeared to accept it implicitly. His incredulity and belief appeared to be one block of the same material, or two sides of the same absolute coin. There was not room for a hair between these two states. They were not two, but one.

Several minutes of dead silence elapsed. His eyes had never winked. His changes had all occurred within one block of concrete undifferentiated blankness. At this period you became aware of a change: but when you looked at him he was completely uniform from moment to moment.

He now addressed me, to my surprise, in my own language. There was every evidence that it had crossed the Atlantic at least once since it had been in his possession; he had not inherited it, but acquired it with the sweat of his brow, it was clear.

"Oh! you're English? It's fine day!"

Now, we are going to begin all over again! And we are going to start, as before, with the weather. But I did not contradict him this time. My opinion of the weather had in no way changed. But for some reason I withdrew from my former perverse attitude.

[8] a person who lives on an income

"Yes," I agreed.

Our eyes met, doubtfully. He had not forgotten my late incivility, and I remembered it at the same time. He was silent again. Evidently he was turning over dully in his mind the signification of this change on my part. My changes I expect presented themselves as occurring in as unruffled uniform a medium as his.

But there was a change now in him. I could both feel and see it. My weak withdrawal, I thought, had been unfortunate. Remembering my wounding obstinacy of five minutes before, a strong resentment took possession of him, swelling his person as it entered. I watched it enter him. It was as though the two sides of his sprawling portmanteau-body had tightened up, and his eyes drew in till he squinted.

Almost threateningly, then, he continued,—heavily, pointedly, steadily, as though to see if there were a spark of resistance anywhere left in me, that would spit up, under his trampling words.

"I guess eet's darn fi' weather, and goin' to laast. A friend of mine, who ees skeeper, sailing for Bilbao this afternoon, said that mighty little sea was out zere, and all fine weather for his run. A skipper ought' know, I guess, ought'n he? Zey know sight more about zee weader than most. I guess zat's deir trade,—an't I right?"

Speaking the tongue of New York evidently injected him with a personal emotion that would not have been suspected, even, in the Frenchman. The strange blankness and impersonality had gone, or rather it had *woken up*, if one may so describe this phenomenon. He now looked at me with awakened eyes, coldly, judicially, fixedly. They were faceted eyes—the eyes of the forty-eight States of the Union. Considering he had crushed me enough, no doubt, he began talking about Paris, just as he had done in french. The one thing linguistically he had brought away from the United States intact was an american accent of almost alarming perfection. Whatever word or phrase he knew, in however mutilated a form, had this stamp of colloquialism and air of being the real thing. He spoke english with a careless impudence at which I was not surprised; but the powerful consciousness of the authentic nature of his *accent* made him still more insolently heedless of the faults of his speech, it seemed, and rendered him immune from all care as to the correctness of the mere english. He was evidently to the full the american, or anglo-saxon american, state of mind: a colossal disdain for everything that does not possess in one way or another an american accent. My english, grammatically regular though it was, lacking the american accent was but a poor vehicle for thought compared with his most blundering sentence.

Before going further I must make quite clear that I have no dislike of the american way of accenting english. American possesses an indolent vigor and dryness which is a most cunning arm when it snarls out its ironies. That accent is the language of Mark Twain, and is the tongue, at once naïve and cynical, of a thousand inimitable humorists. To my mind it is a better accent than the sentimental whimsicality of the Irish.

An illusion of superiority, at the expense of citizens of other states, the American shares with the Englishman. So the "God's Own Country" attitude of some Americans is more anglo-saxon than their blood. I have met many outlandish Americans, from such unamerican cities as Odessa, Trieste and Barcelona. America had done them little good, they tended to become dreamers, drunken with geographical immensities and opportunities they had never had. This man at once resembled and was different from them. The reason for this difference, I concluded, was explained when he informed me that he was a United States citizen. I believed him on the spot, unreservedly. Some air of security in him that only such a ratification can give convinced me.

He did not tell me at once. Between his commencing to speak in english and his announcing his citizenship, came an indetermined phase in our relations. During this phase he knew what he possessed, but he knew I was not yet aware of it. This caused him to make some allowance; since, undivulged, this fact was, for me at least, not yet a full fact. He was constrained, but the situation had not yet, he felt, fully matured.

In the same order as in our conversation in french, we progressed then, from the weather topic (a delicate subject with us) to Paris. Our acquaintance was by this time—scarcely ten minutes had elapsed—painfully ripe. I already felt instinctively that certain subjects of conversation were to be avoided. I knew already what shade of expression would cause suspicion, what hatred, and what snorting disdain. He, for his part, evidently with the intention of eschewing a subject fraught with dangers, did not once speak of England. It was as though England were a subject that no one could expect him to keep his temper about. Should any one, as I did, come from England, he would naturally resent being reminded of it. The other, obviously, would be seeking to take an unfair advantage of him. In fact for the moment the assumption was—that was the only issue from this difficulty —that I was an American.

"Guess you' goin' to Spain?" he said. "Waal, Americans are not like' very much in that country. That country, sir, is barb'rous; you *kant* believe how behind in everything that country is! All you have to do is to *look* smart there to make money. No need to worry there. No, by gosh! Just sit round and ye'll do bett' dan zee durn dagos!"

The american citizenship wiped out the repulsive fact of his southern birth, otherwise, being a Gascon, he would have been almost a dago himself.

"In Guadalquiveer—wall—kind of state-cap'tle, some man-zanas, a bunch shacks, get me?—waal——"

I make these sentences of my neighbor's much more lucid than they in reality were. But he now plunged into this ob-scure and whirling idiom with a story to tell. The story was drowned; but I gathered it told of how, traveling in a motor car, he could find no petrol anywhere in a town of some importance. He was so interested in the telling of this story that I was thrown a little off my guard, and once or twice showed that I did not quite follow him. I did not under-stand his english, that is what unguardedly I showed. He finished his story rather abruptly. There was a deep silence. —It was after this silence that he divulged the fact of his american citizenship.

And now things began to wear at once an ex-ceedingly gloomy and unpromising look.

With the revelation of this staggering fact I lost at one blow all the benefit of that convenient fiction in which we had temporarily indulged—namely, that I was American. It was now incumbent upon him to adopt an air of increased arrogance. The representative of the United States—there was no evading it, that was the dignity that the evulgation of his legal nationality imposed on him. All compromise, all courteous resolve to ignore painful facts, was past. Things must stand out in their true colors, and men too.

As a result of this heightened attitude, he appeared to doubt the sincerity or exactitude of everything I said. His beard bristled round his drawling mouth, his thumbs sought his armpits, his varnished patterned shoes stood up erect and aggressive upon his heels. An insidious attempt on my part to induct the conversation back into french, unhappily detected, caused in him an alarming indignation. I was curious to see the change that would occur in my companion if I could trap him into using again his native speech. The sensation of the humbler tongue upon his lips would have, I was sure, an immediate effect. The perfidy of my intention only gradually dawned upon him. He seemed taken aback. For a few minutes he was silent as though stunned. The subtleties, the *ironics* to which the American is exposed!

"Oui, c'est vrai," I went on, taking a frowning, business-like air, affecting a great absorption in the subject we were discussing, and to have overlooked the fact that I had changed to french, "les Espagnols ont du chic à se chausser. D'ailleurs, c'est tout ce qu'ils savent, en fait de toilette. C'est les Américains surtout qui savent s'habiller!" [9]

His eyes at this became terrible. He had seen through the *manège*, [10] had he not: and now *par surcroît de perfidie*, [11] was I not *flattering* him—flattering Americans; and above all, praising their way of dressing! His cigar protruded from the right-hand corner of his mouth. He now with gnashing and rolling movement conveyed it, in a series of revolutions, to the left-hand corner. He eyed me with a most unorthodox fierceness. In the language of his adopted land, but with an imported wildness in the dry figure that he must affect, he ground out, spitting with it the moist débris of the cigar:

"Yes, *sirr,* and that's more'n zee durn English do!"

No doubt, in his perfect americanism—and at this ticklish moment, his impeccable accent threatened by an unscrupulous foe, who was attempting to stifle it temporarily—a definite analogy arose in his mind. The Redskin and his wiles, the hereditary and cunning foe of the american citizen, came vividly perhaps to his mind. Yes, wiles of that familiar sort were being used against him, Sioux-like, Blackfeet-like maneuvers. He must meet them as the american citizen had always met them. He had at length overcome the Sioux and Cherokee. He turned on me a look as though I

[9] Yes, it's true, Spaniards have stylish footwear. Anyway, that's all they know about dressing. It's the Americans above all who know how to dress.

[10] trick

[11] as the worst perfidy

had been unmasked, and his accent became more raucous and formidable. The elemental that he contained and that often woke in him, I expect, manifested itself in his american accent, the capital vessel of his vitality.

After another significant pause he brusquely chose a new subject of conversation. It was a subject upon which, it was evident, he was persuaded that it would be quite impossible for us to agree. He took a long draft of the powerful fluid served to each diner. I disagreed with him at first out of politeness. But as he seemed resolved to work himself up slowly into a national passion, I changed round, and agreed with him. For a moment he glared at me. He felt at bay before this dreadful subtlety to which his americanism exposed him: then he warily changed his position in the argument, taking up the point of view he had begun by attacking.

We changed about alternately for a while. It was a most diverting game. At one time in taking my new stand, and asserting something, either I had changed too quickly, or he had not done so quite quickly enough. At all events, when he began speaking he found himself *agreeing* with me. This was a breathless moment. It was very close quarters indeed. I felt as one does at a show, standing on the same chair with an uncertain-tempered person. With an anxious swiftness I threw myself into the opposite opinion. The situation, for that time at least, was saved. A moment more, and we should have fallen on each other, or rather, he on me.

He buried his face again in the sinister potion in front of him, and consumed the last vestiges of the fearful food at his elbow. During these happenings we had not been interrupted. A dark figure, that of a Spaniard, I thought, had passed into the kitchen along the passage. From within the muffled uproar of machinery of the kitchen reached us uninterruptedly.

He now with a snarling drawl engaged in a new discussion on another and still more delicate subject. I renewed my tactics, he his. Subject after subject was chosen. His volte-face,[12] his change of attitude in the argument, became less and less leisurely. But my skill in reversing remained more than a match for his methods. At length, whatever I said he said the opposite, brutally and at once. At last, pushing his chair back violently with a frightful grating sound, and

[12] about face

thrusting both his hands in his pockets—at this supreme moment the sort of blank look came back to his face again—he said slowly:

"Waal, zat may be so—you say so—waal! But what say you to England, hein? England! England! England!"

At last it had come! He repeated "England" as though that word in itself were a question—an unanswerable question. "England" was a form of question that a man could only ask when every device of normal courtesy had been exhausted. But it was a thing hanging over every Englishman, at any moment he might be silenced with it.

"England! ha! England! England!" he repeated, as though hypnotized by this word; as though pressing me harder and harder, and finally "chawing me up" with the mere utterance of it.

"Why, mon vieux!" I said suddenly, getting up, "how about the South of France, for that matter—the South of France! the South of France! The bloody Midi, your homeland, you poor bum!" I gnashed my teeth as I said this.

If I had said "America," he would have responded at once, no doubt. But "the South of France!" A look of unspeakable vagueness came into his face. The South of France! This was at once without meaning, a stab in the back, an unfair blow, the sort of thing that was not said, some sort of paralyzing nonsense, that robbed a man of the power of speech. I seemed to have drawn a chilly pall with glove-tight tightness suddenly over the whole of his mind.

I fully expected to be forced to fight my way out of the salle à manger, [13] and was wondering whether his pugilistic methods would be those of Chicago or Toulouse—whether he would skip round me, his fists working like piston rods, or whether he would plunge his head into the pit of my stomach, kick me on the chin and follow up with the "coup de la fourchette," which consists in doubling up one's fist, but allowing the index and little finger to protrude, so that they may enter the eyes on either side of the bridge of the nose.

But I had laid him out quite flat. The situation was totally outside his compass. And the word "bum" lay like a load of dough upon his spirit. My last word had been *american!* As I made for the door, he sat first quite still.

[13] dining room

Then, slightly writhing on his chair, with a painful slowness, his face passed through a few degrees of the compass in an attempt to reach me in spite of the spell I had laid upon him. The fact of my leaving the room seemed to find him still more unprepared. My answer to his final apostrophe was a blow below the belt: I was following it up by vanishing from the ring altogether, as though the contest were over, while he lay paralyzed in the center of the picture. It had never occurred to him, apparently, that I might perhaps get up and leave the dining room.—Sounds came from him, words too—hybrid syllables lost on the borderland between french and english, which appeared to signify protest, pure astonishment, alarmed question. But I had disappeared. I got safely into the kitchen. I sank into that deep hum of internal life, my eye glittering with the battle light of humor.

In the act of taking my candle from the hand of a chambermaid, I heard a nasal roar behind me. I mounted the stairs three steps at a time, the hotel boy at my heels, and the chambermaid breathlessly rushing up in his rear. Swiftly ushered into my room, I thrust outside the panting servants and locked and bolted the door.

Flinging myself on the bed, my blond poll rolling about in ecstasy upon the pillow, I howled like an exultant wolf. This penetrating howl of my kind—the humorous kind—shook the cardboard walls of the room, rattled the stucco frames; but the tumult beneath of the hotel staff must have prevented this sound from getting farther than the area of the bedrooms. My orgasm left me weak, and I lay conventionally mopping my brow, and affectedly gasping. Then, as usually happened with me, I began sentimentally pitying my victim. Poor little chap! My conduct had been unpardonable! I had brutalized this tender flower of the prairies of the West! Why had I dragged in the "bloody Midi" after all? It was too bad altogether. I had certainly behaved very badly. I had a movement to go down immediately and apologize to him, a tear of laughter still hanging from a mournful lash.

My room was at the back. The window looked out to the kitchen; it was just over the stairs leading to the bedrooms. I now got up, for I imagined I heard some intemperate sound thrusting into the general mêlée of mechanical noise. From the naturally unsavory and depressing porthole of my room, immediately above the main caldrons, I was able, I found, to observe my opponent in the murky half-court, half-kitchen, beneath. There he was: by pointing my ear down I could catch sometimes what he was saying. But I found that the noise I had attributed to him had been my fancy only.

Inspected from this height he looked very different. I had not till then seen him on his feet. His yankee clothes, evidently cut beneath his direction by a gascon tailor, made him look as broad as he was long. His violently animated leanness imparted a precarious and toppling appearance to his architecture. He was performing a war dance in this soft national armor just at present, beneath the sodden eyes of the proprietress. It had shuffling, vehement, jazz elements, aided by the gesticulation of the Gaul. This did not seem the same man I had been talking to before. He evidently, in this enchanted hotel, possessed a variety of personalities. It was *not* the same man. Somebody else had leaped into his clothes—which hardly fitted the newcomer—and was carrying on his quarrel. The original and more imposing man had disappeared. I had slain him. This little fellow had taken up his disorganized and overwrought life at that precise moment and place where I had left him knocked out in the dining room, at identically the same pitch of passion, only with fresher nerves, and with the same racial sentiments as the man he had succeeded.

He was talking in spanish—much more correctly than he did in english. She listened with her leaden eyes crawling swiftly and sullenly over his person, with an air of angrily and lazily making an inventory. In his fiery attack on the depths of languor behind which her spirit lived, he would occasionally turn and appeal to one of the nearest of the servants, as though seeking corroboration of something. Of what crime was I being accused? I muttered rapid prayers to the effect that that sultry reserve of the proprietress might prove impregnable. Otherwise I might be cast bodily out of the Fonda del Mundo, and, in my present worn-out state, have to seek another and distant roof. I knew that I was the object of his discourse. What effectively could be said about me on so short an acquaintance? He would, though, certainly affirm that I was a designing ruffian of some sort; such a person as no respectable hotel would consent to harbor, or if it did, would do so at its peril. Probably he might be saying it was my intention to hold up the hotel later on, or he might have influence with the proprietress, be a regular customer and old friend. He might only be saying, "I object to that person; I cannot express to you how I object to that person! I have never objected to anyone to the same fearful degree. All my organs boil at the thought of him. I cannot explain to you how that island organism tears my members this way and that. Out with this abomination! Oh! out with it before I die at your feet from the fever of my *mauvais sang!*" [14]

That personal appeal might prove effective. I went to bed with a feeling of extreme insecurity. I thought that, if nothing else happened, he might set fire to the hotel. But in spite of the dangers by which I was, manifestly, beset in this ill-starred establishment, I slept soundly enough. In the morning an overwhelming din shook me, and I rose with the stink of southern food in my nose.

Breakfast passed off without incident. I concluded that the Complete American was part of the nighttime aspect of the Fonda del Mundo and had no part in its more normal day life.

The square was full of peasants, the men wearing dark blouses and the béret basque. Several groups were sitting near me in the salle à manger. An intricate arrangement of chairs and tables, like an extensive mantrap, lay outside the hotel, extending a little distance into the square. From time to time one or more clumsy peasant would appear to become stuck or somehow involved in these iron contrivances. They would then, with becoming fatalism, sit down and call for a drink. Such was the impression conveyed, at least, by their embarrassed and reluctant movements in choosing a seat. I watched several parties come into this dangerous extension of the Fonda del Mundo. The proprietress would come out occasionally and stare moodily at them. She never looked at me.

A train would shortly leave for the frontier. I bade farewell to the patrona, and asked her if she could recommend me a hotel in Burgos or in Pontaisandra. When I mentioned Pontaisandra, she said at once, "You are going to Pontaisandra?" With a sluggish ghost of a smile she turned to a loitering servant and then said, "Yes, you can go to the Burgaleza at Pontaisandra. That is a good hotel." They both showed a few ragged discolored teeth, only appearing in moments of crafty burlesque. The night before I had told her that my destination was Pontaisandra, and she had looked at me steadfastly and resentfully, as though I had said that

14 diseased blood

my destination was Paradise, and that I intended to occupy
the seat reserved for her. But that was the night before: and
now Pontaisandra appeared to mean something different to
her. The episode of the supper room the night before I now
regarded as an emanation of that place. The Fonda del
Mundo was a mysterious hotel, though in the day its secrets
seemed more obvious. I imagined it inhabited by solitary and
hallucinated beings, like my friend the Perfect American—
or such as I myself might have become. The large kitchen
staff was occupied far into the night in preparing a strange
and excessive table d'hôte. The explanation of this afforded
in the morning by the sight of the crowding peasants did
not efface that impression of midnight though it mitigated it.
Perhaps the dreams caused by its lunches, the visions con-
jured up by its supper, haunted the place. That was the
spirit in which I remembered my overnight affair.

When eventually I started for the frontier, hoping by the
inhalation of a picadura to dispose my tongue to the ordeal
of framing passable castilian, I did not realize that the american adventure was the progenitor of other adventures; nor
that the dreams of the Fonda del Mundo were to go with me
into the heart of Spain.

PART III

BURGOS, I had intended, should be my first stopping place.
But I decided afterwards that San Sebastian and Leon would
be better.

This four days' journeying was an *entr'acte* filled with appropriate music; the lugubrious and splendid landscapes of
Castile, the extremely self-conscious, pedantic and independent spirit of its inhabitants, met with en route. Fate was
marking time, merely. With the second day's journey I
changed trains and dined at Venta de Baños, the junction for
the line that branches off in the direction of Palencia, Leon
and the galician country.

While traveling, the spanish peasant has a marked preference for the next compartment to his own. No sooner has
the train started, than, one after another, heads, arms, and
shoulders appear above the wooden partition. There are times
when you have all the members of the neighboring compartment gazing with the melancholy stolidity of cattle into your
own. In the case of some theatrical savage of the Sierras, who
rears a disheveled head before you in a pose of fierce aban-

don, and hangs there smoking like a chimney, you know that it may be some grandiose recoil of pride that prevents him from remaining in an undignified position huddled in a narrow carriage. In other cases it is probably a simple conviction that the occupants of other compartments are likely to be more interesting.

The whole way from Venta de Baños to Palencia the carriage was dense with people. Crowds of peasants poured into the train, loaded with their heavy vivid horse rugs, gaudy bundles and baskets; which profusion of mere matter, combined with their exuberance, made the carriage appear positively to swarm with animal life. They would crowd in at one little station and out at another a short way along the line, where they were met by hordes of their relations awaiting them. They would rush or swing out of the door, charged with their property or recent purchases, and catch the nearest man or woman of their blood in their arms, with a turbulence that outdid our Northern people's most vehement occasions. The waiting group became twice as vital as average mankind upon the train's arrival, as though so much more blood had poured into their veins. Gradually we got beyond the sphere of this Fiesta, and in the small hours of the morning arrived at Leon.

Next day came the final stages of the journey to the Atlantic seaboard. We arrived within sight of the town that evening, just as the sun was setting. With its houses of green, rose, and white, in general effect a faded bouquet, its tints a scarcely colored reminiscence, it looked like some oriental city represented in the nerveless tempera of an old wall. Its bay stretched between hills for many miles to the ocean, which lay beyond an island of scarcely visible rocks.

On the train drawing up in the central station, the shock troops furnished by every little ragamuffin café as well as stately hotel in the town were hurled against us. I had mislaid the address given me at Bayonne. I wished to find a hotel of medium luxury. The different hotel attendants called hotly out their prices at me. I selected one who named a sum for board and lodging that only the frenzy of competition could have fathered, I thought. Also the name of this hotel was, it seemed to me, the one the patrona at Bayonne had mentioned. I had not then learned to connect Burgaleza with Burgos: this was my first long visit to Spain. With this man I took a cab and was left seated in it at the door of the station, while he went after the heavy luggage. Now one by one, the hotel emissaries came up; their fury of a few minutes before contrasted oddly with their present listless calm. Putting themselves civilly at my disposition, they thrust forward matter-of-factly the card of their establishment, adding that they were sure that I would find out my mistake.

I now felt in a vague manner a tightening of the machinery of Fate—a certain uneasiness and strangeness, in the march and succession of facts and impressions, like a trembling of a decrepit motor bus about to start again. The interlude was over. After a long delay the hotel tout returned and we started. My misgivings were of a practical order. The price named was very low, too low perhaps. But I had found it a capital plan on former occasions to go to a cheap hotel and pay a few pesetas more a day for "extras." My palate was so conservative, that I found in any case that my main fare lay outside the spanish menu. Extras are very satisfactory. You always feel that a single individual has bent over the extra and carefully cooked it, and that it has not been bought in too wholesale a manner. I wished to live on extras—a privileged existence: and extras are much the same in one place as another. So I reassured myself.

The cabman and the hotel man were discussing some local event. But we penetrated farther and farther into a dismal and shabby quarter of the town. My misgivings began to revive. I asked the representative of the Burgaleza if he were sure that his house was a clean and comfortable house. He dismissed my doubtful glance with a gesture full of assurance. "It's a splendid place! You wait and see; we shall be there directly," he added.

We suddenly emerged into a broad and imposing street, on one side of which was a public garden, "El Paseo," I found out afterwards, the Town Promenade. Gazing idly at a palatial white building with a hotel omnibus drawn up before it, to my astonishment I found our driver also stopping at its door. A few minutes later, still scarcely able to credit my eyes, I got out and entered this palace, noticing "Burgaleza" on the board of the omnibus as I passed. I followed the tout, having glimpses in passing of a superbly arrayed table with serviettes that were each a work of art, that one of the splendid guests entertained at this establishment (should I not be among them?) would soon haughtily pull to pieces to wipe his mouth on—tables groaning beneath gilded baskets tottering with a lavish variety of choice fruit. Then came a long hall, darkly paneled, at the end of which I could see several white-capped men shouting fiercely and clashing knives, women answering shrilly and juggling with crashing dishes; a kitchen—the most diabolically noisy and malodorous I had ever approached. We went straight on towards it. Were we going through it? At the very threshold we stopped, and opening the panel-like door in the wall, the porter disappeared with my portmanteau, appearing again without my portmanteau, and hurried away. At this moment my eye caught something else, a door ajar on the other side of the passage and a heavy, wooden, clothless table, with several squares of bread upon it, and a fork or two. In Spain there is a sort of bread for the rich, and a forbidding juice-less papery bread for the humble. The bread on that table was of the latter category, far more like paper than that I had had at Bayonne.

Suddenly the truth flashed upon me. With a theatrical gesture I dashed open again the panel and passed into the pitchy gloom within. I struck a match. It was a cupboard, quite windowless, with just enough room for a little bed; I was standing on my luggage. No doubt in the room across the passage I should be given some cod soup, permanganate of potash and artificial bread. Then, extremely tired after my journey, I should crawl into my kennel, the pandemonium of the kitchen at my ear for several hours.

In the central hall I found the smiling proprietor. He seemed to regard his boarders generally as a gentle joke, and those who slept in the cupboard near the kitchen a particularly good but rather low one. I informed him that I would pay the regular sum for a day's board and lodging, and said I must have another room. A valet accepted the responsibility of seeing that I was given a bedroom. The landlord walked slowly away, his iron-gray side-whiskers, with their traditional air of respectability, giving a disguised look to his rogue's face. I was transferred from one cupboard to another; or rather, I had exchanged a cupboard for a wardrobe—reduced to just half its size by a thick layer of skirts and cloaks, twenty deep, that protruded from all four walls. But still the little open space left in the center ensured a square foot to wash and dress in, with a quite distinct square foot or two for sleep. And it was upstairs.

A quarter of an hour later, wandering along a dark passage on the way back to the hotel lounge, a door opened in a very violent and living way that made me start and look up, and a short rectangular figure, the size of a big square trunk, issued forth, just ahead of me. I recognized this figure fragmentarily—first, with a cold shudder, I recognized an excrescence of hair; then with a jump I recognized a hat held in its hand; then, with an instinctive shrinking, I realized that I had seen these flat traditional pseudo-american shoulders before. With a really comprehensive throb of universal emotion, I then recognized the whole man.

It was the implacable figure of my neighbor at dinner, of the Fonda del Mundo.

He moved along before me with wary rigidity, exhibiting none of the usual signs of recognition. He turned corners with difficulty, a rapid lurch precipitating him into the new path indicated when he reached the end of the wall. On the stairs he appeared to get stuck in much the way that a large american trunk would, borne by a sweating porter. At last he safely reached the hall. I was a yard or two behind him. He stopped to light a cigar, still taking up an unconscionable amount of space. I maneuvered round him, and gained one of the doors of the salle à manger. But as I came within his range of vision, I also became aware that my presence in the house was not a surprise to this sandwich man of Western citizenship. His eye fastened upon me with ruthless bloodshot indignation, an eye-blast as it were crystallized from the episode at Bayonne. But he was so dead and inactive that he seemed a phantom of his former self: and in all my subsequent dealings with him, this feeling of having to deal with a ghost, although a particularly mischievous one, persisted. If before my anger at the trick that had been played on me had dictated a speedy change of lodging, now my anxiety to quit this roof had, naturally, an overwhelming incentive.

After dinner I went forth boldly in search of the wonderful american enemy. Surely I had been condemned, in some indirect way, by him, to the cupboard beside the kitchen. No dungeon could have been worse. Had I then known, as I learned later, that he was the owner of this hotel, the medieval analogy would have been still more complete. He now had me in his castle.

I found him seated, in sinister conjunction with the proprietor or manager, as I supposed he was, in the lobby of the hotel. He turned slightly away as I came up to him with a sulky indifference due to self-restraint. Evidently the time for action was not ripe. There was no pretence of not recognizing me. As though our conversation in the Fonda del

Mundo had taken place a half-hour before, we acknowledged in no way a consciousness of the lapse of time, only of the shifted scene.

"Well, colonel," I said, adopting an allocution of the United States, "taking the air?"

He went on smoking.

"This is a nice little town."

"Vous vous plaisez ici, monsieur? C'est bien!" [15] he replied in french, as though I were not worthy even to *hear* his american accent, and that, if any communication was to be held with me, french must serve.

"I shall make a stay of some weeks here," I said, with indulgent defiance.

"Qui?"

"But not in this hotel."

He got up with something of his Bayonne look about him.

"No, I shouldn't. You might not find it a very comfortable hotel," he said vehemently in his mother tongue.

He walked away hurriedly, as a powder magazine might walk away from a fuse, if it did not, for some reason, want to blow up just then.

That was our last encounter that day. The upstairs and less dreadful dungeon with its layer of clothes would have been an admirable place for a murder. Not a sound would have penetrated its woollen masses and the thick spanish walls enclosing it. But the next morning I was still alive. I set out after breakfast to look for new quarters. My practiced eye had soon measured the inconsistencies of most of the Pensions of the town. But a place in the Calle Real suited me all right, and I decided to stop there for the time. There too the room was only a cupboard. But it was a human cupboard and not a clothes cupboard. It was one of the four tributaries of the dining room. My bedroom door was just beside my place at table—I had simply to step out of bed in the right direction, and there was the morning coffee. The extracting of my baggage from the Burgaleza was easy enough, except that I was charged a heavy toll. I protested with the manager for some time, but he smiled and smiled. "Those are our charges!" He shrugged his shoulders, dismissed the matter, and smiled absentmindedly when I renewed my objections. As at Bayonne, there was no sign of the enemy in the

[15] Are you enjoying yourself here? That's good!

morning. But I was not so sure this time that I had seen the last of him.

That evening I came amongst my new fellow pension-naires for the first time. This place had recommended itself to me, partly because the boarders would probably speak castilian, and so be practice for me. They were mostly not Gallegos, at least, who are the Bretons of Spain, and afford other Spaniards much amusement by their way of expressing themselves. My presence caused no stir whatever. Just as a stone dropped in a small pond which has long been un-touched, and has an opaque coat of green decay, slips dully to the bottom, cutting a neat little hole on the surface, so I took my place at the bottom of the table. But as the pond will send up its personal odor at this intrusion, so these peo-ple revealed something of themselves in the first few min-utes, in an illusive and immobile way. They must all have lived in that Pension together for an inconceivable length of time. My neighbor, however, promised to be a little El Dorado of spanish; a small mine of gossip, grammatical rules and willingness to impart these riches. I struck a deep shaft of friendship into him at once and began work without de-lay. Coming from Madrid, this ore was at least 30 carat, thoroughly thetaed and castilian stuff that he talked. What I gave him in exchange was insignificant. He knew several phrases in french and english, such as "If you please," and "fine day"; I merely confirmed him in these. Every day he would hesitatingly say them over, and I would assent, "quite right," and "very well pronounced." He was a tall, bearded man, head of the orchestra of the principal Café in the town. Two large cuffs lay on either side of his plate during meals, the size of serviettes. Out of them his hands emerged without in any way disturbing them, and served him with his food as far as they could. But he had to remain with his mouth quite near his plate, for the cuffs would not move a hair's breadth. This somewhat annoyed me, as it muffled a little the steady flow of spanish, and even sometimes was a cause of considerable waste. Once or twice without suc-cess I attempted to move the cuff on my side away from the plate. Their ascendancy over him and their indolence was profound.

But I was not content merely to work him for his mother tongue inertly, as it were. I wished to see it in use: to watch this stream of castilian working the mill of general conversa-tion, for instance. Although willing enough for himself, he had no chance in this Pension. On the third day, however, he invited me to come round to the Café after dinner and hear him play. Our dinners overlapped, he leaving early. So the meal over, I strolled round, alone.

The Café Pelayo was the only really parisian establishment in the town. It was the only one where the Madrilenos and the other Spaniards proper, resident in Pontaisandra, went regularly. I entered, peering round in a businesslike way at its monotonously mirrored walls and gilded ceiling. I took up an advantageous position, and settled down to study the idiom.

In a lull of the music, my chef d'orchestre came over to me, and presented me to a large group of people, friends of his. It was an easy matter, from that moment, to become acquainted with everybody in the Café.

I did not approach Spaniards in general, I may say, with any very romantic emotion. Each man I met possessed equally an ancient and admirable tongue, however degenerate himself. He often appeared like some rotten tree, in which a swarm of highly evocative admirable words had nested. I, like a bee cultivator, found it my business to transplant this vagrant swarm to a hive prepared. A language has its habits and idiosyncrasies just like a species of insect, as my first professor comfortably explained; its little world of symbols and parts of speech have to be most carefully studied and manipulated. But above all it is important to observe their habits and idiosyncrasies, and the pitch and accent that naturally accompanies them. So I had my hands full.

When the Café closed, I went home with Don Pedro, chef d'orchestre, to the Pension. Every evening, after dinner—and at lunch time as well—I repaired there. This lasted for three or four days. I now had plenty of opportunity of talking castilian Spanish. I had momentarily forgotten my american enemy.

On the fifth evening, I entered the Café as usual, making towards my most useful and intelligent group. But then, with a sinking of the heart, I saw the rectangular form of my ubiquitous enemy, quartered with an air of demoniac permanence in their midst. A mechanic who finds an unaccountable lump of some foreign substance stuck in the very heart of his machinery—what simile shall I use for my dismay? To proceed somewhat with this image, as this unhappy engineer might dash to the cranks or organ stops of his machine, so I dashed to several of my formerly most willing listeners and talkers. I gave one a wrench and another a screw, but I found that already the machine had become recalcitrant.

I need not enumerate the various stages of my defeat on that evening. It was more or less a passive and moral battle, rather than one with any evident show of the secretly bitter and desperate nature of the passions engaged. Of course, the inclusion of so many people unavoidably caused certain brusqueries here and there. The gradual cooling down of the whole room towards me, the disaffection that swept over the chain of little drinking groups from that center of mystical hostility, that soul that recognized in me something icily antipodean too, no doubt; the immobile figure of America's newest and most mysterious child, apparently emitting these strong waves without effort, as naturally as a fountain: all this, with great vexation, I recognized from the moment of the intrusion of his presence. It almost seemed as though he had stayed away from this haunt of his foreseeing what would happen. He had waited until I had comfortably settled myself and there was something palpable to attack. His absence may have had some more accidental cause.

What exactly it was, again, he found to say as regards me I never discovered. As at Bayonne, I saw the mouth working and experienced the social effects, only. No doubt it was the subtlest and most electric thing that could be found; brief, searching and annihilating. Perhaps something seemingly crude—that I was a spy—may have recommended itself to his ingenuity. But I expect it was a meaningless blast of disapprobation that he blew upon me, an eerie and stinging wind of convincing hatred. He evidently enjoyed a great ascendancy in the Café Pelayo. This would be explained no doubt by his commercial prestige. But it was due, I am sure, even more to his extraordinary character—molded by the sublime force of his illusion. His inscrutable immobility, his unaccountable self-control (for such a person, and feeling as he did towards me), were of course the american or anglo-saxon phlegm and sang-froid as reflected, or interpreted, in this violent human mirror.

I left the Café earlier than usual, before the chef d'orchestre. It was the following morning at lunch when I next saw him. He was embarrassed. His eyes wavered in my direction, fascinated and inquisitive. He found it difficult to realize that his respect for me had to end and give place to another feeling.

"You know Monsieur de Valmore?" he asked.

"That little ape of a Frenchman, do you mean?"

I knew this description of my wonderful enemy was only vulgar and splenetic. But I was too discouraged to be more exact.

This way of describing Monsieur de Valmore appeared to the chef d'orchestre so eccentric, apart from its vulgarity, that I lost at once in Don Pedro's sympathy. He told me, however, all about him; details that did not touch on the real constituents of this life.

"He owns the Burgaleza and many houses in Pontaisandra. Ships, too—Es Americano," he added.

Vexations and hindrances of all sorts now made my stay in Pontaisandra useless and depressing. Don Pedro had generally almost finished when we came to dinner, and I was forced to close down, so to say, the mine. Nothing more was to be extracted, at length, except disobliging monosyllables. The rest of the boarders remained morose and inaccessible. I went once more to the Café Pelayo, but the waiters even seemed to have come beneath the hostile spell. The new Café I chose yielded nothing but gallego chatter, and the garçon was not talkative.

There was little encouragement to try another Pension and stay on in Pontaisandra. I made up my mind to go to Corunna. This would waste time and I was short of money. But there is more gallego than spanish spoken in Galicia, even in the cities. Too easily automatic a conquest as it may seem, Monsieur de Valmore had left me nothing but the Gallegos. I was not getting the practice in spanish I needed, and this sudden deprivation of what I had mainly come into Spain for, poisoned for me the whole air of the place. The task of learning this tiresome language began to be burdensome. I even considered whether I should not take up gallego instead. But I decided finally to go to Corunna. On the following day, some hours before the time for the train, I paraded the line of streets towards the station, with the feeling that I was no longer there. The place seemed cooling down beneath my feet and growing prematurely strange. But the miracle happened. It declared itself with a smooth suddenness. A more exquisite checkmate never occurred in any record of such warfare.

The terrible ethnological difference that existed between Monsieur de Valmore and myself up till that moment, showed every sign of ending in a weird and revolting defeat for me. The "moment" I refer to was that in which I turned out of the High Street, into the short hilly avenue where the post office lay. I thought I would go up to the Correo and see for the last time if a letter for which I had been waiting had arrived.

On turning the corner I at once became aware of three anomalous figures walking just in front of me. They were all three of the proportions known in America as "husky." When I say they were walking, I should describe their movements more accurately as *wading*—wading through the air, evidently towards the post office. Their carriage was slightly rolling, like a ship under way. They occasionally bumped into each other, but did not seem to mind this. Yet no one would have mistaken these three young men for drunkards. But I daresay you will have already guessed. It would under other circumstances have had no difficulty in entering my head. As it was, there seemed a certain impediment of consciousness or inhibition with me which prevented me from framing to myself the word "American." These three figures were three Americans! This seems very simple, I know: but this very ordinary fact trembled and lingered before completely entering into my consciousness. The extreme rapidity of my mind in another sense—in seeing all that this fact, if verified, might signify to me—may have been responsible for that. Then one of them, on turning his head, displays the familiar features of Taffany, a Mississippi friend of mine. I simultaneously recognized Blauenfeld and Morton, the other two members of a trio. A real trio, like real twins, is rarer than one thinks. This one was the remnant of a quartet, however. I had met it first in Paris. Poor Bill (Borden Henneker) was killed in a motor accident. These three had mourned him with insatiable drinking, to which I had been a party for some days the year before. And my first feeling was complicated with a sense of their forlornness, as I recognized their three backs, rolling heavily and mournfully.

In becoming, from any three Americans, three friends of mine, they precipitated in an immediate inrush of the most full-blooded hope the sense of what might be boldly anticipated from this meeting. Two steps brought me up with them: my cordiality if anything exceeded theirs.

"Why, if it isn't Cairo! Look at this! Off what Christmas tree did you drop? Gee, I'm glad to see you, Kire!" shouted Taffany. He was the irrepressible Irishman of the three.

"Why, it's you, that's swell. We looked out for you in

Paris. You'd just left. How long have you been round here?" Blauenfeld ground out cordially. He was the rich melancholy one of the three.

"Come right up to the Correo and interpret for us, Cairo. You know the idioma, I guess. Feldie's a washout," said Morton, who was the great debauchee of the three.

Optimism, consciousness of power (no wonder! I reflected) surged out of them, my simple-hearted friends. Ah, the kindness! the *overwhelming* kindness. I bathed voluptuously in this american greeting—this real american greeting. Nothing naturalized about *that*. At the same time I felt almost awe at the thought of the dangerous nationality. These good fellows I knew and liked so well, seemed for the moment to have some intermixture of the strangeness of Monsieur de Valmore. However, I measured with enthusiasm their egregious breadth of shoulder, the exorbitance of their "pants." I examined with some disappointment these signs of nationality. How english they looked, compared to de Valmore. They were by no means american enough for my taste. Had they appeared in a star-stripe swallow-tail suit like the cartoons of Uncle Sam, I should not have been satisfied.

But I felt rather like some ambitious eastern prince who, having been continually defeated in battle by a neighbor because of the presence in the latter's army of a half-dozen elephants, suddenly becomes possessed of a couple of dozen himself.

I must have behaved oddly. I inquired anxiously about their plans. They were not off at once? No. That was capital. I was most awfully glad that they were not departing at once. I was glad that they had decided to stop. They had booked their rooms? Yes. That was good. So they were here for the night at all events? That was as it should be! You should always stop the night. Yes, I would with very great pleasure interpret for them at the Correo.—I cherished my three Americans as no Americans before have ever been cherished. I was inclined to shelter them as though they were perishable, to see that they didn't get run over, or expose themselves unwisely to the midday sun. Each transatlantic peculiarity of speech or gesture I received with something approaching exultation. Morton was soon persuaded that I was tight. All thoughts of Corunna disappeared. I did not ask at the Poste Restante for my letter.

First of all, I took my trio into a little Café near the

post office. There I told them briefly what was expected of them.

"You have a most distinguished compatriot here," I said.

"Oh. An American?" Morton asked seriously.

"Well, he deserves to be. But he began too late in life, I think. He hails from the southern part of France, and americanism came to him as a revelation when youth had already passed. He repented sincerely of his misguided early nationality. But his years spent as a Frenchman have left their mark. In the meantime, he won't leave Englishmen alone. He persecutes them, apparently, wherever he finds them."

"He mustn't do that!" Taffany said with resolution. "That won't do at all."

"Why, no, I guess he mustn't do that. What makes him want to do that? What's biting him anyway? Britishers are harmless enough, aren't they?" said Blauenfeld.

"I knew you'd look at the matter in that light," I said. "It's a rank abuse of authority; I knew it would be condemned at headquarters. Now if you could only be present, unseen, and witness how I, for instance, am oppressed by this fanatic fellow citizen of yours, and if you could issue forth, and reprove him, and tell him not to do it again, I should bless the day on which you were born in America."

"I wasn't born there anyway," said Morton. "But that's of no importance I suppose. Well, unfold your plan, Cairo."

"I don't see yet what we can do. Do you owe the guy any money? How does it come that he persecutes you like this?" Taffany asked.

"I'm very sorry you should have to complain, Mr. Ker-Orr, of treatment of that sort—but what sort is it anyway?"

I gave a lurid picture of my tribulations, to the scandal and indignation of my friends. They at once placed themselves, and with a humorous modesty their americanism— any quantity of that mixture in their "organisms"—at my disposal.

It appeared to me, to start with, of the first importance that Monsieur de Valmore should not get wind of what had happened. I took my three Americans cautiously out of the Café, reconnoitering before allowing them outside. As their hotel was near the station and not near the enemy's haunts, I encouraged their going back to it. I also supposed that they would wish to make some toilet for the evening, and relied on their good sense to put on their largest clothes, though Taffany was the only one of the three that seemed at all promising from that point of view. The scale of his buttocks did assure a certain outlandish girth that would at once reveal to M. de Valmore the presence of an American.

My army was in excellent form. Robust high spirits possessed them. I kept them out of the way till nightfall, and then after an early dinner, by a circuitous route, approached the Café Pelayo.

Morton was by this time a little screwed: he showed signs that he might become difficult. He insisted on producing a packet of obscene photographs, which he held before him fan-wise, like a hand of cards, some of them upside down. The confused mass of bare legs and arms of the photographs, distorted by this method of holding them, with some highly indecent details occurring here and there, produced the effect of a siamese demon. Blauenfeld was grinning over his shoulder, and seemed likely to forget the purpose for which he was being brought to the Pelayo.

"I know that coon," he insisted, pointing to one of the photos. "I swear I know that coon."

My idea was that the three Americans should enter the Café Pelayo without me. There they would establish themselves, and I had told them where to sit and how to spot their man. They should become acquainted with Monsieur de Valmore. Almost certainly the latter would approach his fellow citizens at once. But if there was any ice to break, it must be broken quickly by Taffany. They must ply him with imitation highballs or some other national drink, which they must undertake to mix for him. For this they could hand the bill to me afterwards. When the ground was sufficiently prepared, Taffany was to sign to me from the door, and I would then, after a further interval, put in my appearance.

Morton was kissing one of the photographs. Should he continue to produce, in season and out of season, his objectionable purchases, and display them, perhaps, to the customers of the Pelayo, although he might gain an ill-deserved popularity, he would certainly convey an impression of a different sort to that planned by me for this all-american evening. After considerable drunken argument I persuaded him to let me hold the photographs until the *coup* had been brought off. That point of discipline enforced, I sent them forward, sheltering, myself, in an archway in an adjoining street, and watched them enter the swing door "ra-raing," as ordered. But I had the mortification of seeing Morton fall down as he got inside, tripping, apparently, over the mat. Cursing this intemperate clown, I moved with some stealth to a small gallego Café within sight of the door of the Pelayo to await events.

I fixed my eyes on the brilliantly lighted windows of the Café. I imagined the glow of national pride, the spasm of delighted recognition, that would invade Monsieur de Valmore, on hearing the "ra-ra" chorus. Apart from the sentimental reason—its use as a kind of battle song—was the practical one that this noisy entrance would at once attract my enemy's attention. Ten minutes passed. I knew that my friends had located Monsieur de Valmore, even if they had not begun operations. Else they would have returned to my place of waiting. I wallowed naïvely in a superb indifference. Having set the machinery going, I turned nonchalantly away, paying no more attention to it. But the stage analogy affected me, in the sense that I became rather conscious of my appearance. I must await my cue, but was sure of my reception. I was the great star that was not expected. I was the unknown quantity. Meantime I pulled out the photographs and arranged them fantastically as Morton had done. From time to time I glanced idly down the road. At last I saw Blauenfeld making towards me, his usual american swing of the body complicated by rhythmical upheavals of mirth into tramplings, stumblings and slappings of his thigh. He was being very american in a traditional way as he approached me. He was a good actor, I thought: I was grateful to him. I paid for my coffee while he was coming up.

"Is it O.K.? Is he spitted?"

"Yep! we've got him fine! Come and have a look at him."

"Did he carry out his part of the program according to my arrangements?"

"Why, yes. We went right in, and all three spotted him at the same time. Taffany walked round and showed himself: he was the decoy. Morty and me coquetted round too, looking arch and *very american*. We could see his old pop-eyes beginning to stick out of his old head, and his old mouth watering. At last he could hold himself no longer. He roared at us. We bellowed at him. Gee, it was a great moment in american history! We just came together with a hiss and splutter of joy. He called up a trayful of drinks, to take off the rawness of our meeting. He can't have seen an American for months. He just gobbled us up. There isn't much left of poor old Taff. He likes him best and me next. Morty's on all fours at present, tickling his legs. He doesn't much care for Morty. He's made us promise to go to his hotel tonight."

I approached the palmy terrace, my mouth a little drawn and pinched, eyebrows raised, like a fastidious expert called in at a decisive moment. I entered the swing door with Blauenfeld, and looked round in a cold and businesslike way, as a doctor might, with the dignified inquiry, "Where is the patient?" The patient was there right enough, surrounded by the nurses I had sent. There he sat in as defenceless a condition of beatitude as possible. He stared at me with an incredulous grin at first. I believe that in this moment he would have been willing to extend to me a temporary pardon —a passe-partout [16] to his Café for the evening. He was so happy I became a bagatelle. Had I wished, an immediate reconciliation was waiting for me. But I approached him with impassive professional rapidity, my eye fixed on him, already making my diagnosis. I was so carried away by their figure of the physician, and adhered so faithfully to the bedside manner that I had decided upon as the most appropriate for the occasion, that I almost began things by asking him to put out his tongue. Instead I sat down carefully in front of him, pulling up my trousers meticulously at the knee. I examined his flushed and astounded face, his bristling mustache, his bloodshot eyes in silence. Then I very gravely shook my head.

No man surprised by his most mortal enemy in the midst of an enervating debauch, or barely convalescent from a bad illness, could have looked more nonplussed. But Monsieur de Valmore turned with a characteristic blank childish appeal to his nurses or boon companions for help, especially to Taffany. Perhaps he was shy or diffident of taking up actively his great role, when more truly great actors were present. Would not the divine America speak, or thunder, through them, at this intruder? He turned a pair of solemn, appealing, outraged dog's eyes upon Taffany. Would not his master repulse and chastise this insolence?

"I guess you don't know each other," said Taffany. "Say, Monsieur de Valmore, here's a friend of mine, Mr. Ker-Orr from London."

[16] skeleton key

My enemy pulled himself together as though the different parts of his body all wanted to leap away in different directions, and he found it all he could do to prevent such disintegration. An attempt at a bow appeared as a chaotic movement, the various parts of his body could not come together for it. It had met other movements on the way, and never became a bow at all. An extraordinary confusion beset his body. The beginning for a score of actions ran over it blindly and disappeared.

"Guess Mr. de Valmore ain't quite comfortable in that chair, Morty. Give him yours."

Then in this chaotic and unusual state he was hustled from one chair to the other, his muffled expostulations being in french, I noticed.

His racial instinct was undergoing the severest revolution it had yet known. An incarnation of sacred America herself had commanded him to take me to his bosom. And, as the scope of my victory dawned upon him, his personal mortification assumed the proportions of a national calamity. For the first time since the sealing of his citizenship he felt that he was only a Frenchman from the Midi—hardly as near an American, in point of fact, as is even a poor god-forsaken Britisher.

The Soldier of Humor is chivalrous, though implacable. I merely drank a bottle of champagne at his expense; made Don Pedro and his orchestra perform three extras, all made up of the most intensely national english light comedy music. Taffany, for whom Monsieur de Valmore entertained the maximum of respect, held him solemnly for some time with a detailed and fabulous enumeration of my virtues. Before long I withdrew with my forces to riot in barbarous triumph at my friends' hotel for the rest of the evening.

During the next two days I on several occasions visited the battlefield, but Monsieur de Valmore had vanished. His disappearance alone would have been sufficient to tell me that my visit to Spain was terminated. And in fact two days later I left Pontaisandra with the Americans, parting with them at Tuy, and myself continuing on the Leon-San Sebastian route back to France, and eventually to Paris. The important letter which I had been expecting had arrived at last and contained most unexpected news. My presence was required, I learned, in Budapest.

Arrived at Bayonne, I left the railway station with what people generally regard as a premonition. It was nothing of course but the usual mechanical working of inference within the fancy. It was already nighttime. Stepping rapidly across the square, I hurried down the hallway of the Fonda del Mundo. Turning brusquely and directly into the dining room of the inn I gazed round me almost shocked not to find what I now associated with that particular scene. Although Monsieur de Valmore had not been there to greet me, as good or better than his presence seemed to be attending me on my withdrawal from Spain. I still heard in this naked little room, as the wash of the sea in the shell, the echo of the first whisperings of his weird displeasure. Next day I arrived in Paris, my spanish nightmare shuffled off long before I reached that humdrum spot.

The Death of the Ankou

"And Death once dead, there's no more dying then."
WILLIAM SHAKESPEARE

ERVOANIK PLOUILLO—meaning the death god of Ploumil-liau; I said over the words, and as I did so I saw the death god.—I sat in a crowded inn at Vandevennec, in the *argoat*, not far from Rot, at the Pardon, deafened by the bitter screech of the drinkers, finishing a piece of cheese. As I avoided the maggots I read the history of the Ankou, that is the armorican death god. The guidebook to the antiquities of the district made plain, to the tourist, the ancient features of this belief. It recounted how the gaunt creature despatched from the country of death traversed at night the breton region. The peasant, late on the highroad and for the most part drunk, staggering home at midnight, felt around him suddenly the atmosphere of the shades, a strange cold penetrated his tissues, authentic portions of the *Néant* [1] pushed in like icy wedges within the mild air of the fields and isolated him from Earth, while rapid hands

[1] nothingness

seized his shoulders from behind, and thrust him into the ditch. Then, crouching with his face against the ground, his eyes shut fast, he heard the hurrying wheels of the cart. Death passed with his assistants. As the complaint of the receding wheels died out, he would cross himself many times, rise from the ditch, and proceed with a terrified haste to his destination.

There was a midnight mass at Ploumilliau, where the Ankou, which stood in a chapel, was said to leave his place, pass amongst the kneeling congregation, and tap on the shoulders those he proposed to take quite soon. These were memories. The statue no longer stood there, even. It had been removed some time before by the priests, because it was an object of too much interest to local magicians. They interfered with it, and at last one impatient hag, disgusted at its feebleness after it had neglected to assist her in a deadly matter she had on hand, introduced herself into the chapel one afternoon and, unobserved by the staff, painted it a pillar-box red. This she imagined would invigorate it and make it full of new mischief. When the priest's eyes in due course fell upon the red god, he decided that that would not do: he put it out of the way, where it could not be tampered with. So one of the last truly pagan images disappeared, wasting its curious efficacy in a loft, dusted occasionally by an ecclesiastical *bonne*.[2]

Such was the story of the last authentic plastic Ankou. In ancient Brittany the people claimed to be descended from a redoubtable god of death. But long passed out of the influence of that barbarity, their early death god, competing with gentler images, saw his altars fall one by one. In a semi-"parisian" parish, at last, the cult which had superseded him arrived in its turn at a universal decline, his ultimate representative was relegated to a loft to save it from the contemptuous devotions of a disappointed sorceress. Alas for Death! or rather for its descendants, thought I, a little romantically: that chill in the bone it brought was an ancient tonic: so long as it ran down the spine the breton soul was quick with memory. So, *alas!*

But I had been reading after that, and immediately prior to my encounter, about the peasant in the ditch, also the blinding of the god. It was supposed, I learned, that formerly the Ankou had his eyesight. As he traveled along in his cart between the hedges, he would stare about him, and spot likely people to right and left. One evening, as his flat, black, breton peasant's hat came rapidly along the road, as he straddled attentively bolt upright upon its jolting floor, a man and his master, in an adjoining field, noticed his approach. The man broke into song. His scandalized master attempted to stop him. But this bright bolshevik continued to sing an offensively carefree song under the nose of the supreme authority. The scandal did not pass unnoticed by the touchy destroyer. He shouted at him over the hedge, that for his insolence he had eight days to live, no more, which perhaps would teach him to sing etcetera! As it happened St. Peter was there. St. Peter's record leaves little question that a suppressed communist of an advanced type is concealed beneath the archangelical robes. It is a questionable policy to employ such a man as doorkeeper, and many popular airs in latin countries facetiously draw attention to the possibilities inherent in such a situation. In this case Peter was as scandalized at the behavior of the Ankou as was the farmer at that of his farmhand.

"Are you not ashamed, strange god, to condemn a man in that way, *at his work?*" he exclaimed. It was the *work* that did it, as far as Peter was concerned. Also it was his interference with work that brought his great misfortune on the Ankou. St. Peter, so the guidebook said, was as touchy as a captain of industry or a demagogue on that point. Though how could poor Death know that work, of all things, was sacred? Evidently he would have quite different ideas as to the attributes of divinity. But he had to pay immediately for his blunder. The revolutionary archangel struck him blind on the spot—struck Death blind; and, true to his character, that of one at all costs anxious for the applause of the *muchedumbre,* he returned to the field, and told the astonished laborer, who was still singing—because in all probability he was a little soft in the head—that he had his personal guarantee of a very long and happy life, and that he, Peter, had punished Death with blindness. At this the laborer, I daresay, gave a hoarse laugh; and St. Peter probably made his way back to his victim well satisfied in the reflection that he had won the favor of a vast mass of mortals.

In the accounts in the guidebook, it was the dating, however, connected with the tapping of owls, the crowing of hens, the significant evolutions of magpies, and especially the subsequent timetable involved in the lonely meetings with the plague-ridden death cart, that seemed to me most effective. If the peasant were overtaken by the cart on the night road towards the morning, he must die within the month. If the encounter is in the young night, he may have anything up to two years still to live. It was easy to imagine all the calculations indulged in by the distracted man after his evil meeting. I could hear his screaming voice (like those at the moment tearing at my ears as the groups of black-coated figures played some game of chance that maddened them) when he had crawled into the large, carved cupboard that served him for a bed, beside his wife, and how she would weigh this living, screaming, man, in the scales of time provided by superstition, and how the death damp would hang about him till his time had expired.

I was persuaded, finally, to go to Ploumilliau, and see the last statue of the blind Ankou. It was not many miles away. *Ervoanik Plouillo*—still to be seen for threepence: and while I was making plans for the necessary journey, my mind was powerfully haunted by that blind and hurrying apparition which had been so concrete there.

It was a long room where I sat, like a gallery: except during a Pardon it was not so popular. When I am reading something that interests me, the whole atmosphere is affected. If I look quickly up, I see things as though they were a part of a dream. They are all penetrated by the particular medium I have drawn out of my mind. What I had last read on this occasion, although my eyes at the moment were resting on the words *Ervoanik Plouillo*, was the account of how it affected the person's fate at what hour he met the Ankou. The din and smoke in the dark and crowded gallery was lighted by weak electricity, and a set and lowering daylight beyond. Crowds of umbrellas moved past the door which opened on to the square. Whenever I grew attentive to my surroundings, the passionate movement of whirling and striking arms was visible at the tables where the play was in progress, or a furious black body would dash itself from one chair to another. The "celtic screech" meantime growing harsher and harsher, sharpening itself on caustic snarling words, would soar to a paroxysm of energy. "Garce!" was the most frequent sound. All the voices would clamor for a moment together. It was a shattering noise in this dusky tunnel.—I had stopped reading, as I have said, and I lifted my eyes. It was then that I saw the Ankou.

With revulsed and misty eyes almost in front of me, an imperious figure, apparently armed with a club, was forcing its way insolently forward towards the door, its head up, an eloquently moving mouth hung in the air, as it seemed, for its possessor. It forced rudely aside everything in its path. Two men who were standing and talking to a seated one flew apart, struck by the club, or the scepter, of this king amongst afflictions. The progress of this embodied calamity was peculiarly straight. He did not deviate. He passed my table and I saw a small, highly colored face, with waxed mustaches. But the terrible perquisite of the blind was there in the staring, milky eyeballs: and an expression of ascetic ponderous importance weighted it so that, mean as it was in reality, this mask was highly impressive. Also, from its bitter immunity and unquestioned right-of-way, and from the habit of wandering through the outer jungle of physical objects, it had the look that some small boy's face might acquire, prone to imagine himself a steamroller, or a sightless Juggernaut.

The blinded figure had burst into my daydream so unexpectedly and so pat, that I was taken aback by this sudden close-up of so trite a tragedy. Where he had come was compact with an emotional medium emitted by me. In reality it was a private scene, so that this overweening intruder might have been marching through my mind with his taut convulsive step, club in hand, rather than merely traversing the eating room of a hotel, after a privileged visit to the kitchen. Certainly at that moment my mind was lying open so much, or was so much exteriorized, that almost literally, as far as I was concerned, it was inside, not out, that this image forced its way. Hence, perhaps, the strange effect.

The impression was so strong that I felt for the moment that I had met the death god, a garbled version with waxed mustaches. It was noon. I said to myself that, as it was noon, that should give me twelve months more to live. I brushed aside the suggestion that day was not night, that I was not a breton peasant, and that the beggar was probably not Death. I tried to shudder. I had not shuddered. His attendant, a sad-faced child, rattled a lead mug under my nose. I put two sous in it. I had no doubt averted the omen, I reflected, with this bribe.

The weather improved in the afternoon. As I was walking about with a fisherman I knew, who had come in twenty miles for this Pardon, I saw the Ankou again, collecting pence. He was strolling now, making a leisurely harvest from the pockets of these religious crowds. His attitude was, however, peremptory. He called out hoarsely his requirements, and turned his empty eyes in the direction indicated by his acolyte, where he knew there was a group who had not paid. His clothes were smart, all in rich, black broadcloth and black velvet, with a ribboned hat. He entered into every door he found open, beating on it with his clublike stick. I did not notice any *Thank you!* pass his lips. He appeared to snort when he had received what was due to him, and to turn away, his legs beginning to march mechanically like a man mildly shell-shocked.

The fisherman and I both stood watching him. I laughed. "Il ne se gêne pas!" [3] I said. "He does not *beg*. I don't call that a *beggar*."

"Indeed, you are right.—That is Ludo," I was told.

"Who is Ludo, then?" I asked.

"Ludo is the king of Rot!" my friend laughed. "The people round here spoil him, according to my idea. He's only a beggar. It's true he's blind. But he takes too much on himself."

He spat.

"He's not the only blind beggar in the world!"

"Indeed, he is not," I said.

"He drives off any other blind beggars that put their noses inside Rot. You see his stick? He uses it!"

We saw him led up to a party who had not noticed his approach. He stood for a moment shouting. From stupidity they did not respond at once. Turning violently away, he dragged his attendant after him.

"He must not be kept waiting!" I said.

"Ah, no. With Ludo you must be nimble!"

The people he had left remained crestfallen and astonished.

"Where does he live?" I asked.

"Well, he lives, I have been told, in a cave, on the road to Kermarquer. That's where he lives. Where he banks I can't tell you!"

Ludo approached us. He shouted in breton.

"What is he saying?"

"He is telling you to get ready; that he is coming!" said

my friend. He pulled out a few sous from his pocket, and said: "Faut bien! Needs must!" and laughed a little sheepishly.

I emptied a handful of coppers into the mug.

"Ludo!" I exclaimed. "How are you? Are you well?"

He stood, his face in my direction, with, except for the eyes, his mask of an irritable Jack-in-office, with the waxed mustaches of a small pretentious official.

"Very well! And you?" came back with unexpected rapidity.

"Not so bad, touching wood!" I said. "How is your wife?"

"Je suis garçon! I am a bachelor!" he replied at once.

"So you are better off, old chap!" I said. "Women serve no good purpose, for serious boys!"

"You are right," said Ludo. He then made a disgusting remark. We laughed. His face had not changed its expression. Did he try, I wondered, to picture the stranger, discharging remarks from empty blackness, or had the voice outside become for him or had it always been what the picture is to us? If you had never seen any of the people you knew, but had only talked to them on the telephone— what under these circumstances would So-and-So be as a voice, I asked myself, instead of mainly a picture?

"How long have you been a beggar, Ludo?" I asked.

"Longtemps!" he replied. I had been too fresh for this important beggar. He got in motion and passed on, shouting in breton.

"Quel type!" he said. "When we were in Penang, no, it was at Bankok, at the time of my service with the fleet, I saw just such another. He was a blind sailor, an Englishman. He had lost his sight in a shipwreck.—He would not beg from the black people."

"Why did he stop there?"

"He liked the heat. He was a *farceur*.[4] He was such another as this one."

Two days later I set out on foot for Kermarquer. I remembered as I was going out of the town that my friend had told me that Ludo's cave was there somewhere. I asked a woman working in a field where it was. She directed me.

I found him in a small, verdant enclosure, one end of it full of half-wild chickens, with a rocky bluff at one side, and a stream running in a bed of smooth boulders. A chimney stuck out of the rock, and a black string of smoke

4 droll fellow

wound out of it. Ludo sat at the mouth of his cave. A large
dog rushed barking towards me at my approach. I took up a
stone and threatened it. His boy, who was cooking, called off
the dog. He looked at me with intelligence.

"Good morning, Ludo!" I said. "I am an Englishman. I
met you at the Pardon, do you remember? I have come to
visit you, in passing. How are you? It's a fine day."

"Ah, it was you I met? I remember. You were with a
fisherman from Kermanec?"

"The same."

"So you're an Englishman?"

"Yes."

"Tiens!"

I did not think he looked well. My sensation of mock
superstition had passed. But although I was now familiar
with Ludo, when I looked at his staring mask I still experienced a faint reflection of my first impression, when he
was the death god. That impression had been a strong one,
and it was associated with superstition. So he was still a
feeble death god.

The bodies of a number of esculent frogs lay on the
ground, from which the back legs had been cut. These the
boy was engaged in poaching.

"What is that you are doing them in?" I asked him.

"White wine," he said.

"Are they best that way?" I asked.

"Why, that is a good way to do them," said Ludo. "You
don't eat frogs in England, do you?"

"No, that is repugnant to us."

I picked one up:

"You don't eat the bodies?"

"No, only the thighs," said the boy.

"Will you try one?" asked Ludo.

"I've just had my meal, thank you all the same."

I pulled out of my rucksack a flask of brandy.

"I have some eau-de-vie here," I said. "Will you have a
glass?"

"I should be glad to," said Ludo.

I sat down, and in a few minutes his meal was ready.
He disposed of the grenouilles with relish, and drank my
health in my brandy, and I drank his. The boy ate some
fish that he had cooked for himself, a few yards away from
us, giving small pieces to the dog.

After the meal Ludo sent the boy on some errand. The dog did not go with him. I offered Ludo a cigarette which he refused. We sat in silence for some minutes. As I looked at him I realized how the eyes mount guard over the face, as well as look out of it. The faces of the blind are hung there like a dead lantern. Blind people must feel on their skins our eyes upon them: but this sheet of flesh is rashly stuck up in what must appear far outside their control, an object in a foreign world of sight. So in consequence of this divorce, their faces have the appearance of things that have been abandoned by the mind. What is his face to a blind man? Probably nothing more than an organ, an exposed part of the stomach, that is a mouth.

Ludo's face, in any case, was *blind;* it looked the blindest part of his body, and perhaps the deadest, from which all the functions of a living face had gone. As a result of its irrelevant external situation, it carried on its own life with the outer world, and behaved with all the disinvolture of an internal organ, no longer serving to secrete thought any more than the foot. For after all to be lost *outside* is much the same as to be hidden in the dark *within.*—What served for a face for the blind, then? What did they have instead, that was expressive of emotion in the way that our faces are? I supposed that all the responsive machinery must be largely readjusted with them, and directed to some other part of the body. I noticed that Ludo's hands, all the movement of his limbs, were a surer indication of what he was thinking than was his face.

Still the face registered something. It was a health chart perhaps. He looked very ill I thought, and by that I meant, of course, that his *face* did not look in good health. When I said, "You don't look well," his hands moved nervously on his club. His face responded by taking on a sicklier shade.

"I'm ill," he said.

"What is it?"

"I'm indisposed."

"Perhaps you've met the Ankou." I said this thoughtlessly, probably because I had intended to ask him if he had ever heard of the Ankou, or something like that. He did not say anything to this, but remained quite still, then stood up and shook himself and sat down again. He began rocking himself lightly from side to side.

"Who has been telling you about the Ankou, and all those tales?" he suddenly asked.

"Why, I was reading about it in a guidebook, as a matter of fact, the first time I saw you. You scared me for a moment. I thought you might be he."

He did not reply to this, nor did he say anything, but his face assumed the expression I had noticed on it when I first saw it, as he forced his way through the throngs at the inn.

"Do you think the weather will hold?" I asked.

He made no reply. I did not look at him. With anybody with a face you necessarily feel that they can see you, even if their blank eyes prove the contrary. His fingers moved nervously on the handle of the stick. I felt that I had suddenly grown less popular. What had I done? I had mentioned an extinct god of death. Perhaps that was regarded as unlucky. I could not guess what had occurred to displease him.

"It was a good Pardon, was it not, the other day?" I said.

There was no reply. I was not sure whether he had not perhaps moods in which, owing to his affliction, he just entered into his shell, and declined to hold intercourse with the outside. I sat smoking for five minutes, I suppose, expecting that the boy might return. I coughed. He turned his head towards me.

"Vous êtes toujours là?" he asked.

"Oui, toujours," I said. Another silence passed. He placed his hand on his side and groaned.

"Is there something hurting you?" I asked.

He got up and exclaimed:

"Merde!"

Was that for me? I had the impression, as I glanced towards him to inquire, that his face expressed fear. Of what?

Still holding his side, shuddering and with an unsteady step, he went into his cave, the door of which he slammed. I got up. The dog growled as he lay before the door of the cave. I shouldered my rucksack. It was no longer a hospitable spot. I passed the midden on which the bodies of the grenouilles now lay, went down the stream, and so left. If I met the boy I would tell him his master was ill. But he was nowhere in sight, and I did not know which way he had gone.

I connected the change from cordiality to dislike on the part of Ludo with the mention of the Ankou. There seemed no other explanation. But why should that have affected

him so much? Perhaps I had put myself in the position of
the Ankou, even—unseen as I was, a foreigner and, so, ultimately dangerous—by mentioning the Ankou, with which
he was evidently familiar. He may even have retreated into
his cave, because he was afraid of me. Or the poor devil was
simply ill. Perhaps the frogs had upset him: or maybe the
boy had poisoned him. I walked away. I had gone a mile
probably when I met the boy. He was carrying a covered
basket.

"Ludo's ill. He went indoors," I said. "He seemed to be
suffering."

"He's not very well today," said the boy. "Has he gone
in?"

I gave him a few sous.

Later that summer the fisherman I had been with at the
Pardon told me that Ludo was dead.

Inferior Religions

PART I

To introduce my puppets, and the Wild Body, the generic
puppet of all, I must project a fanciful wandering figure to be
the showman to whom the antics and solemn gambols of
these wild children are to be a source of strange delight. In
the first of these stories he makes his appearance. The fascinating imbecility of the creaking men machines, that some
little restaurant or fishing boat works, was the original subject of these studies, though in fact the nautical set never
materialized. The boat's tackle and dirty little shell, or the
hotel and its technique of hospitality, keeping the limbs of
the men and women involved in a monotonous rhythm from
morning till night, that was the occupational background,
placed in Brittany or in Spanish Galicia.

A man is made drunk with his boat or restaurant as he is
with a merry-go-round: only it is the staid, everyday
drunkenness of the normal real, not easy always to detect.
We can all see the ascendance a "carousal" has on men,

driving them into a set narrow intoxication. The wheel at Carisbrooke imposes a set of movements upon the donkey inside it, in drawing water from the well, that it is easy to grasp. But in the case of a hotel or fishing boat, for instance, the complexity of the rhythmic scheme is so great that it passes as open and untrammeled life. This subtle and wider mechanism merges, for the spectator, in the general variety of nature. Yet we have in most lives the spectacle of a pattern as circumscribed and complete as a theorem of Euclid. So these are essays in a new human mathematic. But they are, each of them, simple shapes, little monuments of logic. I should like to compile a book of forty of these propositions, one deriving from and depending on the other. A few of the axioms for such a book are here laid down.

These intricately moving bobbins are all subject to a set of objects or to one in particular. Brotcotnaz [1] is fascinated by one object, for instance; one at once another vitality. He bangs up against it wildly at regular intervals, blackens it, contemplates it, moves round it and dreams. He reverences it: it is his task to kill it. All such fascination is religious. The damp napkins of the innkeeper are the altar cloths of his rough illusion, as Julie's bruises are the markings upon an idol; with the peasant, Mammon dominating the background. Zoborov and Mademoiselle Péronnette struggle for a Pension de Famille, unequally. Zoborov is the "polish" cuckoo of a stupid and ill-managed nest.

These studies of rather primitive people are studies in a savage worship and attraction. The innkeeper rolls between his tables ten million times in a realistic rhythm that is as intense and superstitious as are the figures of a war dance. He worships his soup, his damp napkins, the lump of procreative flesh probably associated with him in this task. Brotcotnaz circles round Julie with gestures a million times repeated. Zoborov camps against and encircles Mademoiselle Péronnette and her lover Carl. Bestre is the eternal watchdog, with an elaborate civilized ritual. Similarly the Cornac is engaged in a death struggle with his "Public." All religion has the mechanism of the celestial bodies, has a dance. When we wish to renew our idols, or break up the rhythm of our naïveté, the effort postulates a respect which is the summit of devoutness.

[1] Brotcotnaz and all the characters mentioned in this paragraph and the next are found in the stories published in *The Wild Body*.

PART II

I would present these puppets, then, as carefully selected specimens of religious fanaticism. With their attendant objects or fetishes they live and have a regular food and vitality. They are not creations, but puppets. You can be as exterior to them, and live their life as little, as the showman grasping from beneath and working about a Polichinelle. They are only shadows of energy, not living beings. Their mechanism is a logical structure and they are nothing but that.

Boswell's Johnson, Mr. Veneering, Malvolio, Bouvard and Pécuchet, the "commissaire" in *Crime and Punishment,* do not live; they are congealed and frozen into logic, and an exuberant hysterical truth. They transcend life and are complete ciphers, but they are monuments of dead imperfection. Their only significance is their egoism. So the great intuitive figures of creation live with the universal egoism of the poet. This "Realism" is satire. Satire is the great Heaven of Ideas, where you meet the titans of red laughter; it is just below intuition, and life charged with black illusion.

PART III

When we say "types of humanity," we mean violent individualities, and nothing stereotyped. But Quixote, Falstaff, and Pecksniff attract, in our memory, a vivid following. All difference is energy, and a category of humanity a relatively small group, and not the myriads suggested by a generalization.

A comic type is a failure of a considerable energy, an imitation and standardizing of self, suggesting the existence of a uniform humanity,—creating, that is, a little host as like as ninepins; instead of one synthetic and various ego. It is the laziness that is the habit-world or system of a successful personality. It is often part of our own organism become a fetish. So Boswell's Johnson or Sir John Falstaff are minute and rich religions.

That Johnson was a sort of god to his biographer we readily see. But Falstaff as well is a sort of english god, like the rice-bellied gods of laughter in China. They are illusions hugged and lived in; little dead totems. Just as all gods are a repose for humanity, the big religions an immense refuge and rest, so are these little grotesque fetishes. One reason for this is that, for the spectator or participator, it is a world within the world, full of order, even if violent.

All these are forms of static art, then. There is a great deal of divine olympian sleep in english humor, and its delightful dreams. The most gigantic spasm of laughter is sculptural, isolated, and essentially simple.

PART IV

I WILL catalogue the attributes of Laughter.

1. Laughter is the Wild Body's song of triumph.
2. Laughter is the climax in the tragedy of seeing, hearing, and smelling self-consciously.
3. Laughter is the bark of delight of a gregarious animal at the proximity of its kind.
4. Laughter is an independent, tremendously important, and lurid emotion.
5. Laughter is the representative of tragedy, when tragedy is away.
6. Laughter is the emotion of tragic delight.
7. Laughter is the female of tragedy.
8. Laughter is the strong elastic fish, caught in Styx, springing and flapping about until it dies.
9. Laughter is the sudden handshake of mystic violence and the anarchist.
10. Laughter is the mind sneezing.
11. Laughter is the one obvious commotion that is not complex, or in expression dynamic.
12. Laughter does not progress. It is primitive, hard and unchangeable.

PART V

THE Wild Body, I have said, triumphs in its laughter. What is the Wild Body?

The Wild Body, as understood here, is that small, primitive, literally antediluvian vessel in which we set out on our adventures. Or regarded as a brain, it is rather a winged magic horse, that transports us hither and thither, sometimes rushing, as in the chinese cosmogonies, up and down the outer reaches of space. Laughter is the brain-body's snort of exultation. It expresses its wild sensation of power and speed; it is all that remains physical in the flash of thought, its friction: or it may be a defiance flung at the hurrying fates.

The Wild Body is this supreme survival that is us, the stark apparatus with its set of mysterious spasms; the most profound of which is laughter.

PART VI

THE chemistry of personality (subterranean in a sort of cemetery, whose decompositions are our lives) puffs up in frigid balls, soapy Snowmen, arctic carnival masks, which we can photograph and fix.

Upwards from the surface of existence a lurid and dramatic scum oozes and accumulates into the characters we see. The real and tenacious poisons, and sharp forces of vitality, do not socially transpire. Within five yards of another man's eyes we are on a little crater, which, if it erupted, would split up as would a cocoa tin of nitrogen. Some of these bombs are ill-made, or some erratic in their timing. But they are all potential little bombs. Capriciously, however, the froth-forms of these darkly contrived machines twist and puff in the air, in our legitimate and liveried masquerade.

Were you the female of Bestre or Brotcotnaz and beneath the counterpane with him, you would be just below the surface of life, in touch with a tragic organism. The first indications of the proximity of the real soul would be apparent. You would be for hours beside a filmy crocodile, conscious of it like a bone in an X ray, and for minutes in the midst of a tragic wallowing. The soul lives in a cadaverous activity; its dramatic corruption thumps us like a racing engine in the body of a car. The finest humor is the great play-shapes blown up or given off by the tragic corpse of life underneath the world of the camera. This futile, grotesque, and sometimes pretty spawn, is what in this book is snapshotted by the imagination.

Any master of humor is an essential artist; even Dickens is no exception. For it is the character of uselessness and impersonality which is found in laughter (the anarchist emotion concerned in the comic habit of mind) that makes a man an "artist." So when he begins living on his laughter, even in spite of himself a man becomes an artist. Laughter is that arch complexity that is really as simple as bread.

PART VII

IN this objective play-world, corresponding to our social

consciousness, as opposed to our solitude, no final issue is decided. You may blow away a man-of-bubble with a burgundian gust of laughter, but that is not a personality, it is an apparition of no importance. But so much correspondence it has with its original that, if the cadaveric travail beneath is vigorous and bitter, the dummy or mask will be of a more original grotesqueness. The opposing armies in the early days in Flanders stuck up dummy men on poles for their enemies to pot at, in a spirit of ferocious banter. It is only a shell of that description that is engaged in the sphere of laughter. In our rather drab revel there is a certain category of spirit that is not quite inanimate and yet not very funny. It consists of those who take, at the Clarkson's [2] situated at the opening of their lives, some conventional Pierrot costume. This is intended to assure them a minimum of strain, of course, and so is a capitulation. In order to evade life we must have recourse to those uniforms, but such a choice leaves nothing but the white and ethereal abstraction of the shadow of laughter.

So the King of Play is not a phantom corresponding to the sovereign farce beneath the surface. The latter must always be reckoned on: it is the Skeleton at the Feast, potentially, with us. That soul or dominant corruption is so real that he cannot rise up and take part in man's festival as a Falstaff of unwieldy spume. If he comes at all it must be as he is, the skeleton or bogey of veritable life, stuck over with corruptions and vices. As such he could rely on a certain succès d'estime: nothing more.

PART VIII

A SCORNFUL optimism, with its confident onslaughts on our snobbism, will not make material existence a peer for our energy. The gladiator is not a perpetual monument of triumphant health: Napoleon was harried with Elbas: moments of vision are blurred rapidly, and the poet sinks into the rhetoric of his will.

But life is invisible, and perfection is not in the waves or houses that the poet sees. To rationalize that appearance is not possible. Beauty is an icy douche of ease and happiness at something *suggesting* perfect conditions for an organism: it remains suggestion. A stormy landscape, and a pigment

2 Theatrical costumer

consisting of a lake of hard, yet florid waves; delight in each brilliant scoop or ragged burst was John Constable's beauty. Leonardo's consisted in a red rain on the shadowed side of heads, and heads of massive female aesthetes. Uccello accumulated pale parallels, and delighted in cold architecture of distinct color. Korin found in the symmetrical gushing of water, in waves like huge vegetable insects, traced and worked faintly, on a golden pâte, his business. Cézanne like cumbrous, democratic slabs of life, slightly leaning, transfixed in vegetable intensity.

Beauty is an immense predilection, a perfect conviction of the desirability of a certain thing, whatever that thing may be. It is a universe for one organism. To a man with long and consumptive fingers, a sturdy hand may be heaven. We can aim at no universality of form, for what we see is not the reality. Henri Fabre was in every way a superior being to a Salon artist, and he knew of elegant grubs which he would prefer to the Salon's painter's nymphs.—It is quite obvious though, to fulfil the conditions of successful art, that we should live in relatively small communities.

from BLAST, 1914

THE ENEMY OF THE STARS

ADVERTISEMENT

THE SCENE.   **SOME BLEAK CIRCUS, UNCOVERED, CAREFULLY CHOSEN, VIVID NIGHT. IT IS PACKED WITH POSTERITY, SILENT AND EXPECTANT. POSTERITY IS SILENT, LIKE THE DEAD, AND MORE PATHETIC.**

CHARACTERS.

TWO HEATHEN CLOWNS, GRAVE BOOTH ANIMALS CYNICAL ATHLETES.

DRESS.   **ENORMOUS YOUNGSTERS, BURST-ING EVERYWHERE THROUGH HEAVY TIGHT CLOTHES, LABORED IN BY DULL EXPLOSIVE MUSCLES, full of fiery dust and sinewy energetic air, not sap. BLACK CLOTH CUT SOME-WHERE, NOWADAYS, ON THE UPPER BALTIC.**

VERY WELL ACTED BY YOU AND ME.

ENEMY OF THE STARS

ONE IS IN IMMENSE COLLAPSE OF CHRONIC PHILOSOPHY. YET HE BULGES ALL OVER, COMPLEX FRUIT, WITH SIMPLE FIRE OF LIFE. GREAT MASK, VENUSTIC AND VERIDIC, TYPE OF FEMININE BEAUTY CALLED "MANNISH."

FIRST HE IS ALONE. A HUMAN BULL RUSHES INTO THE CIRCUS. THIS SUPER IS NO MORE IMPORTANT THAN LOUNGING STAR OVERHEAD. HE IS NOT EVEN A "STAR." HE RUSHES OFF, INTO THE EARTH.

CHARACTERS AND PROPERTIES BOTH EMERGE FROM GANGWAY INTO GROUND AT ONE SIDE.

THEN AGAIN THE PROTAGONIST REMAINS NEGLECTED, AS THOUGH HIS TWO FELLOW ACTORS HAD FORGOTTEN HIM, CAROUSING IN THEIR PROFESSIONAL CAVERN.

SECOND CHARACTER, APPALLING "GAMIN," BLACK BOURGEOIS ASPIRATIONS UNDERMINING BLATANT VIRTUOSITY OF SELF.

His criminal instinct of intemperate bilious heart, put at service of unknown Humanity, our King, to express its violent royal aversion to Protagonist, statue-mirage of Liberty in the great desert.

Mask of discontent, anxious to explode, restrained by qualms of vanity, and professional coyness. Eyes grown venturesome in native temperatures of Pole—indulgent and familiar, blessing with white nights.

Type of characters taken from broad faces where Europe grows arctic, intense, human and universal.

"Yet you and me: why not from the English metropolis?" —Listen: it is our honeymoon. We go abroad for first scene of our drama. Such a strange thing as our coming together requires a strange place for initial stages of our intimate ceremonious acquaintance.

THERE ARE TWO SCENES.

STAGE ARRANGEMENTS.

RED OR STAINED COPPER PREDOMINANT COLOR. OVERTURNED CASES AND OTHER IMPEDIMENTA HAVE BEEN COVERED, THROUGHOUT ARENA, WITH OLD SAIL CANVAS.

HUT OF SECOND SCENE IS SUGGESTED BY CHARACTERS TAKING UP THEIR POSITION AT OPENING OF SHAFT LEADING DOWN INTO MINE'S QUARTERS.

A GUST, SUCH AS IS MET IN THE CORRIDORS OF THE TUBE, MAKES THEIR CLOTHES SHIVER OR FLAP, AND BLARES UP THEIR VOICES. MASKS FITTED WITH TRUMPETS OF ANTIQUE THEATER, WITH EFFECT OF TWO CHILDREN BLOWING AT EACH OTHER WITH TIN TRUMPETS.

AUDIENCE LOOKS DOWN INTO SCENE, AS THOUGH IT WERE A HUT ROLLED HALF ON ITS BACK, DOOR UPWARDS, CHARACTERS GIDDILY MOUNTING IN ITS OPENING.

ARGHOL.

INVESTMENT OF RED UNIVERSE.

EACH FORCE ATTEMPTS TO SHAKE HIM.

CENTRAL AS STONE. POISED MAGNET OF SUBTLE, VAST, SELFISH THINGS.

HE LIES LIKE HUMAN STRATA OF INFERNAL BIOL-
OGIES. WALKS LIKE WARY SHIFTING OF BODIES IN
DISTANT EQUIPOISE. SITS LIKE A GOD BUILT BY AN
ARCHITECTURAL STREAM, FECUNDED BY MAD BLASTS
OF SUNLIGHT.

———

The first stars appear and Arghol comes out of the hut.
This is his cue. The stars are his cast. He is rather late and
snips into its place a test button. A noise falls on the cream
of Posterity, assembled in silent banks. One hears the gnats'
song of the Thirtieth centuries.

They strain to see him, a gladiator who has come to
fight a ghost, Humanity—the great Sport of Future Mankind.

He is the prime athlete exponent of this sport in its palmy
days. Posterity slowly sinks into the hypnotic trance of Art,
and the Arena is transformed into the necessary scene.

THE RED WALLS OF THE UNIVERSE NOW SHUT THEM
IN, WITH THIS CONDEMNED PROTAGONIST.

THEY BREATHE IN CLOSE ATMOSPHERE OF TERROR
AND NECESSITY TILL THE EXECUTION IS OVER, THE
RED WALLS RECEDE, THE UNIVERSE SATISFIED.

THE BOX OFFICE RECEIPTS HAVE BEEN ENORMOUS.

———

THE ACTION OPENS.

THE YARD.

The Earth has burst, a granite flower, and disclosed the scene.

A wheelwright's yard.

Full of dry, white volcanic light.

Full of emblems of one trade: stacks of pine, iron, wheels stranded.

Rough Eden of one soul, to whom another man, and not EVE, would be mated.

A canal at one side, the night pouring into it like blood from a butcher's pail.

Rouge mask in aluminum mirror, sunset's grimace through the night.

A leaden gob, slipped at zenith, first drop of violent night, spreads cataclysmically in harsh water of coming. Caustic Reckett's stain.

Three trees, above canal, sentimental, black and conventional in number, drive leaf flocks, with jeering cry.

Or they slightly bend their joints, impassible acrobats; step rapidly forward, faintly incline their heads.

Across the mud in pod of the canal their shadows are gawky toy crocodiles, sawed up and down by infant giant?

Gollywog of Arabian symmetry, several tons, Arghol drags them in blank nervous hatred.

THE SUPER.

Arghol crosses yard to the banks of the canal: sits down.

"Arghol!"

"I am here."

His voice raucous and disfigured with a catarrh of lies in the fetid bankrupt atmosphere of life's swamp: clear and splendid among Truth's balsamic hills, shepherding his agile thoughts.

"Arghol!"

It was like a child's voice hunting its mother.

A note of primitive distress edged the thick bellow. The figure rushed without running. Arghol heeled over to the left. A boot battered his right-hand ribs. These were the least damaged: it was their turn.

Upper lip shot down, half covering chin, his body reached methodically. At each blow, in muscular spasm, he made the pain pass out. Rolled and jumped, crouched and flung his groveling Enceladus weight against it, like swimmer with wave.

The boot, and heavy shadow above it, went. The self-centered and elemental shadow, with whistling noise peculiar to it, passed softly and sickly into a doorway's brown light.

The second attack, pain left by first shadow, lashing him, was worse. He lost consciousness.

THE NIGHT.

His eyes woke first, shaken by rough moonbeams. A white, crude volume of brutal light blazed over him. Immense bleak electric advertisement of God, it crushed with wild emptiness of street.

The ice field of the sky swept and crashed silently. Blowing wild organism into the hard splendid clouds, some will cast its glare, as well, over him.

The canal ran in one direction, his blood, weakly, in the opposite.

The stars shone madly in the archaic blank wilderness of the universe, machines of prey.

Mastodons, placid in electric atmosphere, white rivers of power. They stood in eternal black sunlight.

Tigers are beautiful imperfect brutes.

Throats iron eternities, drinking heavy radiance, limbs towers of blatant light, the stars poised, immensely distant, with their metal sides, pantheistic machines.

The farther, the more violent and vivid, Nature: weakness crushed out of creation! Hard weakness, a flea's size, pinched to death in a second, could it get so far.

He rose before this cliff of cadaverous beaming force, imprisoned in a messed socket of existence.

Will Energy some day reach Earth like violent civilization, smashing or hardening all? In his mind a chip of distant hardness, tugged at dully like a tooth, made him ache from top to toe.

But the violences of all things had left him so far intact.

HANP.

I.

Hanp comes out of hut, coughing like a goat, rolling a cigarette. He goes to where Arghol is lying. He stirs him with his foot roughly.

Arghol strains and stretches elegantly, face over shoulder, like a woman.

"Come, you fool, and have supper." Hanp walks back to hut, leaving him.

Arghol lies, hands clasped around his knees. This new kick has put him into a childish lethargy. He gets to his feet soon, and walks to hut. He puts his hand on Hanp's shoulder, who has been watching him, and kisses him on the cheek.

Hanp shakes him off with fury and passes inside hut.

Bastard violence of his half disciple, métis of an apache of the icy steppe, sleek citizen, and his own dumbfounding soul.

Fungi of sullen violet thoughts, investing primitive vegetation. Hot words drummed on his ear every evening: abuse: question. Groping hands strummed toppling Byzantine organ of his mind, producing monotonous black fugue.

Harsh bayadere-shepherdess of Pamir, with her Chinese beauty: living on from month to month in utmost tent with wastrel, lean as mandrake root, red and precocious: with heavy black odor of vast Manchurian garden—deserts, and the disreputable muddy gold squandered by the unknown sun of the Amur.

His mind unlocked, free to this violent hand. It was his mind's one cold flirtation, then cold love. Excelling in beauty, marked out for Hindu fate of sovereign prostitution, but clear of the world, with furious vow not to return. The deep female strain succumbed to this ragged spirit of crude manhood, masculine with blunt wilfulness and hideous stupidity of the fecund horde of men, phallic wand-like cataract incessantly poured into God. This pip of icy spray struck him on the mouth. He tasted it with new pleasure, before spitting it out: acrid.

To be spat back among men. The young men foresaw the event.

They ate their supper at the door of the hut. An hour passed in wandering spacious silence.

"Was it bad tonight?" a fierce and railing question often repeated.

Arghol lay silent, his hands a thick shell fitting back of head, his face gray vegetable cave.

"Can't you kill him, in the name of God? A man has his hands, little else. Mote and speck, the universe illimitable!" Hanp gibed. "It is true he is a speck, but all men are. To you he is immense."

They sat, two grubby shadows, unvaccinated as yet by the moon's lymph, sickened by the immense vague infections of night.

"That is absurd. I have explained to you. Here I get routine, the will of the universe manifested with directness and persistence. Figures of persecution are accidents or adventures for some. Prick the thin near heart, like a pea, and the bubble puffs out. That would not be of the faintest use in my case."

Two small black flames, wavering, as their tongues moved, drumming out thought, with low earth draughts and hard sudden winds dropped like slapping birds from climaxes in the clouds.

No Morris-lens would have dragged them from the key of vastness. They must be severe midgets, brain specks of the vertiginous, seismic vertebrae, slowly-living lines, of landscape.

"Self, sacred act of violence, is like murder on my face and hands. The stain won't come out. It is the one piece of property all communities have agreed it is illegal to possess. The sweetest-tempered person, once he discovers you are that sort of criminal, changes any opinion of you, and is on his guard. When mankind cannot overcome a personality, it has an immemorial way out of the difficulty. It becomes it. It imitates and assimilates that Ego until it is no longer one. This is success.

Between Personality and Mankind it is always a question of dog and cat; they are diametrically opposed species. Self is the ancient race, the rest are the new one. Self is the race that lost. But Mankind still suspects Egotistic plots, and hunts Pretenders.

My uncle is very little of a relation. It would be foolish to kill him. He is an échantillon,[1] acid advertisement slipped in letter box: space's storerooms dense with frivolous originals. I am used to him, as well."

Arghol's voice had no modulations of argument. Weak now, it handled words numbly, like tired compositor. His body was quite strong again and vivacious. Words acted on it as rain on a plant. It got a stormy neat brilliance in this soft shower. One flame balanced giddily erect, while other larger one swerved and sang with speech coldly before it.

They lay in a pool of bleak brown shadow, disturbed once by a rat's plunging head. It seemed to rattle along, yet slide on oiled planes. Arghol shifted his legs mechanically. It was a hutch with low loft where they slept.

Beyond the canal, brute lands, shuttered with stony clouds, lay in heavy angels of sand. They were squirted in by twenty ragged streams; legions of quails hopped parasitically in the miniature cliffs.

Arghol's uncle was a wheelwright on the edge of the town.

Two hundred miles to north the Arctic circle swept. Sin-

1 sample

ister tramps, its winds came wandering down the high road, fatigued and chill, doors shut against them.

"First of all; lily pollen of Ideal on red badge of your predatory category. Scrape this off and you lose your appetite. Obviously.—But I don't want in any case to eat Smith, because he is tough and distasteful to me. I am too vain to do harm, too superb ever to lift a finger when harmed.

A man eats his mutton chop, forgetting it is his neighbor; drinks every evening blood of the Christs, and gossips of glory.

Existence; loud feeble sunset, blaring like lumpish, savage clown, alive with rigid tinsel, before a misty door: announcing events, tricks and a thousand follies, to penniless herds, their eyes red with stupidity.

To leave violently slow monotonous life is to take header into the boiling starry cold. (For with me some guilty fire of friction unspent in solitariness, will reach the stars.)

Hell of those Heavens uncovered, whirling pit, every evening! You cling to any object, dig your nails in earth, not to drop into it."

The night plunged gleaming nervous arms down into the wood, to wrench it up by the roots. Restless and rhythmical, beyond the staring red-rimmed doorway, giddy and expanding in drunken walls, its heavy drastic lights shifted.

Arghol could see only ponderous arabesques of red cloud, whose lines did not stop at door's frame, but pressed on into shadows within the hut, in tyrannous continuity. As a cloud drove eastward, out of this frame, its weight passed, with spiritual menace, into the hut. A thunderous atmosphere thickened above their heads.

Arghol, paler, tossed clumsily and swiftly from side to side, as though asleep.

He got nearer the door. The clouds had room to waste themselves. The land continued in dull form, one percent animal, these immense bird-amoebas. Nerves made the earth pulse up against his side and reverberate. He dragged hot palms along the ground, caressing its explosive harshness.

All merely exterior attack.

His face calm seismograph of eruptions in Heaven.

Head of black, eagerly carved, herculean Venus, of iron tribe, hyperbarbarous and ascetic. Lofty tents, sonorous with October rains, swarming from vast bright doll-like Asiatic lakes.

Faces following stars in blue rivers, till sea-struck, thundering engine of red water.

Pink idle brotherhood of little stars, passed over by rough cloud of sea.

Cataclysm of premature decadence.

Extermination of the resounding, somber, summer tents in a decade, furious mass of images left: no human.

Immense production of barren muscular girl idols, wood verdigris, copper, dull paints, flowers.

Hundred idols to a man, and a race swamped in hurricane of art, falling on big narrow souls of its artists.

Head heavy and birdlike, weighted to strike, living on his body, ungainly red Atlantic wave.

"To have read all the books of the town, Arghol, and to come back here to take up this life again."

Coaxing: genuine stupefaction: reproach, a trap.

Arghol once more preceded him through his soul, unbenevolent. Doors opened on noisy blankness, coming through from calm, reeling noon-loudness beyond. Garrets waking like faces. A shout down a passage to show its depth, horizon as well. Voice coming back with suddenness of expert pugilistics.

Perpetual inspector of himself.

"I must live, like a tree, where I grow. An inch to left or right would be too much.

In the town I felt unrighteous in escaping blows, home anger, destiny of here.

Selfishness, flouting of destiny, to step so much as an inch out of the bull's-eye of your birth. (When it is obviously a bull's-eye!)

A visionary tree, not migratory: visions from within.

A man with headache lies in deliberate leaden inanimation. He isolates his body, floods it with phlegm, sucks numbness up to his brain.

A soul wettest dough, doughest lead: a bullet. To drop down Eternity like a plummet.

Accumulate in myself, day after day, dense concentration of pig life. Nothing spent, stored rather in strong stagnation, till rid at last of evaporation and lightness characteristic of men. So burst Death's membrane through, slog beyond, not float in appalling distances.

Energy has been fixed on me from nowhere—heavy and astonished: resigned. Or is it for remote sin! I will use it, anyway, as prisoner his bowl or sheet for escape: not as means of idle humiliation.

One night Death left his card. I was not familiar with the name he chose: but the black edge was deep. I flung it back. A thousand awakenings of violence.

Next day I had my knife up my sleeve as my uncle came at me, ready for what you recommend. But a superstition, habit, is there, curbing him mathematically: that of not killing me. I should know an ounce of effort more.—He loads my plate, even. He must have palpable reasons for my being alive."

———

A superb urchin watching some center of angry commotion in the street, his companion kept his puffed slit eyes, generously cruel, fixed on him. God and Fate, constant protagonists, one equivalent to Police, his simple sensationalism was always focused on. But God was really his champion. He longed to see God fall on Arghol, and wipe the earth with him. He egged God on: then egged on Arghol. His soft rigid face grinned with intensity of attention, propped contemplatively on hand.

Port—prowler, serf of the capital, serving its tongue and gait within the grasp and aroma of the white, mat, immense sea. Abstract instinct of sullen seafarer, dry-salted in slow acrid airs, aerian flood not stopped by shore, dying in dirty warmth of harbor-boulevards.

His soul like ocean-town; leaned on by two skies. Lower opaque one washes it with noisy clouds: or lies giddily flush with street crevices, wedges of black air, flooding it with red emptiness of dead light.

It sends ships between its unchanging slight rock of houses periodically, slowly to spacious center. Nineteen big ships, like nineteen nomad souls for its amphibious sluggish body, locked there.

II.

"What is destiny? Why yours to stay here, more than to live in the town or cross to America?"

"My dear Hanp, your geography is so up-to-date!"

"Geography doesn't interest me. America is geography.

I've explained to you what the town is like.

Offenses against the discipline of the universe are registered by a sort of conscience, prior to the kicks. Blows rain on me. Mine is not a popular post. It is my destiny right enough: an extremely unpleasant one.

"It is not the destiny of a man like you to live buried in this cursed hole."

"Our soul is wild, with primitiveness of its own. Its wilderness is anywhere—in a shop, sailing, reading psalms, its greatest good our destiny.

Anything I possess is drunk up here on the world's brink, by big stars, and returned me in the shape of thought heavy as a meteorite. The stone of the stars will do for my seal and emblem. I practice with it, monotonous putting, that I may hit Death when he comes."

"Your thought is buried in yourself."

"A thought weighs less in a million brains than in one. No one is conjuror enough to prevent spilling. Rather the bastard form infects the original. Famous men are those who have exchanged themselves against a thousand idiots. When you hear a famous man has died penniless and diseased, you say, 'Well served.' Part of life's arrangement is that the few best become these cheap scarecrows.

The process and condition of life, without any exception, is a grotesque degradation, and "souillure" [2] of the original solitude of the soul. There is no help for it, since each gesture and word partakes of it, and the child has already covered himself with mire.

Anything but yourself is dirt. Anybody that is. I do not feel clean enough to die, or to make it worthwhile killing myself."

A laugh, packed with hatred, not hoping to carry, snapped like a fiddle cord.

"Sour grapes! That's what it's all about! And you let yourself be kicked to death here out of spite.

Why do you talk to me, I should like to know? Answer me that?"

Disrespect or mocking is followed, in spiritualistic seances, with offended silence on part of the spooks. Such silence, not discernedly offended, now followed.

The pseudo-rustic Master, cavernously, hemicycally real,

2 stain, blemish

but anomalous shamness on him in these circumstances, poudre de riz [3] on the face of knights sleeping effigy, lay back indifferent, his feet lying, two heavy closed books, before the disciple.

Arghol was a large open book, full of truths and insults.

He opened his jaws wide once more in egotistic self-castigation.

"The doctoring is often fouler than disease.

Men have a loathsome deformity called Self; affliction got through indiscriminate rubbing against their fellows: Social excrescence.

Their being is regulated by exigencies of this affliction. Only one operation can cure it: the suicide's knife.

Or an immense snuffling or taciturn parasite, become necessary to victim, like abortive poodle, all nerves, vice and dissatisfaction.

I have smashed it against me, but it still writhes, turbulent mess.

I have shrunk it in frosty climates, but it has filtered filth inward through me, dispersed till my deepest solitude is impure.

Mire stirred up desperately, without success is subsequent hygiene."

This focused disciple's physical repulsion: nausea of humility added. Perfect tyrannic contempt: but choking respect, curiosity; consciousness of defeat. These two extremes clashed furiously. The contempt claimed its security and triumph: the other sentiment baffled it. His hatred of Arghol for perpetually producing this second sentiment grew. This would have been faint without physical repulsion to fascinate him, make him murderous and sick.

[3] face powder

He was strong and insolent with consciousness stuffed in him in anonymous form of vastness of Humanity: full of rage at gigantic insolence and superiority, combined with utter uncleanness and despicableness—all back to physical parallel—of his Master.

The more Arghol made him realize his congenital fatuity and cheapness, the more a contemptible matter appeared accumulated in the image of his Master, sunken mirror. The price of this sharp vision of mastery was contamination.

Too many things inhabited together in this spirit for cleanliness or health. Is one soul too narrow an abode for genius?

To have humanity inside you, to keep a doss-house! At least impossible to organize on such a scale.

People are right who would disperse these impure monopolies! Let everyone get his little bit, intellectual Ballam rather than Bedlam!

III.

In sluggish but resolute progress towards the City and center, on part of young man was to be found cause of Arghol's ascendancy in first place. Arghol had returned some months only from the great city of their world.

He showed Hanp picture postcards. He described the character of each scene. Then he had begun describing more closely. At length, systematically he lived again there for his questioner, exhausted the capital, put it completely in his hands. The young man had got there without going there. But instead of satisfying him, this developed a wild desire to start off at once. Then Arghol said:

"Wait a moment."

He whispered something in his ear.

"Is that true?"

"Aye and more."

He supplemented his description with a whole life of comment and disillusion. The young man felt now that he had left the city. His life was being lived for him. But he forgot this and fought for his first city. Then he began taking a pleasure in destruction.

He had got under Arghol's touch.

But when he came to look squarely at his new possession, which he had exchanged for his city, he found it wild, incredibly sad, hateful stuff.

Somehow, however, the City had settled down in Arghol. He must seek it there, and rescue it from that tyrannic abode. He could not now start off without taking this unreal image city with him. He sat down to invest it, Arghol its walls.

IV.

Arghol had fallen. His Thébaide had been his Waterloo.

He now sat up slowly.

"Why do I speak to you?

It's not to you but myself. I think it's a physical matter: simply to use one's mouth.

My thoughts to walk abroad and not always be stuffed up in my head: ideas to banjo this resounding body.

You seemed such a contemptible sort of fellow that there was some hope for you. Or to be clear, there was NOTHING to hope from your vile character.

That is better than little painful somethings!

I am amazed to find that you are like me.

I talk to you for an hour and get more disgusted with myself.

I find I wanted to make a naif yapping Poodle-parasite of you. I shall always be a prostitute.

I wanted to make you myself; you understand?

Every man who wants to make another HIMSELF, is seeking a companion for his detached ailment of a self.

You are an unclean little beast, crept gloomily out of my ego. You are the world, brother, with its family objections to me.

Go back to our Mother and spit in her face for me!

I wish to see you no more here! Leave at once. Here is money. Take train at once: Berlin is the place for your pestilential little carcass. Get out! Here! Go!"

Amazement had stretched the disciple's face back like a mouth, then slowly it contracted, the eyes growing smaller, chin more prominent, old and clenched like a fist.

Arghol's voice rang coldly in the hut, a bell beaten by words.

Only the words, not tune of bell, had grown harder. At last they beat virulently.

When he had finished, silence fell like guillotine between them, severing bonds.

———

The disciple spoke with his own voice, which he had not used for some weeks. It sounded fresh, brisk and strange to him, half live garish salt fish.

His mouth felt different.

"Is that all?"

Arghol was relieved at sound of Hanp's voice, no longer borrowed, and felt better disposed towards him. The strain of this mock life, or real life, rather, was tremendous on his underworld of energy and rebellious muscles. This cold outburst was not commensurate with it. It was twitch of loud bound nerve only.

"Bloody glib-tongued cow! You think you can treat me that way!"

Hanp sprang out of the ground, a handful of furious movements: flung himself on Arghol.

Once more the stars had come down.

Arghol used his fists.

To break vows and spoil continuity of instinctive behavior, lose a prize that would only be a trophy tankard never drunk from, is always fine.

Arghol would have flung away his hoarding and scraping of thought as well now. But his calm, long instrument of thought was too heavy. It weighed him down, resisted his swift anarchist effort, and made him giddy.

His fear of death, anti-manhood, words coming out of caverns of belief—synthesis, that is, of ideal life—appalled him with his own strength.

Strike his disciple as he had abused him. Suddenly give way. Incurable self taught you a heroism.

The young man brought his own disgust back to him. Full of disgust: therefore disgusting. He felt himself on him. What a cause of downfall!

V.

The great beer-colored sky, at the fuss, leapt in fête of green gaiety.

Its immense lines bent like whalebones and sprang back with slight deaf thunder.

The sky, two clouds, their two furious shadows, fought.

The bleak misty hospital of the horizon grew pale with fluid of anger.

The trees were wiped out in a blow.
The hut became a new boat inebriated with electric milky human passion, poured in.

It shrank and struck them; struck, in its course, in a stirred-up unmixed world, by tree, or house-side grown wave.

First they hit each other, both with blows about equal in force—on face and head.

Soul perched like aviator in basin of skull, more alert and smaller than on any other occasion. Mask stoic with energy: thought cleaned off slick—pure and clean with action. Bodies grown brain, black octopi.

Flushes on silk epiderm and fierce card-play of fists between: emptying of "hand" on soft flesh-table.

Arms of gray windmills, grinding anger on stone of the new heart.

Messages from one to another, dropped down anywhere when nobody is looking, reaching brain by telegraph: most desolating and alarming messages possible.

The attacker rushed in drunk with blows. They rolled, swift jagged rut, into one corner of shed: large insect scuttling roughly to hiding.

Stopped astonished.

Fisticuffs again: then rolled kicking air and each other, springs broken, torn from engine.

Hanp's punch wore itself out, soon, on herculean clouds, at mad rudder of boat on Arghol.

Then like a punch ball, something vague and swift struck him on face, exhausted and white.

Arghol did not hit hard. Like something inanimate, only striking as rebound and as attacked.

He became soft, blunt paw of Nature, taken back to her bosom, mechanically; slowly and idly winning.

He became part of responsive landscape: his friend's active punch key of the commotion.

Hanp fell somewhere in the shadow: there lay.

Arghol stood rigid.

As the nervous geometry of the world in sight relaxed, and went on with its perpetual mystic invention, he threw himself down where he had been lying before.

A strong flood of thought passed up to his fatigued head, and at once dazed him. Not his body only, but being was out of training for action: puffed and exhilarated. Thoughts fell on it like punches.

His mind, baying mastiff, he flung off.

In steep struggle he rolled into sleep.

Two clear thoughts had intervened between fight and sleep.

Now a dream began valuing, with its tentative symbols, preceding events.

———

A black jacket and shirt hung on nails across window: a gas jet turned low to keep room warm, through the night, sallow chill illumination: dirty pillows, black and thin in middle, worn down by rough head, but congested at each end.

Bedclothes crawling over bed never made, like stagnant waves and eddies to be crept beneath.—Picture above pillow of Rosa Bonheur horses trampling up wall like well fed toffyish insects. Books piled on table and chair, open at some page.

Two texts in Finnish. Pipes half smoked, collars: past days not effaced beneath perpetual tidyness, but scraps and souvenirs of their accidents lying in heaps.

His room in the city, nine feet by six, grave big enough for the six corpses that is each living man.

Appalling tabernacle of Self and Unbelief.

He was furious with this room, tore down jacket and shirt, and threw the window open.

The air made him giddy.

He began putting things straight.

The third book, stalely open, which he took up to shut, was the "Einige und Sein Eigenkeit." [4]

Stirner.

One of seven arrows in his martyr mind.

Poof! he flung it out of the window.

A few minutes, and there was a knock at his door. It was a young man he had known in the town, but now saw for the first time, seemingly. He had come to bring him the book, fallen into the roadway.

"I thought I told you to go!" he said.

The young man had changed into his present disciple.

Obliquely, though he appeared now to be addressing Stirner.

"I thought I told you to go?"

His visitor changed a third time.

A middle-aged man, red-cropped head and dark eyes, self-possessed, loose, free, student—sailor, fingering the book:

[4] "The Ego and Its Own"

coming to a decision. Stirner as he had imagined him.

"Get out, I say. Here is money."

Was the money for the book?

The man flung it at his head; its cover slapped him sharply.

"Glib-tongued cow! Take that!"

A scrap ensued, physical experiences of recent fight recurring, ending in eviction of this visitor, and slamming of door.

"These books are all parasites. Poodles of the mind, Chows and King Charles; eternal prostitute.

The mind, perverse and gorgeous.

All this Art life, posterity and the rest, is wrong. Begin with these."

He tore up his books.

A pile by door ready to sweep out.

He left the room, and went round to Café to find his friends.

"All companions of parasite Self. No single one a brother.

My dealings with these men is with their parasite composite selves, not with Them."

The night had come on suddenly. Stars like clear rain soaked chillily into him.

No one was in the street.

The sickly houses oozed sad human electricity.

He had wished to clean up, spiritually, his room, obliterate or turn into deliberate refuse, accumulations of Self.

Now a similar purging must be undertaken among his companions preparatory to leaving the city.

But he never reached the Café.

His dream changed; he was walking down the street in his native town, where he now was, and where he knew no one but his schoolmates, workmen, clerks in export of hemp, grain and wood.

Ahead of him he saw one of the friends of his years of study in Capital.

He did not question how he had got there, but caught him up. Although brusquely pitched elsewhere, he went on with his plan.

"Sir, I wish to know you!"

Provisional smile on face of friend, puzzled.

"Hallo, Arghol, you seem upset."

"I wish to make your acquaintance."

"But, my dear Arghol, what's the matter with you?

We already are very well acquainted."

"I am not Arghol."

"No?"

The good-natured smug certitude offended him.

This man would never see anyone but Arghol he knew. —Yet he on his side saw a man, directly beneath his friend imprisoned, with intolerable need of recognition.

Arghol, that the baffling requirements of society had made, impudent parasite of his solitude, had foregathered too long with men, and borne his name too variously, to be superseded.

He was not sure, if they had been separated surgically,

in which self life would have gone out and in which remained.

"This man has been masquerading as me."

He repudiated Arghol, nevertheless.

If eyes of his friends-up-till-then could not be opened, he would sweep them, along with Arghol, into rubbish heap.

Arghol was under a dishonoring pact with all of them.

He repudiated it and him.

"So I am Arghol."

"Of course. But if you don't want——"

"That is a lie. Your foolish grin proves you are lying. Good day."

Walking on, he knew his friend was himself. He had divested himself of something.

The other steps followed, timidly and deliberately: odious invitation.

The sound of the footsteps gradually sent him to sleep.

Next, a Café; he, alone, writing at table.

He became slowly aware of his friends seated at other end of room, watching him, as it had actually happened before his return to his uncle's house. There he was behaving as a complete stranger with a set of men he had been on good terms with two days before.

"He's gone mad. Leave him alone," they advised each other.

As an idiot, too, he had come home; dropped, idle and sullen, on his relative's shoulders.

VI.

Suddenly, through confused struggles and vague successions of scenes, a new state of mind asserted itself.

A riddle had been solved.

What could this be?

He was Arghol once more.

Was that a key to something? He was simply Arghol.

"I am Arghol."

He repeated his name—like sinister word invented to launch a new Soap, in gigantic advertisement—toilet-necessity, he, to scrub the soul.

He had ventured in his solitude and failed. Arghol he had imagined left in the city.—Suddenly he had discovered Arghol who had followed him, in Hanp. Always à deux!

───────

Flung back to extremity of hut, Hanp lay for some time recovering. Then he thought. Chattel for rest of mankind, Arghol had brutalized him.

Both eyes were swollen pulp.

Shut in: thought for him hardly possible so cut off from visible world.

Sullen indignation at Arghol ACTING, he who had not the right to act. Violence in him was indecent; again question to taste.

How loathsome heavy body, so long quiet, flinging itself about: face strained with intimate expression of act of love.

Firm grip still on him; outrage.

"Pudeur," [5] in races accustomed to restraint, is the most violent emotion, in all its developments. Devil ridicule,

5 shame

heroism of vice, ideal, god of taste. Why has it not been taken for root of great Northern tragedy?

Arghol's unwieldly sensitiveness, physical and mental, made him a monster in his own eyes, among other things. Such illusion, imparted with bullet-like directness to a companion, falling on suitable soil, produced similar conviction.

This humility and perverse asceticism opposed to vigorous animal glorification of self.

He gave men one image with one hand, and at same time a second, its antidote, with the other.

He watched results a little puzzled.

The conflict never ended.

Shyness and brutality, chief ingredients of their drama, fought side by side.

Hanp had been "ordered off," knocked about. Now he was going. Why? Because he had been sent off like a belonging.

Arghol had dragged him down: had preached a certain life, and now insolently set an example of the opposite.

Played with, debauched by a mind that could not leave passion in another alone.

Where should he go? Home. Good-natured drunken mother, recriminating and savage at night.

Hanp had almost felt she had no right to be violent and resentful, being weak when sober. He caught a resemblance to present experiences in tipsy life stretching to baby-hood.

He saw in her face a look of Arghol.

How disgusting she was, his own flesh. Ah! That was the sensation! Arghol, similarly disgusted through this family feeling, his own flesh: though he was not any relation.

Berlin and nearer city was full of Arghol. He was comfortable where he was.

Arghol had lived for him, worked: impaired his will. Even wheel making had grown difficult, whereas Arghol acquitted himself of duties of trade quite easily.

WHOSE energy did he use?

Just now the blows had leaped in his muscles towards Arghol, but were sickened and did not seem hard. Would he never be able again to hit? Feel himself hard and distinct on somebody else?

That mass, muck, in the corner, that he hated: was it hoarded energy, stolen or grabbed, which he could only partially use, stagnating?

Arghol was brittle, repulsive and formidable through this sentiment.

Had this passivity been holy, with charm of a Saint's?

Arghol was glutted with others, in coma of energy.

He had just been feeding on him—Hanp!

He REFUSED to act, almost avowedly to infuriate: prurient contempt.

His physical strength was obnoxious: muscles affecting as flabby fat would in another.

Energetic through self-indulgence.

Thick sickly puddle of humanity, lying there by door.

Death, taciturn refrain of his being.

Preparation for Death.

Tip him over into caldron in which he persistently gazed: see what happened!

This sleepy desire leaped on to young man's mind, after a hundred other thoughts—clown in the circus, springing on horse's back, when the elegant riders have hopped, with obsequious dignity down gangway.

VII.

Bluebottle, at first unnoticed, hurtling about, a snore rose quietly on the air.

Drawn out, clumsy, self-centered! It pressed inflexibly on Hanp's nerve of hatred, sending hysteria gyrating in top of diaphragm, flooding neck.

It beckoned, filthy, ogling finger.

The first organ note abated. A second at once was set up: stronger, startling, full of loathsome unconsciousness.

It purred a little now, quick and labial. Then virile and strident again.

It rose and fell up center of listener's body, and along swollen nerves, peachy, clotted tide, gurgling back in slimy shallows. Snoring of a malodorous, bloody sink, emptying its water.

More acutely, it plunged into his soul with bestial regularity, intolerable besmirching.

Aching with disgust and fury, he lay dully, head against ground. At each fresh offence the veins puffed faintly in his temples.

All this sonority of the voice that subdued him sometimes: suddenly turned bestial in answer to his vision.

"How can I stand it! How can I stand it!"

His whole being was laid bare: battened on by this noise. His strength was drawn raspingly out of him. In a minute he would be a flabby yelling wreck.

Like a sleek shadow passing down his face, the rigor of his discomfort changed, sly volte-face of Nature.

Glee settled thickly on him.

The snore crowed with increased loudness, glad, seemingly, with him; laughing that he should have at last learned to appreciate it. A rare proper world if you understand it!

He got up, held by this foul sound of sleep, in dream of action. Rapt beyond all reflection, he would, martyr, relieve the world of this sound.

Cut out this noise like a cancer.

He swayed and groaned a little, peeping through patches of tumified flesh, boozer collecting his senses; fumbled in pocket.

His knife was not there.

He stood still wiping blood off his face.

Then he stepped across shed to where fight had occurred.

The snore grew again: its sonorous recoveries had amazing and startling strength. Every time it rose he gasped, pressing back a clap of laughter.

With his eyes, it was like looking through goggles.

He peered round carefully, and found knife and two coppers where they had slipped out of his pocket a foot away from Arghol.

He opened the knife, and an ocean of movements poured into his body. He stretched and strained like a toy wound up.

He took deep breaths: his eyes almost closed. He opened one roughly with two fingers, the knife held stiffly at arm's length.

He could hardly help plunging it in himself, the nearest flesh to him.

He now saw Arghol clearly: knelt down beside him.

A long stout snore drove his hand back. But the next instant the hand rushed in, and the knife sliced heavily the impious meat. The blood burst out after the knife.

Arghol rose as though on a spring, his eyes glaring down on Hanp, and with an action of the head, as though he were about to sneeze. Hanp shrank back, on his haunches. He overbalanced, and fell on his back.

He scrambled up, and Arghol lay now in the position in which he had been sleeping.

There was something incredible in the dead figure, the blood sinking down, a moist shaft, into the ground. Hanp felt friendly towards it.

There was only flesh there, and all our flesh is the same. Something distant, terrible and eccentric, bathing in that milky snore, had been struck and banished from matter.

Hanp wiped his hands on a rag, and rubbed at his clothes for a few minutes, then went out of the hut.

The night was suddenly absurdly peaceful, trying richly to please him with gracious movements of trees, and gay processions of arctic clouds.

Relief of grateful universe.

A rapid despair settled down on Hanp, a galloping blackness of mood. He moved quickly to outstrip it, perhaps.

Near the gate of the yard he found an idle figure. It was his master. He ground his teeth almost in this man's face, with an aggressive and furious movement towards him. The face looked shy and pleased, but civil, like a mysterious domestic.

Hanp walked slowly along the canal to a low stone bridge.

His face was wet with tears, his heart beating weakly, a boat slowed down.

A sickly flood of moonlight beat miserably on him, cutting empty shadow he could hardly drag along.

He sprang from the bridge clumsily, too unhappy for instinctive science, and sank like lead, his heart a sagging weight of stagnant hatred.

from THE LITTLE REVIEW, 1917

Cantleman's Spring Mate

CANTLEMAN walked in the strenuous fields, steam rising from them as though from an exertion, dissecting the daisies specked in the small wood, the primroses on the banks, the marshy lakes, and all God's creatures. The heat of a heavy premature Summer was cooking the little narrow belt of earth-air, causing everything innocently to burst its skin, bask abjectly and profoundly. Everything was enchanted with itself and with everything else. The horses considered the mares immensely appetizing masses of quivering shiny flesh: was there not something of "je ne sais quoi" about a mare, that no other beast's better-half possessed? The birds with their little gnarled feet, and beaks made for fishing worms out of the mold, or the river, would have considered Shelley's references to the skylark—or any other poet's paeans to their species—as lamentably inadequate to describe the beauty of birds! The female bird, for her particular part, reflected that, in spite of the ineptitude of her sweetheart's latest song, which he insisted on deafening her with, never seemed to tire of, and was so persuaded that she liked as much as he did himself, and although outwardly he remained strictly critical and vicious: that all the same and nevertheless, chock, chock, peep, peep, he was a fluffy object from which certain satisfaction could be derived! And both the male and the female reflected together as they stood a foot or so apart looking at each other with one eye, and at the landscape with the other, that of all nourishment the red earthworm was the juiciest and sweetest! The sow, as she watched her hog, with his splenetic energy, and guttural articulation, a sound between content and complaint, not noticing the untidy habits of both of them, gave a sharp grunt of sex hunger, and jerked rapidly towards him. The only jarring note in this vast mutual admiration society was the fact that many of its members showed their fondness for their neighbor in an embarrassing way: that is they killed and ate them.

But the weaker were so used to dying violent deaths and being eaten that they worried very little about it. The West was gushing up a harmless volcano of fire, obviously intended as an immense dreamy nightcap.

Cantleman in the midst of his cogitation on surrounding life, surprised his faithless and unfriendly brain in the act of turning over an object which humiliated his meditation. He found that he was wondering whether at his return through the village lying between him and the Camp, he would see the girl he had passed there three hours before. At that time he had not begun his philosophizing, and without interference from conscience, he had noticed the redness of her cheeks, the animal fullness of the child-bearing hips, with an eye as innocent as the bird or the beast. He laughed without shame or pleasure, lit his pipe and turned back towards the village. His field boots were covered with dust: his head was wet with perspiration and he carried his cap, in unmilitary fashion, in his hand. In a week he was leaving for the Front, for the first time. So his thoughts and sensations all had, as a philosophic background, the prospect of death. The Infantry, and his commission, implied death or mutilation unless he were very lucky. He had not a high opinion of his luck. He was pretty miserable at the thought, in a deliberate, unemotional way. But as he realized this he again laughed, a similiar sound to that that the girl had caused.—For what was he unhappy about? He wanted to remain amongst his fellow insects and beasts, which were so beautiful, did he then: Well well! On the other hand, who was it that told him to do anything else? After all, supposing the values they attached to each other of "beautiful," "interesting," "divine," were unjustified in many cases on cooler observation:—nevertheless birds were more beautiful than pigs: and if pigs were absurd and ugly, rather than handsome, and possibly chivalrous, as they imagined themselves; then equally the odor of the violet was pleasant, and there was nothing offensive about most trees. The newspapers were the things that stank most on earth, and human beings anywhere were the most ugly and offensive of the brutes because of the confusion caused by their consciousness. Had it not been for that unmaterial gift that some bungling or wild hand had bestowed, our sisters and brothers would be no worse than dogs and sheep. That they could not reconcile their little meager stream of sublimity with the needs of animal life should not be railed at. Well then, should not the sad human amalgam, all it did, all it willed, all it demanded, be thrown over, for the fake and confusion that it was, and should not such as possessed a greater quantity of that wine of reason, retire, metaphorically, to the wilderness, and sit forever in a formal and gentle elation, refusing to be disturbed? Should such allow himself to be disturbed by the quarrels of jews, the desperate perplexities, resulting in desperate dice throws, of politicians, the crack-jaw and unreasoning tumult?

On the other hand, Cantleman had a little more human, as well as a little more divine, than those usually on his left and right, and he had had, not so long ago, conspicuous hopes that such a conjuncture might produce a new human chemistry. But he must repudiate the human entirely, if that were to be brought off. His present occupation, the trampling boots upon his feet, the belt that crossed his back and breast, was his sacrifice, his compliment to, the animal.

He then began dissecting his laugh, comparing it to the pig's grunt and the bird's cough. He laughed again several times in order to listen to it.

At the village he met the girl, this time with a second girl. He stared at her "in such a funny way" that she laughed. He once more laughed, the same sound as before, and bid her good evening. She immediately became civil. Inquiries about the village, and the best way back to camp across the marsh, put in as nimble and at the same time rustic a form as he could contrive, lay the first tentative brick of what might become the dwelling of a friend, a sweetheart, a ghost, anything in the absurd world! He asked her to come and show him a short cut she had indicated.

"I *couldn't!* My mother's waiting for *me!*" in a rush of expostulation and semi-affected alarm. However, she concluded, in a minute or two, that she could.

He wished that she had been some Anne Garland, the lady whose lips were always flying open like a door with a defective latch. He had made Anne's acquaintance under distressing circumstances.

On his arrival at Gideon brook, the mighty brand-new camp on the edge of the marsh, he found that his colleague in charge of the advance party had got him a bed-space in a room with four officers of another regiment. It had seemed impossible that there were any duller men than those in the mess of his particular battalion: but it was a dullness he had become accustomed to.

He saw his four new companions with a sinking of the heart, and steady gnawing anger at such concentration of furious foolishness.

Cantleman did not know their names, and he hated them in order as follows:

A. he hated because he found him a sturdy, shortish young man with a bull-like stoop and energetic rush in his walk, with flat feet spread out to left to right, and slightly bowed legs. This physique was enhanced by his leggings: and not improved, though hidden, in his slacks. He had a swarthy and vivacious face, with a sort of semitic cunning and insolence painted on it. His cheeks had a broad carmine flush on general sallowness. The mind painted on this face for the perusal of whoever had the art of such lettering, was as vulgar stuff, in Cantleman's judgment, as could be found. To *see* this face constantly was like *hearing* perpetually a cheap and foolish music. A. was an officer, but naturally not a gentleman.

B. he disliked, because, being lean and fresh colored, with glasses, he stank, to Cantleman's peculiar nose, of Jack London, Summer Numbers of magazines, bad flabby Suburban Tennis, flabby clerkship in inert, though still prosperous, city offices. He brought a demoralizing dullness into the room with him, with a brisk punctiliousness, several inches higher from the ground than A.

C. he resented for the sullen stupidity with which he moved about, the fat having settled at the bottom of his cheeks, and pulled the corners of his mouth down, from sheer stagnation. His accent dragged the listener through the larger slums of Scotland, harrowing him with the bestial cheerlessness of morose religion and poverty. The man was certainly, from every point of view, social prestige, character, intelligence, far less suited to hold a commission than most of the privates in his platoon.

D. reproduced the characteristics of the other three, in different quantities: his only personal contribution being a senile singsong voice, from the North, and a blond beam, or partially toothless grin, for a face.

This was the society into the midst of which Cantleman had been dropped on his arrival at Gideon brook, ten days previous to this. They had all looked up (for it was always *all*, they having the inseparability of their kind) with friendly welcome, as brother officers should. He avoided their eyes, and sat amongst them for a few days, reading the *Trumpet-*

Major, belonging to B. He had even seemed to snatch Hardy away from B. as though B. had no business to possess such books. Then they avoided his eye as though an animal disguised as an officer and gentleman like themselves had got into their room, for whom, therein, the *Trumpet-Major* and nothing else exercised fascination. He came among them suddenly, and not appearing to see them, settled down into a morbid intercourse with a romantic abstraction. The Trumpet-Major, it is true, was a soldier, that is why he was there. But he was an imaginary one, and imbedded in the passionate affairs of the village of a mock county, and distant time. Cantleman bit the flesh at the side of his thumbs, as he surveyed the Yeomanry Cavalry reveling in the absent farmer's house, and the infantile Farnese Hercules, with the boastfulness of the Red, explaining to his military companions the condescensions of his infatuation. Anne Garland stood in the moonlight, and Loveday hesitated to reveal his rival, weighing a rough chivalry against self-interest.

Cantleman eventually decamped with the *Trumpet-Major,* taking him across to Havre, and B. never saw his book again. Cantleman had also tried to take a book away from A. (a book incompatible with A's vulgar physique). But A. had snatched it back, and mounted guard surlily and cunningly over it.

In his present rustic encounter, then, he was influenced in his feelings towards his first shepherdess by memories of Wessex heroines, and the something more that being the daughter of a landscape painter would give. Anne, imbued with the delicacy of the Mill, filled his mind to the injury of this crude marsh plant. But he had his program. Since he was forced back, by his logic and body, among the madness of natural things, he would live up to his part.

The young woman had, or had given herself, the unlikely name of Stella. In the narrow road where they got away from the village, Cantleman put his arm around Stella's waist and immediately experienced all the sensations that he had been divining in the creatures around him; the horse, the bird and the pig. The way in which Stella's hips stood out, the solid blood-heated expanse on which his hand lay, had the amplitude and flatness of a mare. Her lips had at once no practical significance, but only the aesthetic blandishment of a bull-like flower. With the gesture of a fabulous Faust he drew her against him, and kissed her with a crafty gentleness.

Cantleman turned up that evening in his quarters in a state of baffling good humor. He took up the *Trumpet-Major* and was soon surrounded by the breathing and scratching of his roommates, reading and writing. He chuckled somewhere where Hardy was funny. At this human noise the others fixed their eyes on him in sour alarm. He gave another, this time gratuitous, chuckle. They returned with disgust at his habits, his peculiarity, to what he considered their maid-servant's fiction and correspondence. Oh Christ, what abysms! Oh Christ, what abysms! Cantleman shook noisily in the wicker chair like a dog or a fly-blown old gentleman.

Once more on the following evening he was out in the fields, and once more his thoughts were engaged in recapitulations.—The miraculous camouflage of Nature did not deceive this observer. He saw everywhere the gun pits and the "nests of death." Each puff of green leaves he knew was in some way as harmful as the burst of a shell. Decay and ruins, it is true, were soon covered up, but there was yet that parallel, and the sight of things smashed and corruption. In the factory town ten miles away to the right, whose smoke could be seen, life was just as dangerous for the poor, and as uncomfortable, as for the soldier in his trench. The hypocrisy of Nature and the hypocrisy of War were the same. The only safety in life was for the man with the soft job. But that fellow was not conforming to life's conditions. He was life's paid man, and had the mark of the sneak. He was making too much of life, and too much out of it. He, Cantleman, did not want to owe anything to life, or enter into league or understanding with her! The thing was either to go out of existence: or, failing that, remain in it unreconciled, indifferent to Nature's threat, consorting openly with her enemies, making a war within her war upon her servants. In short, the spectacle of the handsome English spring produced nothing but ideas of defiance in Cantleman's mind.

As to Stella, she was a sort of Whizbang. With a treachery worthy of a Hun, Nature tempted him towards her. He was drugged with delicious appetites. Very well! He would hoist the unseen power of his own petard. He would throw back Stella where she was discharged from (if it were allowable, now, to change her into a bomb), first having relieved himself of this humiliating gnawing and yearning in his blood.

As to Stella, considered as an unconscious agent, all women were contaminated with Nature's hostile power and might be treated as spies or enemies. The only time they could be trusted, or were likely to stand up to Nature and show their teeth, was as mothers. So he approached Stella with as much falsity as he could master.

At their third meeting he brought her a ring. Her melting gratitude was immediately ligotted with long arms, full of the contradictory and offending fire of the spring. On the warm earth consent flowed up into her body from all the veins of the landscape. The nightingale sang ceaselessly in the small wood at the top of the field where they lay. He grinned up towards it, and once more turned to the devouring of his mate. He felt that he was raiding the bowels of Nature: not fecundating the Aspasias of our flimsy flesh, or assuaging, or competing with, the nightingale. Cantleman was proud that he could remain deliberate and aloof, and gaze bravely, like a minute insect, up at the immense and melancholy night, with all its mad nightingales, piously folded small brown wings in a million nests, night-working stars, and misty useless watchmen. They got up at last: she went furtively back to her home. Cantleman on his way to camp had a smile of severe satisfaction on his face. It did not occur to him that his action might be supremely unimportant as far as Stella was concerned. He had not even asked himself if, had he not been there that night, someone else might or might not have been there in his place. He was also convinced that the laurels were his, and that Nature had come off badly. He was still convinced of this when he received six weeks afterwards, in France, a long appeal from Stella, telling him that she was going to have a child. She received no answer to that nor any subsequent letter. They came to Cantleman with great regularity in the trenches; he read them all through from beginning to end, without comment of any sort. And when he beat a German's brains out, it was with the same impartial malignity that he had displayed in the English night with his Spring mate. Only he considered there too that he was in some way outwitting Nature; he had no adequate realization of the extent to which, evidently, the death of a Hun was to the advantage of the animal world.

from THE LITTLE REVIEW, 1918

The Ideal Giant

The Action occurs in the Restaurant Gambetta, in German London, in October, 1914. Belgian "refugees" have found it out in numbers; the poor ones do not get so far. These people are very composed.

The Restaurant is French in its staff and traditions. An Austrian, at present, keeps it.

A cream-lace curtain, hanging from brass hooks, runs all along its face, shoulder high.

A very large brass vase in the middle, and a Russian wood-painting of a Virgin and Child on narrow wall between the two windows, gives the German cultured touch.

The peculiar situation of this Restaurant makes it indispensable to a few people.

The Proprietor is interesting.

The Proprietor follows his stomach about the Restaurant constantly while the Action is proceeding, playing with it like a large ball. He comes right up to John Porter Kemp often and then at the last moment whisks it away, and wheels in another direction, head thrown back, with heroic contraction of brows like a Russian dancer.

FIRST SCENE.

Characters:
MR. JOHN FINGAL.
MR. JOHN PORTER KEMP.

The Restaurant is behind the two central figures in each scene. The dialogues occur in a little brightly lighted box at the front of the stage. It is a recess at the back of the Restaurant, which is seen behind it in a perfectly square frame made by the limits of the recess. The boxlike recess is painted shiny white with large brass hooks to the left for the coats.

113

It is sanitary, doll-like and conventional.

Fingal's sienna brown suit, and Kemp's rather vivid blue, under the bright electric light, and Miss Godd's green jersey in 3rd scene, add to the appearance of freshness and artificial bloom.

SCENE I.

MR. JOHN FINGAL *is found seated at table, on left-hand side, his right-hand profile to you. He is reading a green evening paper.*

Mr. John Fingal is a robust, un-English-looking Adonis, like rank and file stocky Paris cubist; jowl, phlegm, professional classes. He is thirty-six, a solid adventurer, studying art. He does a little dealing. He is flippant, and methodically aggressive in a snobbish way. He sees himself as "fine old gentleman," très fin; also as a beautiful young man, the memory of personal triumphs at Cambridge maintained.

He likes speaking French. He does so with careful clumsiness and only so much attempt at a good accent as is compatible with dignity and comfort.

The tables beyond in the body of the Restaurant are occupied by various people, chiefly Belgians.

JOHN PORTER KEMP *comes in from street at far end of stage. He is tall, dog-lean, in first bloom of middle age.*

He is a writer; journalism takes up most of his time.

(Red-haired people seem mongrels—common to every country, like women. Kemp's is a shabby strong mixture, giving him rather a colonial entrée into the civilized world. It carries him back, down the ages, in any case, in an energetic ancestral trail, without the interruptions you must always count on with colorless crops.)

FINGAL *looks up toward back of stage, and with immediate concentration makes a sign to Kemp, and kicks the chair back on the other side of the table.*

FINGAL.   Hallo. Come here, have lunch here—

KEMP.   Good morning. What's the news?

FINGAL.   Oh. I don't know. Much the same.

　　　(Fingal shakes the paper.)

KEMP.   Yes.

　　　(Kemp sits down. He does not prune himself, rub his cheeks or hands, or stretch his eyelids. He looks at Menu.)

FINGAL.   Oh. I don't know. Much the same.

KEMP.   You've seen the Goeben's been doing something again?   (*Fingal glances across paper.*)

FINGAL.   Yes.

> (*Kemp orders his dinner. A duck and potatoes and salsifé[1] arrive for Fingal. Kemp stares at the Belgians at the back of the Restaurant, his large raw eye full of pleasure, like a golden patine.[2]*)

FINGAL.   Did you get that book all right?

KEMP.   Yes. They hadn't got it at the Times Book Club. I went to the Figaro. They got it for me. What a nice family that is over there! How shiny their faces are! They really are nice greasy lumps.

> (*Fingal looks round at Belgian family, sees what he expected after a minute, and laughs. Kemp turns back to the table.*)

KEMP.   I wish we were more like that. At least I wish we had that air of being in a tavern they have; or just come out of a heavy bedroom, like immense dolls out of the box of an erotic game. They don't mind dying as much as we do, because their blood is the same oil as the Earth's. With them continuity is not so broken by demise.

FINGAL.   You are romancing.

KEMP.   Of course I'm not. Look at Cézanne's race and then look at us. See how much harder they work at getting their children. Their pictures, too. But it doesn't show so much in our children.

FINGAL.   Do they? I should have thought——

KEMP.   They are much more like the things they eat. They all have a good deal of pig, horse and dog in them. They yap and snort and their noses sniff and twitch.

FINGAL.   Do you want to be like a pig?

KEMP.   It might improve me. I should be willing to try it.

> (*They laugh with indulgence and digestive grace.*)

FINGAL.   Are you doing much work? I saw you were writing in the *London Monthly* the other day. I intended to get it.

KEMP.   Yes. There's no reviewing now, during the war. I shall have to turn strategist, I suppose. I shall not make a good one. I can never make head or tail of what they're doing over there.

---

[1] oyster plant or scorzonera
[2] patina

FINGAL.   Aren't they going to begin to print other news again soon?

KEMP.   Heaven knows.

(*A duck and boiled potatoes and salsifé arrive for Kemp: a bottle of Teinach. Fingal's are taken away; The garçon is built compactly for body service. His eyes are round and blue, and bring to mind Swiss Lakes and mean popular sentimentalities. He is your respectful friend and abject servant. He bends down and advises with a candor and carefulness that makes you turn your head away. He stares into the distance when he is not busy. This is his menial cachet.*)

KEMP.   I wonder if any of these Belgians have been ruined? I expect it is chiefly the working people who have been done for.

FINGAL.   I tried to get a Refugee the other day to come and work for me. My little servant girl is going away. I couldn't find one for love or money.

KEMP.   I suppose the poor ones get looked after, and drafted off as soon as they arrive.

(*A Pêche Melba is brought for Fingal.*)

KEMP.   What is that? Pêche Melba? I must have that. Albert! A Pêche Melba.

FINGAL.   Our friend Radac here is pretty busy.

KEMP.   If things become very bad I shall get Radac to take me on as garçon. I should enjoy inducting food into those mouths.

(*A Pêche Melba is brought to Kemp.*)

FINGAL.   Miss Godd was here yesterday

KEMP.   Was she? But damn Miss Godd.

FINGAL.   Damn Miss Godd? She was here about two. Just after you'd gone.

KEMP.   I know. I saw her last night.

(*Fingal smiles, but keeps temperately within that demonstration. Miss Godd is a mystery. Fingal has not been asked to meet her. He does not know in what relation Miss Godd and Kemp stand to each other. He sees them at the Restaurant gesticulating in the distance. Kemp does not encourage communication on the subject of his friend. Kemp exaggerates his appetite. Nature with him substituted food for drink as a stimulant. A little food is enough. He has not a strong head. Rendered abnormally communicative and aggressive by the duck and other food, his eye more and*

*more often approaches Fingal, with a progressive
ritual like that of a large fly. At last it settles full in
the middle of his face. In a few minutes he is grinning at him, talking, twitching his great animal's nose
as though it had been surrounded by Grauben gnats.)*

KEMP. Do you sleep well?

FINGAL. Not really well. I vary. I sometimes sleep for
eight hours right off, sometimes only four. My average is a
bit below the necessary, I should say.

*(This punctilious answer was in order to save time,
and was the result of experience of Kemp. Kemp and
Fingal's talks resembled those arranged between the
Proprietor of the Circus and the Clown. Fingal would
display the meticulous credulity of the toff in evening
dress. Kemp does not want to know, however, about
Fingal's powers of sleep. It is one of his feints. This
is his way of "working.")*

KEMP. Are you sensitive about your shell?

FINGAL. No. No.

KEMP. The husk you shed at night?

FINGAL. Ah. No.

*(Kemp pulls his chair forward a little and leans
across the table. He constantly shoots his eye up,
while speaking, at an imaginary third person in the
middle distance. Sometimes he fixes this myth with
his blank red-rimmed disk of an eye, and stops his
discourse. Or he will lower his voice as though to
prevent this third person from overhearing his most
harmless remarks.)*

KEMP. Life for some people is full of the nuisance of
symmetries and forms. When you put your pen down, do you
begin worrying about its position in relation to the inkpot?

FINGAL. I can't say I do.

KEMP. *Some people*—have a certain personal arrangement
with their clothes at night. This is very common. I, for myself,
have to tie my bootlaces symmetrically. Have you never stepped in every second or third stone of a pavement, and been
afflicted if you were compelled to miss one? I know a man
who walked all the way back from Oxford Circus to Waring
and Gillows to plant his foot on a stone he had been compelled to miss!

FINGAL. That is bad neurasthenia, isn't it?

KEMP. Of course. And therefore should be fought and
broken up from time to time.

FINGAL.   I agree with you.

> (*Kemp sits back in his chair as though his bolt were shot, and the argument closed. This is more feinting and personal play of his high spirits. He then comes forward again in his chair.*)

KEMP.   Truth, at all events, is a thing like that. Our truthfulness. Some people—have an uneasiness and sense of something wrong, out of place, crying to be put right, if they have been compelled or have elected to tell an untruth. There is something in such and such a person's mind, placed there by them, and that should not be there. Or it should not be there in that form. It is "the thing which is not" of the Horses.[3]

> (*Kemp draws a cigar out of his pocket, cuts the end off, and lights it.*)

KEMP.   This meticulous sense will induce a man to describe very carefully something he has seen, if he describe it at all, and to suffer if, from laziness or other motive, he has slurred or misrepresented. This is the common base of wisdom and beauty. It is the famous generic madness at the bottom of genius.

It is the madness known as "Exactitude" in America.

> (*Kemp fixes Fingal with his eye, Ancient Mariner fashion, and shows him by a pause, that the preamble is over. He takes several deep breaths, inhaling his very bad cigar. Fingal disturbs the maneuvering of his eye.*)

FINGAL.   What would the clever Horses find to call your stories? Those "things that are not" fill your brains.

KEMP.   The transference is so complete in creative life of any sort. *Reality* is the "thing which is not," for the creative artists. An artist would have precisely that feeling of "malaise" and disgust if he had put in another man's head the *real truth*—the actual biological appearance of Nature, that my ideally truthful man would feel if he had lied.

FINGAL.   The arranging of the clothes; or the symmetry of the bootlace; is a sign of a feeling for order. Whereas the squeamishness about "the truth" in another man's head is a slavish timidity.

KEMP.   I don't think so. I don't see the contradiction. In the sphere of practical life it is essential to have facts. People can only base their actions on facts. If you put in a person's

---

[3] Reference to the wise horses in Swift's *Gulliver's Travels*.

head something purporting to be a fact, which is not a fact, it is liable to cause the utmost confusion and disorder.

But the point for my argument is the *physical* uneasiness about this thing said, whether fact or not, the "hallucination of the Object."

The "truth" is only another way of saying "the substantial." In life the "substantial" is the "fact."

FINGAL. I'm afraid I don't see what you're driving at.

> (*Gruff and cold contemplation from the lofty general entrenched beside Kemp's nose, conducting the affairs of the world, ensues. The eye sweeps over Fingal slowly like a searchlight.*)

KEMP. Do you tell many lies?

> (*Kemp fixes his eye stonily.*)

FINGAL. (*grinning*). Sometimes. But I'm a particular man. I am an esprit d'ordre.[4]

KEMP. I am the same. I am the same—I never lie—

> (*Kemp beams, in sudden immense thawing. A pause, in which Kemp inundates Fingal with smiles of nauseating richness. Renewed pretence that this is the bourn of his argument: namely, that he never tells lies.*)

FINGAL. Garçon. L'addition s'il vous plait.

> (*Fingal accepts this feint, and prepares to break up the séance. The waiter comes, and stooping down to the table, makes up the bill.*)

WAITER. Attendez. Il y avait deux légumes.[5]

FINGAL. Oui. Un salsifés.

WAITER. Oh yes. Salsifés. Thank you Mr. Fingal.

> (*Fingal pays the bill, but does not at once get up. Kemp leans forward and puts his hand on Fingal's arm.*)

KEMP. Today I have been lying steadily ever since I got up. The last two or three times we've met, I have told you several lies; which you did not notice.

I feel as though I should never tell the truth again.

> (*Kemp sits back and stares at Fingal.*)

FINGAL. I noticed all your lies, and was distressed.

KEMP. That is not true.

FINGAL. Oh yes. Perfectly. You told me you paid two-pence each for those cigars.

KEMP. Well, so I did.

[4] man of order
[5] Wait. There are two vegetables.

FINGAL.   Am I to take that as a lie; or, to put it another way, regard it as a proof, under the circumstances, that you did not pay that for them?

KEMP.   I paid twopence for this excellent cigar.

(*Kemp holds it up, and blows out his gingercream cheeks at its gilded label.*)

FINGAL.   Then why did you tell——?

(*Kemp springs up and calls the waiter.*)

KEMP.   Bring me a "Flor de Cijas."

(*He throws his cigar away, sits down and holds up his finger, then hooks it over his nose. He has seen some fat mid-European man with a cigar do this, and the fact of his smoking a cigar, a habit to which he has lately taken, suggests this action.*)

KEMP.   I am found out. This will not make me down-hearted. As a matter of fact I do not mind being found out. That is not material. I am not setting out to deceive, but only to cure myself of a superstition and rigid manner of feeling.

(*While handling Radac's much more satisfactory cigar, Kemp explains his latest regimen.*)

KEMP.   For instance, this arm of mine attracted attention this morning.

(*His arm is bandaged, and cased in a black leather trough which he takes off to eat. Kemp is getting over blood-poisoning in the wrist and forearm.*)

KEMP.   I posed as a Mons hero, with this, yesterday evening, in a pub. It was a triumph for me. Education and natural integrity revolt against the stupid action. We will admit it is not in my line. But I am too shy. Such things are excellent discipline. They harden, humble and invigorate. They are a medicine made up of the acrid harshness of the flash scum of a city.

The Ego's worst enemy is Truth. This gives truth the slap in the face good for us.

(*The Proprietor approaches; stands in the middle of the square opening, his stomach pointing rudely at them, head and eye frowning down on Kemp. They look at him in silence. He suddenly whisks his stomach away, wheels, and moves shoulderingly back into restaurant.*)

KEMP (*continuing*).   Self. Self. One must rescue that sanity. Truth, duty—are insanity.

FINGAL.   You are talking for the times. There are times when Self, Self—

KEMP.   Yes, perhaps. But if we have not War, we have Art——

FINGAL.   Now we have both—

KEMP.   But Art is much the purer and stronger, and against its truths and impositions we must revolt or at least react. The "pure artist" is a Non-sense.

The gentleman, likewise, must be shown his place.

The Prussian exploits the psychology of the commis-voyageur to harden himself into a practical aggressor—

FINGAL.   Do not let us be like the Prussian, for—

KEMP.   Heaven forbid; ah yes, forbid. We could not be if we tried. We therefore could introduce a little of his methods without the danger he runs of foolishness and vulgarity.

FINGAL.   Quite. Then you mean—

KEMP.   We, as individuals, are at a disadvantage in a struggle with the community. It contains, invariably, inevitably, criminal energy, stoicism and vulgarity of a high order.

FINGAL.   But why do you make this opposition between the individual and the community?

KEMP.   *I* did not make it.

FINGAL.   But does it exist to the extent you—

KEMP.   It exists. It exists like this. A hundred men is a giant.

> (*Kemp makes his points with a finger flattened out on the table. The Proprietor brings his stomach forward. Kemp waves it hurriedly away with his flat, stiff finger.*)

KEMP.   A hundred men is a giant. A giant is always rather lymphatic and inclined to be weak intellectually, we are told. He is also subject to violent rages. Just as legendary men were always at war with the giants, so are individuals with society.

That exceptional men can be spoiled by the world is a commonplace. But consider another thing. See how two or three distinguished people lose personal value in a mob—at a dinner, at a meeting. Their personalities deteriorate in a moment—for an hour or two. They hardly ever become the head and brain of the Giant.

FINGAL.   That doesn't apply to all men. It is due to some weakness in the personality. Some shine most.

KEMP.   Ah, yes. But examine those shiners by themselves, and look steadily at their words and acts. Theirs is a practical and relative success. The *solitary* test is the only searching one. The fine personality loses, in every case, by association. *The problem in life is to maintain the Ideal Giant.*

The artist is the Ideal Giant or Many. The Crowd at its moments of heroism also is. But Art is never at its best without the assaults of Egotism and of Life.

For the health of the Giant as much as for that of the individual, conflict and its alértes are necessary.

Revolution is the normal proper state of things.

FINGAL.   Paraguay or Venezuela offering the picture of the Ideal State.

KEMP.   They are not States. They are just Revolutions. They should be called the "Revolution of Venezuela," etcetera, etcetera.

> (*Fingal leans back against the wall and stretches.*)

FINGAL.   Well, as though we hadn't war enough already! Here you are trying to stir up a new war—a World War, too, I suppose.

KEMP.   No, I'm afraid one war might make us forget our other wars.

FINGAL.   I wish it would!

> (*Fingal stares back into the Restaurant. Two tables away a stout Belgian woman is eating, with her leg heavily bandaged resting on a chair. Kemp turns towards Restaurant, pivoting on his chair, one elbow on table.*)

KEMP.   Did the Germans do that?

FINGAL.   No. She comes from Louvain, but she did that herself.

KEMP.   Has not she the grace to attribute it to the Germans? She comes from Louvain, bandaged, at a moment like this! It is a case for the police. She must be in German pay.

FINGAL.   Quite likely. And as we are the only people she impresses— (*The Proprietor approaches from door at left.*)

THE PROPRIETOR.   Miss Godd wishes to speak to you on the telephone.

> (*Kemp gets up.*)

KEMP.   I must go and telephone.

> (*Fingal gets up.*)

FINGAL.   I must go.

KEMP.   I shall see you soon again, perhaps?

FINGAL.   Yes. I'm going North for a few days. I shall be back the beginning of next week.

(They both walk back into Restaurant, Kemp going out through door at left, half way down the wall, Fingal through street door at farther end of Restaurant.)

SCENE II.

Characters:
MR. JOHN PORTER KEMP.

Scene:—A dark recess, about 6 feet long, with a telephone desk on wall, on which John Kemp is leaning and speaking at telephone. At the back is a staircase, on which several people go up and down during action. His nose occasionally obscures the telephone mouthpiece as he bends his head and listens. When he answers his nose seems fighting and fuming, or drawing itself up solemnly, admonishing the mouth into which he is speaking. His face is red, the veins protruding on the side of his forehead, partly from the effect of holding the ear piece up to his ear.

KEMP.   No, I did not say that. What I meant was that honesty was a rhythm; it must be broken up. I found myself becoming the first cousin to George Washington. I really couldn't tell a lie! I became the slave of any bloody fact. Similarly, but oppositely, in my writing, *I did not introduce a single real character taken from life, for over a year!* I was becoming in both cases a *maniac.* In the case of art a man I met every day in the Restaurant might coincide, except for some irrelevant details, with my last dream or will-picture! But I steered all round him askance, and never touched him as though he had been a ghost! He was something, I felt, that was too true to be true. Do you see? Not to consider life partially a dream, or fancy partially a substance, is utter madness! My fancies are so matter-of-fact, shameless and conceited, that they march about the streets like Golyadkin's double. I have refused to accept them as *real,* up till now simply because they happened to be *there!* It is absurd! What? Absurd!

(Kemp inclines his head and listens crossly. The voice speaking in his ear evidently annoys him.)

KEMP.   Yes. I mentioned Golyadkin: he—But that is wandering from the point.

(*His face becomes a confused mass of irony, shame, and irritation.*)

KEMP.   Your father's spoons are excellent. Yes. That shows the right spirit. But it is not by pawning a spoon. What?

(*Kemp seems no longer listening. He says, "What!" occasionally and then relapses into staring at the ground. He at last begins speaking with impatient emphasis; putting two more pennies into the machine.*)

KEMP.   My point is plain. It is entirely a question of whole hogging, and escaping from the dreariness and self-contempt of *play*. We *play* at everything here—at love, art, winning and losing—don't we? We do! The artists take *them!* They are the rottenest and most contemptible crowd discoverable—rotten as most artists-crowds are, anywhere in the world; one of the worst sort of crowds. Chelsea! It is a name today that does not leave us many memories, alas, of genuinely Guinevere-loving able dreamer. It is the most pestiferous haunt of dilettantism, snobbery, and bourgeois selfishness. Consider that "rag" we went to last week! Oh my God! But all that we are agreed on. Now, at least all *that* we must not be! How shall we avoid becoming that play-acting, bickering, pretending trash? Easily, for you require years of selfish nursing to become that. You say: When there is fire and intelligence and will all round you, you will become modeled to a reality that spits on that! Your quiet will not be contaminated: your dreaming will ignore the mess in which it sits and contrives. Not quite! We owe ourselves a sacrifice. I would rather be out there with the soldiers than here with the playmen of the —Western World! But when you think of battles you cannot help remembering that it is that art-crowd that are being fought for, instead of the "Our women and children" for whom you are to "lend our strong right arm." Women can always look after themselves, can't they?

"We are the civilization for which you are fighting!" I read today in a newspaper that one of the "Café Royalties," as the delighted paper called them, had said that. And then, having uttered that boast, he departed to a studio rag; and the next morning he sculpted his daily sculp, or pawed on to his canvas his daily slop, probably German as regards its emotions and intelligence; indubitably vomit. No! action, for me, does not lie that way. And then again if you don't remember the art-crowd, you remember other equally nauseous ones that linger behind and contaminate the War, actually dirtying with their existence the bitterest heroism, degrading death.

Yet *action*, if you could find the right action, is the "sovereign cure for our ills."

And it is maddening to live with such a profusion of action suddenly poured out, most wasted; at least not curing what requires that cure.

> (*Kemp places two more pennies in the box, muttering, "what porridge had John Keats?" He seems pursuing some parallel between his oratory and the pennies.*)

KEMP. Yes. Well then, I doubt if you *can* act now, in the sense I mean, any more than you can swim without water. But at least avoid degrading *substitutes* for action. If you act, in however slight a way, *act*. If you are not *doing* anything, do not pretend that you are. Do *nothing*. It is the only clean proceeding when conditions are against some particular form of action. Do not shrink from misfortune. It will not hurt you. Then—I can hold this thing no longer to my ear. I must go, as well. Are you at your father's house? Alone? I shouldn't interfere with his property anymore! Ha! Ha! We meet to-morrow. Farewell.

> (*Kemp places the receiver up, and walks quickly back through the door into the Restaurant.*)

SCENE III.

(Same as Scene 1. Time: next day, 1:30.)

Characters:

MR. JOHN PORTER KEMP.
MISS ROSE GODD.
Detective: WILLIAM DRUCE.

Rose Godd and Kemp are sitting opposite each other at table. Rose Godd is a very large-boned flat-faced woman of twenty years. When she stands up she is very tall and strong looking, with a small head and thick neck. The Mongol intensity of her face is mitigated by self-consciousness. Her lips are painted a bright red in the midst of her yellow skin. She is always perfectly calm. She feels that her intelligence is not quite good enough for her company: but pride in what she considers her latent power of action brings her into steadfastness. Kemp, as he looks at her, wonders sometimes whether the "action" he preaches will not be found in his case in Rose Godd flinging herself on him and trying to tear him to pieces. But he is satisfied on reflection (and turns from the fact with distaste, usually) that it is a softer conflict that she desires. But as between Rose Godd and himself that action could not be disguised into the rôle of discovery.

KEMP.   Will you have coffee? Albert! Two coffees please!

WAITER.   Two coffees, sir? Yes sir!

KEMP.   That is the situation and there is no preamble. But Hakluyt traveled into lands we could never discover. He went on millions of leagues further than we could ever go. We are thrown back on ourselves in that sense. That is *action*. The old way is something divorced from ourselves: the appetite for, and the conditions to attain to, the New. To fit out a high wooden ship, with a poop and a carved figure on the bow, at Plymouth, to sail to El Dorado or even Rio Grande, would be neither venturesome nor intelligent. It would be a reconstruction as foolish as Don Quixote's was wise. Yet we suffer from this shriveling up of our horizons. We need those horizons, and action and adventure as much as our books need exercise. We have been rendered sedentary by perfected transport. Our minds have become home-keeping. We do not *think* as boldly: our thoughts do not leap out in the same way.

Well, in the case of the Earth there is nothing to be done. If it were suddenly increased to twenty times its present size we should not be impressed, or see Giants now, intellectual or other. That something subtle and multitudinous that is the Poet, is not so easy to describe: for to say that he is "great" is not the point, although it satisfied our Victorian forefathers to see him as a perfect, very big, and muscular *man*, with philological credentials, a Konig, a canny-man: a Can-Man. He was a cloud-squatting Jehovah's athletic twin brother. Then when we hear this war referred to as "the Greatest War of all time," we laugh irritably. It is not by a counting of heads, or poor corpses, that the blank in our imagination can be filled! They were evil fellows who stole our visions. He would be a great savior who could get them back again! Meantime it is a female's game to go on pretending this, and playing at that! We must contrive; find a new Exit. Any wildly subversive action should be welcomed. *We must escape from the machine in ourselves! Smash it up: renew ourselves.*

> (*The Proprietor brings his stomach slowly up. It appears like an emblem of the Earth to Kemp, who points to it with a fork as a schoolmaster might, at a class-*

room globe. But it has come too late. Miss Godd and Kemp stare stupidly at it together. They at last begin laughing, and Rodac carries it swiftly away, frowning over his shoulder.)

KEMP. But I think you misunderstood me with your spoons! *(He smiles slowly and archly at her, wagging his head. She looks at him with such fixity that his smile is gradually driven off his face. He remains staring at her in a sobered, cross, astonishment.)*

KEMP. I am sorry. Have I hurt you? Did you put much store in the spoons?

(She shakes her head. Two or three tears roll down her cheeks.)

KEMP. But your spoons are no more ineffective than my lies. What did you get for them?

MISS GODD. Not much.

(Kemp looks down at his plate. Their entente today does not seem the same as on other occasions. Her face appears at once reproachful, insolently claiming something, antagonistically reserved. She appears looking at him out of armor in which she has implicit confidence. Kemp is embarrassed, and when he begins speaking again takes up the subject truculently. He attributes her attitude, for want of a better explanation, to his reasoning. He feels he has not held his audience.)

KEMP. I feel that my lies and your spoons were about as playful as some of the absurdities with which we reproach our art friends. Compared to death on a barricade, or the robber Garnier's Swedish exercises while he was in hiding in the suburbs of Paris, they are slight exploits. The blood that spurts from a tapped probiscus is not enough. A spoon will not thrust you into jail for so long that you forget what the Earth looks like. For the hair to turn white, the heart to turn gray, in an hour, you require the real thing, ma mie.

MISS GODD. Yes.

(Kemp looks at her sideways. Her face is green and her eyes shining. He reverts once more to the hypothesis of a wrestling match with Rose Godd. He looks at her large muscular hands. She follows the direction of his eyes. With a sudden look of panic she places them under the table, and between her knees, and she seems almost hissing at him.)

MISS GODD.   What are you looking at, Kemp? What are you looking at?

KEMP.   At your hands.   (*She works them up and down spasmodically as if they were cold.*)

KEMP.   But "it is the principle." A great violence, unless you were sure you had your finger on the spot, would be no better. So long as you are *pretending* to do anything desperate or the reverse. The objective I indicate is different. Whether it is extreme or puerile is as it happens.

MISS GODD.   As it happens?

KEMP.   You seem rather odd, Miss *Godd!*

MISS GODD.   Give me a cigarette.

KEMP.   You ask for it like a criminal on the scaffold!

> (*He gives Miss Godd a cigarette. A man has entered the door of the Restaurant. He is talking to Radac, the Proprietor. Kemp watches him idly for a moment. He then notices that the Proprietor and the newcomer are both looking at the table where Rose Godd and himself are seated. He glances over to Rose Godd, and finds her eyes are fixed on him, with a senseless fiery questioning.*)

KEMP.   What is the matter?

MISS GODD.   Nothing, I wondered something——But your standards are so high!

KEMP.   I can't help my standards being a bit cocked up.

MISS GODD.   I mean in this respect: in connection with what we talk about so much.

KEMP.   What?——

MISS GODD.   You must torment me with your denseness. Your standards for *action* are so difficult. You don't accept an action. You look at an action as critically as you do at a thought. Most actions won't stand that. They are delicate little things, or rough undeveloped things, or mad things. If you *look* at them too hard—as that man is looking at me—(*Miss Godd indicates the man who is talking to Radac*) they might shrivel up, they do get small. I *pity* all actions. They are so unimportant compared to thought. For all their blood, men sniff at them and dissect them.

KEMP.   There need not be blood.

MISS GODD.   You don't have to dig far for blood.

> (*Radac and the man who has been talking to him have come up, and are standing a few yards from the table now, listening to the conversation of Kemp and Miss Godd.*)

KEMP. No, it is true. But the avoir-du-poids amount of violence is no criterion of action. It would have taken no more force and would be no more bloody an action, to kill Napoleon than any contemporary bourgeois in France. But it would have been a more important action. And *any* action, however bloodless, that hamstrung that destructive personality, would have been a more important action than to cut a grocer's throat.

MISS GODD. Or a Banker's.

KEMP. Why a Banker?

MISS GODD. Because—he *was* a banker.

KEMP. Who? Napoleon?

MISS GODD. This gentleman will tell you.

(*Miss Godd looks up sideways at the man with Radac.*)

KEMP. What the devil are you standing there for?

DETECTIVE WILLIAM DRUCE. Steady—steady. None of your devils to me, please. *You* may be the Devil, for all I know. I am a Police Officer. You are Miss Rose Godd, I believe?

MISS GODD. (*looking at him blackly*). Yes, that's my name.

DETECTIVE WILLIAM DRUCE. I have come to arrest you, Rose Godd, for the murder of Nicolas Godd.

KEMP. Murder! Murder of whom?

MISS GODD. (*laughs*). Napoleon!

DETECTIVE WILLIAM DRUCE. Come with me, please.

(*The detective watches Rose Godd with wary attention. Rose Godd gets up, her face a dark white, her lips hard factitious crimson.*)

MISS GODD. Good-bye!

KEMP. Haven't you——. Is Nicolas Godd your father?

MISS GODD. I have acted.

(*The Detective springs at Rose Godd, catching her by the wrists, and a small bottle falls on the table. They roll on the floor together, and the back of the restaurant becomes full of a crowd of people—diners, Radac, and some folk from the street.*

Kemp sits with his white profile, and large eye distorted with shame and perplexity. He springs up, partly disappearing behind the table, where he is noticed to have seized the Detective by the collar.)

CURTAIN.

The Bishop's Fool

1.

RETURNING from Sweden a short while ago, in the M.S. *Volsung*, a sumptuous ship, I experienced the utter peace which only sea travel can provide. A few passengers, I among them, had made their way to the sun lounge beyond the American bar. We wallowed in deep cushioned receptacles, rocked upon the gently heaving sea; a music program of the Swedish radio crooned away at a suitable distance. Like all peace it was artificial, and no doubt a little sugary, but all of us were conditioned to appreciate any kind of peace. It was one of the appropriate amenities of a neutral vessel: we were going back to blood, sweat, and tears No. 3. Even the boastful growl of the alcoholic American which could be heard from within, nearer the bar where he crouched over a table, vainglorious but confidential, even this was soothing, like the rumbling of a volcano not in eruption. And upstairs three young Englishmen, innocent of vulgar emulation, hurled deck quoits or whatever they were called, and when their quoit was expelled from its transitory nest complimented the other fellow and obviously preferred to be the loser. Success is always a little beastly. It is less glorious to sit upon another fellow's chest than to be sat on by another fellow—if he is a decent fellow. For this voyage at least we were all to be out of reach of human passions. Even the unseemly effort involved in the propulsion of this luxurious monster from one side of the North Sea to the other was only felt as a muffled throb, an agreeable subterranean tom-tom.

For some reason I began to think just then of Rymer. Were Rymer on board, I said to myself, what a different ship this would be. He would be arguing with the American within, or with one of these peace-loving inmates of the all-glass sun lounge, arguing that Soviet Russia was maligned by Press magnates, and that the North Koreans were as a matter of fact in no way connected with the Kremlin: that the South Koreans (very corrupt and scheming puppets) had been the first to attack, and were of course the actual aggressors, though the Press unanimously asserted the opposite. Then on the upper deck, where the quoit players were, Rymer would have taken a quoit from one of the young Englishmen and proceeded to demonstrate how the game ought really to be played. There is little doubt that before we had reached Tilbury the captain would have received some valuable tips as to how to navigate his ship, and had Rymer got into the engine-room the chief engineer would soon have acquired a good deal more knowledge about the handling of marine engines than he had possessed twenty-four hours before. Finally, should this energetic friend of mine have happened to be crossing at a week-end with Sunday supervening, he would have insisted upon holding divine service anglo-catholicly for English passengers, with a parade of Roman formularies, which (few English tourists today belonging to classes susceptible to ritual) would not have been well received. But whatever the special circumstances, with Rymer on board the ship would have ceased to be at peace. Such pacific bliss as I have dwelt upon would have been out of the question: politics, religion, and the itch-to-teach would have combined, a trinity of irritants, to sow disquiet in the ship from one end to the other.

Whether this is the best way to approach the subject of Rymer I hardly know, but there is this: you are introduced not to the man-in-the-flesh, with all his physical irrelevancies, but to disembodied action. You see only ideally what he *does,* what only *he* would do, like the action of a Poltergeist: an invisible something, with the famous Yorkshire name of Rymer. So, anyway we start with the functional essence of Rymer. Having begun with the effect I will turn to the cause; give an account of this unusual creature, whom you may judge to be a Christian pest, a dangerous busybody, or a saint in motley.

We met in the following manner. It was not in fact a *meeting* but he had the next place to me in the Reading Room of the British Museum. This accident has no more significance than sitting next to somebody in a bus—it does not, happily, constitute a "meeting": and if it is converted into a meeting by one of the parties, is properly resented.

Not a Webb addict, I had on this occasion, by the purest chance, put in a slip for some Fabian tracts and this was the uppermost of a half-dozen books awaiting me on my return from lunch. I should perhaps add, for the benefit of those unacquainted with the B. M. Reading Room, that the official ticket protruding from each book brought by the attendant displays the name as well as the seat number of the reader for whom it is destined. This may be a relevant fact.

I was preparing to begin work when a shadowy figure existing only in the corner of my eye, occupying the chair and desk space to my right, unexpectedly thrust out a hand and gave the Fabian tracts an emphatic slap.

"Splendid stuff, Mr. Wyndham Lewis!" was the unwelcome oral accompaniment of the pawing of my book. Then there was another vigorous pat. I looked fixedly and coldly at the intrusive hand, ignoring the shadow in the corner of my right eye to which it belonged and from which it had strayed uninvited into my reading territory. I turned to the left, presenting my back to so unduly extrovert an organism. This is all I remember, beyond the fact that when I had finished my reading and stood up to go, I noticed that the chair to my right was vacant.

It was ten days later that a letter arrived, with a Midland postmark, at the foot of which I read Samuel Hartley Rymer (Rev). This was fairly carefully written: for these were the only words in the whole letter that I felt absolutely certain about. However, I thought I gathered that my correspondent —"if not," as he feared, "quite beyond my means"—desired to purchase a work of mine: "a small painting? or a drawing which is probably all I could afford." I disentangled these sentences from the shapeless jumble of his script. Finally, he was reminding me, it came to light, of the impertinent stranger who had spoken to me in the Reading Room of the Museum. "I am afraid that was me." So! My neighbour who had smacked my pile of books was a parson? I saw at once how that might be.

The Museum episode was not calculated to recommend me to Mr. Rymer but I thought I would see him. It was two hundred years since the Enlightenment and six centuries since the Age of Faith. And of course I knew that in its "dry" form the Rot was in the wood roof of the churches, in reredos, in pulpit, and in pew. It was my idea that this might be a good opportunity to learn whether the Rot had entered into the Cloth. Did it rage beneath the surplice and eat away the roots of faith, in the impalpable center of belief? For though faith began to die in the flock half a millennium ago, I have always supposed that a priest must secrete a little of it.

When I went to the door in answer to Rymer's knock, a large passionate and weary and frustrated face was thrust up towards mine—a not unhandsome one I thought. (We are of the same height, but it was thrust up because of the clerical crouch, and there was the prayerful angle of the supplicant's eyes.)

To a Frenchman, in my place, *a slovenly overgrown schoolboy* would have been standing there on the doorstep: which would have been to overlook or ignore the English tradition of expressing superiority by means of shabby garments: and then the fact that it is not the Englishman's idea to get *mature*. Maturity pertains to another ethos, continental and not insular. Let me add in this context, that irresponsible boyish "mischief" is a favorite alibi with the Anglo-Saxon.

But to return from the general to the particular, my visitor was a hulking forty-something, hatless, spectacled. Not come as the well-heeled patron, surely. Just dropped up from a by-no-means fashionable watering place to get a glass of milk, trying to look at once commanding and appealing as the farmer's wife comes to the door.

My first impressions I was obliged later very radically to scrap, to Rymer's advantage, I mean. I am the possessor of a tough eye. It does not soften what it sees: it hands me everything like a photographer's untouched photograph. In this case, it noted with a relentless acuity what had narrowly escaped being a lantern jaw, which it was only prevented from degenerating into by his masterful vitality. It registered the eloquent feminine mouth which pursed itself almost primly and then shot out its lips at right angles, the rest of the mouth not moving, to be a spout for speech to rabble rouse or to exhort—as urchins do in their word battles. He reads verse better than anyone I have ever heard: he was the quietest crooner, he was soft like a man talking to himself about something he had seen, at once matter-of-fact and unearthly. And he knew the weight in Heaven of every word in the dictionary.

As I saw him for the first time I observed of course the

eyes of a somewhat worried, but stubbornly amused, big dog. I saw that the nose was shapely, the brow large. Those first impressions did not have to be modified: but in the end one would forget the ecclesiastical chinline; one would assess at their proper value the disfigurement associated with eloquent verbal discharges—such as the spoutlike propensities of the shooting lips, the wildly wrinkled brow.

There was no clerical collar on his large weather-beaten neck. It was framed instead with the gaping collar of a soft blue shirt. "Where is your collar?" I demanded. Minus his master's name upon a brass-plate, collarless and unidentifiable, this big dog was at large in London. But, "Got it in my pocket!" came popping out the brisk rejoinder: "Do you want me to put it on?" He had produced it and held it in his hand. "Not before coming in," I said. "Not at once," he echoed, putting the collar back in the pocket.

The collar had looked authentic. "Please come this way," said I, leading my incognito man-of-god upstairs, into my workroom. I looked narrowly at him of course. We were there under the vast sculptor's window: he exposed his rugged worried countenance to the glare of the sky without an unbecoming diffidence, but quite simply as if to say, "Well here I am. Since you seem inclined to scrutinize my person, this is what I look like." I was searching for signs of the Rot, of course.

What he actually said was: "You must have thought it great cheek for me to write to you. I feel I am here under false pretences." "You must not feel that," I said. "Why should you?"

"It is very good of you to say so."

"Please sit down," I told him as I sat down myself. He followed suit, silently. Rather stiffly expectant he sat there as if awaiting my next move. I sat studying him, however, and he did not look at me.

It was not that he really felt in a false position, I'm sure of that: and there is nothing shy about Rymer. At this first meeting, for a little while, I had a sense of a youthful manner: of an attempt rather curious in view of his massive maturity—to suggest the early years of manhood. This did not survive our first meeting. It was perhaps a manner he adopted, under certain circumstances, with strangers. I think he produces (however battered it may be) the undergraduate he once was. In any case, it was a very different approach to the aggressive book slapping of the Museum.

"You like pictures?" I inquired, as I saw him looking at a Rowlandson which hung near him.

"I do very much. I have some. Two or three, perhaps you might like."

"I understand you wish to add to your collection?" I then said, for *this* patron would have to be brought to the point, if he was a patron. And if he was not, it was best to find out what his errand was. His response was satisfactorily prompt and clear.

"Yes. I should like to acquire a work of yours, unless it is altogether beyond my means."

After I had produced two small canvases, and perhaps a dozen drawings, he stuck one of the drawings up against the back of a chair, returned to where he had been sitting and proceeded to examine it (from much too far off, as a matter of fact). It was a large, strongly colored, gouache of a number of nude horsemen. Rigidly stylized, certainly; but with the black arcs of the horses' legs against a shining lagoon, and so on, possessing enough romantic literary appeal to recommend it to an intelligent clergyman. I knew it would look far better on his walls than he could foresee.

I left him in front of the drawing, and went downstairs to answer the telephone. When I returned he was standing up. He asked me whether I would sell the drawing—he liked it very much. I told him I was glad and the price of it was thirty pounds.

He began making out a check, saying as he did so, "May I take it away with me?" There was no objection of course, and shortly he handed me that check and received the drawing wrapped in brown paper, with an arrow to show where it should be held. I pushed cigarettes over; he took a horrific pipe from his pocket and asked if he might be allowed to smoke. We neither of us wished to terminate the interview with the production of the check (I was quite prepared to find that it bounced). We talked for a short while about pictures—my hours of work, my training in Paris—the disadvantages of the naked overhead sky as a source of light. Then he had pipe trouble, and when we were able to converse again I asked him about himself. What manner of life did he live at Bagwick Rectory and if he came up to London?

No, he did not come to London often. He could not afford to: and very quickly I found we had passed into astonishingly uninhibited intercourse. Yielding to my discreet invitations he opened up, and I looked in, as if into a woman's handbag. I must confess that what I saw there in the matter of hard cash embarrassed me for a moment. The thirty pounds in my pocket (in the form of a check) had left about tuppence three farthings; all mixed up with the bus tickets and hairpins and little girlish secrets. And far from being averse, I found, from laying bare economic secrets, he relished exposing them. Somewhat abashed, as I have said, by his unexpected exhibitions, I steered off on to more general subjects. I attempted to distract him with *racontars* [1] and perhaps a few caustic indiscretions. In these early hours of our friendship, I recall, Rymer played the parson a little. For instance, in response to one of my exposures of a colleague's vanity he exclaimed "you wicked man!" as parsons had in England in the heyday of the Cloth, over muffins and seed cake—the parsons the inimitable du Maurier, and Trollope, too, of course, were acquainted with.

While these pleasantries were occurring I had time to think. My new patron's annual income as Rector of Bagwick was, he disclosed, theoretically six pounds a week, but naturally it was not tax-free and neither he nor his wife had any means of their own. The pound sterling slides downhill all the time, but there is one thing that is stationary as a rock in England, namely the clergyman's stipend. That does not rise correspondingly. Clergymen cannot strike so their wages are not adjustable to meet rises in the cost of living. Had I unaware got a dustman for a patron I should have been amused: as it was I said a little crossly, "So you are paying me a month's salary?" "Yes," with firm relish he assented—it amused him as much as if he had been a ragpicker: "Yes—about."

I privately examined the likelihood of his being a phony. Of course I could have given him the thing. If he was really so poor a clergyman I would do that. I decided to be cautious. Then I enquired, "Why are you indulging, Mr. Rymer, in this absurd extravagance?" and something like the following dialogue ensued:

Myself. "You have about five shillings a week pocket money?"

1 gossip

Rev. Rymer. "Sometimes!"

Myself. "Is not this drawing an absurd extravagance?"

Rev. Rymer. "That's what my daughter says!" (In a classy rhetorical whine—apt to terminate in a comic wail—to which he was sometimes addicted.)

Myself. "You're a wicked man!"

Rev. Rymer. "Yes," with unabated promptitude, "I'm a miserable sinner!"

Myself (*kindly*). "Does not your conscience prick you?"

Rev. Rymer. "Ought it to?" (Parsonically quizzical.)

Myself. "I know mine ought to, if I accept money for that drawing, now I know your circumstances."

Rev. Rymer. "That is absurd. It was generous of you to let me have it so cheaply. I make a little money on the side."

Myself. "How?"

Rev. Rymer. "Oh, by coaching. Not very much, but it is a little. I only spend *that,* on my London trips—and this, of course."

Myself. "I have a special cheap rate for poor men of religion, 'rich of holy thought and work.' You could have availed yourself of that. Had I known. . . ."

Rev. Rymer. "Have you a special fee?" (He gurgled merrily.) "Have you many of us as clients?"

Myself. "Quite a few. But you can't even afford . . . You would be straining your resources if you bought a picture-postcard *Sunflower* of Van Gogh!"

Rev. Rymer. "Oh well, provided we can laugh at such embarrassments."

Myself. "Poverty is not a laughing matter—for an artist. For a priest it is the preordained condition and affluence is disgraceful. You can go on laughing."

Rev. Rymer. "But I am not really poor. I live in the country. You do not realize how inexpensive life is at Bagwick."

Myself. "You six-quid-a-week capitalist!"

Rymer is an individual not without dignity. He is large and serious and worried. And he is quite exceptionally arrogant. If he heard this he would not like it, but he is the most aggressive dogmatist I know, as was indicated in my preamble. If your electric oven is a serious problem, or your studio painfully hot in summer, he will, with his invariable promptitude and patness, and with an affectation of salesmanship technique, propose a gadget to regulate the first, and install (in theory) a novel ventilation system to correct the second. There is no handicap he will not convert in the twinkling of an eye into a triumphant asset. Should you suffer from asthma he will be your doctor: if you are a philosopher assailed with doubt he will overhaul your system—or if you do not fancy a system, he will show you the best way to get on without one, as a light-hearted empiricist.

It is easy to see how a village priest is apt to develop into a wiseacre, and where this technique might be highly appropriate. Of course with me he has to behave himself up to a point, but he would be a bad man to have around if one were in a worldly position defenceless against this amateur lawgiver. Though a kind man, he could not resist the opportunity. He literally boils with the heat of his private absolute. Sometimes I have had to wrestle jovially for hours with this didactic dragon.

If this is a fault which takes up a good deal of room here, out of proportion to its importance, his virtues are unusual. He is one of those men with whom one finds oneself conversing at once with the freedom of two tramps meeting at a dusty crossroad, open to one another in the free masonry of the propertyless. He is touched with the heroism of the destitute, even if it is *malgré lui* [2] that he is of that caste. He is not a throwback to the religious mendicant, he is an advance copy (imperfect but authentic) of the hobo-holiness of Tomorrow. So actually we get on because both are poor, and a fastidious absence of dignity (the intelligent hallmark of English education) neutralizes, in its operation, such faults as the relic of class bossiness, in its parsonic form, which I have described. Oxford has cooked Rymer so successfully that whatever else he may be he is not raw. At times I have felt he is overcooked, or perhaps it would be better to say *overoxfordized*.

A clerical playboy he emphatically is not. But at times *il en a l'air*. [3] Much is, as I have suggested, mannerism induced by *métier*. [4] I hope the man of parts I write of is not disappearing beneath such elaboration: not this poor clergyman who forgets he has no money, who yearns for

[2] despite himself
[3] he has style, an air
[4] profession

honor—who certainly has dreamed of fame, but who dreams incessantly now of social justice and a new, bright, bossy, fraternal world—a new Jerusalem. He comes from a part of England that has bred rebels like rabbits. His verse is of a wizard elegance, the song of a rather mechanically cheerful bird, on the highest and frostiest bough in a frost like the last frost of all, celebrating the winter of our discontent as though it were the morning of the world.

With a brave curl of the chapped lip Rymer is ready to take on his cavernous jaw whatever buffet, in spite of his prayers, cruel Providence swings at him. This, if not mute, inglorious Rymer, eating his heart out in a remote rectory, risks going short of fuel or food every time he buys a ticket for King's Cross for no strictly clerical purpose—just to come up for air: to spend a few days in London, go to hear Grosser preach, go to see a highbrow film at the Academy, or stare at paintings in the small Galleries.

It took quite some time to digest Rymer. It was like overcoming the flamboyance of French prose in an author who by chance has something to say. His verse is the reverse of the personality however. If he conversationally bludgeons his way through the world, if that is the outer animal, within he is attentive and quiet. On top of all is social splashings, but beneath there abides in the Rymerian deeps something which is only seen in his verse, which has at times a submerged quality of great intensity. It might be the noiseless canticle of a cephalopod. I shall have to take back the wintry mechanical bird, this is a better image.

How it was we came, at our first meeting, to be communicating with such rugged readiness immediately will be a little plainer presently perhaps. Rymer did not come in as a stranger you see—almost with a "hallo!" He refuses to be a stranger to anybody. He has the secret I think of his divine Master, he is no mere official of the Church. Within five minutes, with someone he had never seen before in his life, he would be telling him how to fix his lighter, the best way to get to sleep at night, or in what to invest his money.

The talk about his status as a patron, to go back to that, died down. Further personal revelations however followed. His situation looked to me a very ugly one. At this point the actual fieldwork began. What he was telling me, now, concerned his position as Rector, and it was related to the new standing of all the rural clergy in England. The final ruin of the landed society was factor number one, though Heaven knows no traditional Squire would have tolerated Rymer—he himself representing a new brand of parson. However, before I proceed I ought to say that the information I am about to impart was not all acquired on the first day we met. Nor, of course, was Rymer the Rymer I now know yet. The process of progressive understanding by means of which density is acquired by the phantom stranger, even with such an extrovert as Rymer demands some little time. Again, the facts he divulged concerning his life at Bagwick I only fully grasped the meaning of when a little later I passed some time in the different parts of the postwar English countryside. I went where he lived and functioned too, and checked at firsthand. So what is the narrative proper will now begin, ending with the last news I have had of him —most disagreeable events which I fear will change his life for the worse.

English village life until quite recently was, of course, dominated by the Squire: the old order, which had long ceased to have any meaning in the towns, clung on in the English villages. It was with the Squire that the Rector, or Vicar, had to deal. Often he owed his appointment to the local big landowner, and in any case he was apt to have the most say in questions relating to the Church. That is still the position in many places, certainly, though it is manifest that this faint shadow of the feudal situation is about to disappear completely. From the fifteenth to the twentieth century has been an interminable fade-out. In what an American magazine described as "the Crippsean Ice Age" there is no room for the "country gentleman"; even a clergyman in the old sense must be an outrageous exotic.

Those of the landowning class who have disposed of their "seats," parks and estates, may even now not be the majority. Comedy to which they are not averse, lightens the lot of those who will not be frozen out of their seats, or who retain a toehold in some cumbersome seventeenth-century Renaissance palace. Some convert their country seats into apartment houses for local businessmen (I know of such cases in Wales for instance), themselves occupying a modest suite in one of the flanking towers—from which vantage point they can keep an eye on their lodgers. One, I know, lived alone with a manservant and his now decrepit nannie, in a house about the size of Wellington Barracks. The Park is now a golflinks, the Clubhouse a hundred yards or so from the Hall: tradesmen from the neighboring city put and stibble all around the main entrance. Then I remember being told of a well known Marquess and his Marchioness who dig and hoe side by side in the vegetable garden adjacent to their palace (which they would describe of course as a "country house"), inhabiting the few rooms that can be kept clean with a vacuum cleaner wielded by an elderly domestic or by the not very robust Marchioness. Finally, there are those who live in a gardener's house upon the estate and act as cicerone to sightseers come to visit the huge and ostentatious shell where one of the greatest lords of England used to live in state. There is one case of this sort in which a handsome young Countess, a former "school teacher," married to the earl during the blitz, escorts parties around. It is reported that she levels some very caustic cracks at her husband's ancestors, whose portraits snootily placard the towering walls of the rooms of state.

Seeing how long ago the feudal age ended, it is remarkable how intense a sentiment of pleasurable inferiority still subsisted in the English countryside as late as the first years of the present century, from which the Church derived advantage, and which sentiment it encouraged. Anyone familiar with the countryside before the radio and the automobile, would be inclined to feel that the end of the Manor must mean the end of the Church. But Rymer has a quite different destiny for the Church. What he would really like, I believe, is that it should replace the Manor.

However, a new power has come on the scene, most unexpectedly, in many parts of the country, and automatically has occupied the place left vacant by the Squire. I refer to the new-rich Farmer (rich partly owing to Government subsidies). The men who have the big farms, of a thousand acres up, are the new variety of big bug, once you get outside the town, for they are in fact the biggest thing in sight. Wherever a Squire, or other aristocratic authority, has dropped out, the force of circumstances, if not their own volition, pushes these other agricultural bosses in. The Farmer's tenure of power will be brief: but there he is. He will remain until such time as this Government, or the next, as it must be, much more radical, collectivizes his property. Who can say, without unwarrantable optimism, that he will not be shot as a Kulak?

In the rural parish of which Rymer is the agent of salvation such a transference of power as I have indicated has taken place—much to his disgust. A farmer possessed of fifteen hundred acres, himself coming of a long line of yeomen farmers, but (odious complication) grammar-schooled at the school once attended as a day boy by Rymer himself, and hovering between yeoman and gentleman, is the big man in the eyes of the village now. Most of his laborers in fact live there.

The Squire is a highly intelligent man, not cut out to play that part at all. He has sold his farms and other property, is seldom down at Bagwick—which is a perfectly hideous place, though the Manor is a fine specimen of the Dutch Gable period proper in the manorial architecture of England. So he has little say in village affairs, and the fact that he is well-disposed to my friend does not alter the situation. It is Jack Cox, the young farmer, with whom Rymer for his sins is confronted. This little rustic capitalist is Samuel Hartley Rymer's cross. For Jack Cox neither likes Rymer's politics, nor his brand of religion (Anglo-Catholic), nor his big sweet worried argumentative face.

For ten years Farmer and Rector have not spoken to one another: or if the latter has proffered a Christian greeting, the former—the farmer—had disdainfully declined to return it. Rather, this *was* the position until only the other day, to which I will come later on. The farmer's aggressiveness has become much more marked since the war: he has addressed complaints personally to the Bishop; then he drew up a petition, for which he obtained a number of signatures in the neighborhood, for Rymer's removal. Several times my friend has been visited by the Archdeacon who acts as a one-man Gestapo, the Bishop's emissary detailed to investigate any case of this kind and report. If a few vague and desultory inquiries can be called a cross-examination, Rymer underwent that at the hands of the Archdeacon. The Rural Dean has bent a puzzled eye upon him. So poor Rymer has been the object of too much attention to be comfortable. But the last time the meek envoy of the Cathedral showed up, with elaborate casualness he observed: "Let us see, Rymer, did I not hear it said that you wrote—er—articles? It seems to me I did." When Rymer agreed that he had indeed done that, the Archdeacon added, smiling a little slyly and shyly, "And *verse*—or am I wrong?" Rymer made no difficulty about admitting that he was married to immortal verse. But the interpretation he put upon this interrogatory surprised me at first. He regarded it as a very favorable omen. His literary habits, he felt, would excuse a good deal, especially the writing of verse. The farmer's indictment would melt away confronted with that fact, or at least would be blunted.

The charges brought by the farmer, it seems, are multiple. First, there is the usual one with which all clergymen have to contend, namely that he is lazy, lies down on the job, keeps the church in a dirty condition, never visits the sick for fear of infection: that he just draws his pay and lazes around, except for an hour or two of very hot air on Sunday—which does not however warm the church and the children come home sneezing their heads off, and old people who were fond of going there had stopped doing so because it was too dangerous after October the first.

Next come his papist habits: the stink of incense that one can smell half the way down the road, the flexing of the knees and other ungodliness. All farmers like a "broad churchman" and dislike and suspect a "high churchman," and Jack Cox was no exception to the rule. But there was another charge that may have carried far more weight, if only because it is not often heard. Jack Cox accused the Rector of being a "red"—the farmer's bane—of stirring up his laborers, of contaminating the parish with radical doctrine, of being a disturbing and immoral influence.

When first Rymer disclosed this latter charge I stared at him. I said "A Red, too!" He gave his little short breathless laugh, his eyes never participating. "Yes. It is true," he told me, "that I am in favor of telling the United States to keep its beastly dollars, and to trade with Russia instead." He stirred about vigorously in his chair, I noticed. Any mention of the United States inflamed him, but because of his sacred calling he was obliged to smother the flames within, or to bottle them up. This engendered a physical uneasiness.

"Is that being *a red?*" he asked, "If so I am one."

"But you advertise a desire for more social justice?"

"Certainly!" he protested. "Don't you?"

"Well, you are a socialist."

"Call it that, if you like."

"Which of course would make Mr. Attlee 'a red'."

"Exactly."

That was as far as I got upon that occasion. He did tell me a little later that he had "sat on the same platform" as the Red Dean (of Canterbury). I, of course, do not know everything. The farmer had a case, I suppose. He could be described as a "political priest," no doubt, which is all, under certain circumstances, the farmer would need. But those circumstances did not exist as it happened.

The Archdeacon, dispatched by the Cathedral the first time, unseen by Rymer, poked around the neighborhood in his shabby clerical automobile, discussed with some the weather, with others the crops, learned that Rymer was a total abstainer, that he affected to smoke a pipe—but there was rarely any tobacco in it: that he had never been known to make passes at the maid at the rectory (there had never been any there). The Archdeacon had had some practice in mollifying parishioners on the score of the "redness" (or "liberalism," as he had learned to call it) of their vicars. He had got rather to enjoy doing this, as people who play a game well welcome opportunities of displaying their skill.

As for Anglo-Catholicism, that was apple pie to the Archdeacon. One might almost say that he had been specially trained in the art of turning people's minds away from the swinging of the censers in the churches of the diocese—and he had had reason to observe that a certain "redness" or "pinkness" was frequently associated with these liturgical eccentricities. The Bishop no one could accuse of a tendency to totalitarianism; on the other hand he was one of the "highest" bishops in the country. So of course this conjunction of the "pink" and the "high" was not invariable.

As an ecclesiastical administrator the Bishop was no man of iron. A rather picturesque-looking aristocrat, he would listen, his eyes half-closed, the graceful silver-curling head bowed far more in sorrow than in anger, to the reports of his clerical watchdog—who was not a very fierce dog either. "Ah!" the Bishop would intone despondently as the Archdeacon uttered the dreadful word *drink*. "Mum!" the Bishop would softly ejaculate as the Archdeacon muttered *young girls of fifteen* (or *choirboys in the Vestry*) as he reported his findings in connection with some poison pen letter, or on some accusation leveled at a curate who was said to use scent.

But it is probable that were Rymer discovered (to make use of an extreme illustration), when the teller's back was turned, with his hand in the till of the local branch bank in the nearby market town, the Bishop would only murmur, "Rymer is an extremely impetuous clergyman, defective in judgment, I think. He is apt, don't you agree, to forget that he is now a weighty and responsible incumbent and acts as wild curates sometimes do. In the present case he would undoubtedly have returned the bundle of five-pound notes later: for I assume he was testing the vigilance of the bank clerk. It is most like him to interfere in what does not concern him. Poor Rymer! Always his actions rather resemble those of the practical joker." And were it further alleged that Rymer, when discovered, had produced a gun, which he pointed at the teller, the Bishop would have observed: "A revolver? Rymer would be more likely to blow *himself* up with such a weapon than to harm anyone else. It was clearly some prank—everything points to that, I think. Poor Rymer! I have often thought Rymer missed his vocation, he should have been an actor. However, I regard him as the right man for Bagwick, quite the right man. The people like him. And . . . as a living Bagwick is not a very attractive proposition." Were Rymer on the other hand to murder the gamekeeper of a neighboring Coal Board executive, it would not be because the famished Rymer had been caught poaching— no. It would be because Rymer had mistaken the gamekeeper for a poacher. There was no imaginable crime of which a clergyman stood accused, which would not have received this treatment—been melted away in the mellow mildness of the Bishop's mind.

It was the Bishop of Storby's invariable belief that clergymen in his diocese were *popular*. Then, the anglican priesthood is the worst-paid calling in Great Britain today. This is a major fact that must be ever present to the mind of a high functionary of the Church. Indeed, should any man be so eccentric as to express a desire to join the greatly depleted ranks of the clergy, a warm welcome would be given to a ticket-of-leave man, an ex-Borstal boy, or a tubercular hunchback who could with difficulty sign his name. It is as bad as that: and in this particular diocese the position was exceptionally acute, because of the county's marked absence of amenities. As it was, nearly half the clergy made themselves responsible for two churches. Should the pound sterling continue to lose its value, many churches would have to be closed down, clergymen seeking other work. Rural populations would have in their midst a large empty building, standing in a graveyard, symbolizing the vacuum where once there was Faith. The ex-Anglican parishes would become the missionary field for the witch doctors of a variety of cults.

Accordingly anyone prepared to face the rigors involved in entering holy orders, is eligible—rigors which might make a holy calling of this again. In the rural diocese of which

Rymer's parish formed a part, one of the vicars was an ex-hairdresser. He made a first-rate clergyman and on Saturdays cut his parishioners' hair free of charge. Though he lacked the equipment to give them a "perm," he interviewed local belles at the vicarage and advised them as to the style of dressing most suited to their hair and personality. So you can see that it really was not much use signing petitions to have a clergyman removed. And were Rymer removed the See would be obliged to find him another living—such, it seems, is the law of the Church. The rectory he vacated might quite well remain untenanted, its church padlocked, its bell unrung, a bad advertisement for Jesus. In view of all this Rymer (as he put it in his letters) "sat back." Why should he worry? It was tails I win, heads you lose. He felt completely master of the situation—up to June 28. But he was a fretful, discontented man, his bubbling masterful surface-self, his big arrogant poker-face the bluff, as he recklessly played his hand, of a very pessimistic player.

2.

On my first visit to Bagwick I decided I would go unannounced. First I would spend a night at the cathedral city, then drive over to Bagwick, have a drink at the village pub, see what sort of flock Rymer's was, and afterwards walk up to the Rectory. The eastering Midlands are the dullest part of England from the window of a train. Storby, my destination, does not impress: it has never been very important, has no charter, it is a county town no more. The county, I have always found, has not much identity, it has to be hunted for on the map: being on the small side; being a county that fits in, not that stands out; not upon the sea (and having a coastline always helps one to remember the position of a county): lastly, with a name which is too long, and one not written in large letters upon our palates, like Devonshire Cream, or Worcester Sauce, or Yorkshire Pudding, or Dundee Cake. Upon its eastern side, for half its length, it melts into a bleak-fen county, on the other side it is blackened by a forest of chimneys, where the furnaces of its big industrial neighbors are producing mechanical legs, taxi cabs and toy locomotives. Storby is on its eastern border, which is why it stands in so flat a landscape. Bagwick lies directly west of the city. Once you have crossed six miles or so of plain as flat as a billiard table the land begins to rise, but of course not very much. It is a county that never rises into the air more than the height of Box Hill.

The spire of Storby's Cathedral stuck up like a spike out of the perfectly flat collection of roofs. As there are no other steeples or buildings of any size, it causes on arrival one to feel that the Cathedral possessed of this unusually tapering horn is all that is outstanding in this cold and lonely community. In fact, once you are part of the flatness yourself, that is inside the city, it is found to be swarming with people on bicycles and others selling barrowsful of flowers, and a goodly amount of ribaldry can be heard passing between bicycle and flower-laden barrow. There is much vitality in the large marketplace upon a river bank, and entire streets that are still medieval. The inhabitants get more out of them that way than if they demolished the open-timber houses bulging over the ancient cobbles, and erected prosaic contemporary abodes, touristically unprofitable. The aura of antiquity extends to the hotels, no *good* hotel being of later date than Queen Anne.

Storby's Cathedral dominated the market, as a Cathedral should. Fans of Perpendicular became delirious as they approached it, sticking up propped and buttressed as in the stone age of building it must be. It is entirely deserted by the clergy—you would expect to see one *corbeau* [5] from time to time. But like Rymer I suppose they all wear sports jackets and sports shirts. There seemed to be a lot of people about, it is true, obviously not enthusiasts of the Perpendicular: they may have been some of the staff off-duty. I saw no one anywhere in the city who showed any sign of being a clergyman. What might be described as *the flight from the Cloth* certainly makes the churches and cathedrals seem more derelict even than they are.

When on the way to my hotel from the railway station, the taxi crossed a river. "What is the name of the river?" I inquired of the young taxi man as we were moving over the bridge. He drove on in silence. "Is it perhaps the Stor?" I suggested. He muttered, and it appeared he actually did not know. He was a native of Storby. I suppose the war had come before he had got around to asking the name of anything, and once he got back (at about the age of twenty-three at a guess) he had other things to think about. However when I laughed understandingly he began speaking again,

[5] black crow, that is, priest

saying that for *his* part he could not see why people came
to Storby (he thought English Perpendicular was my weakness
of course), he could see nothing very exciting about Storby
and in fact took every opportunity of getting out of it.
Having got this off his chest, in Storby idiom and half-said
to himself, he resumed his eloquent silence. I gave him a
handsome tip, he was the sort of citizen I like.

Next day, as I had planned to do, I was driven out to
Bagwick in a hired car. If anyone is interested in fields,
hundreds and hundreds of them, tilted up and all running the
same way, with telegraph poles to give variety to the scene,
it must be a lovely drive. After fourteen or fifteen miles
of implacable farmland but no sign of man or beast we
entered Bagwick. There was no one there either. It was a
sizeable village, with a pub and a few shops. Its street was
not straight, it kept bearing round to the left. As we moved
forward we came in sight of a solitary figure, coming in our
direction, followed by a barking dog. Towards this infuriated
animal the solitary figure turned, appeasement visibly his
policy, but it was the wrong dog, to judge from the disap-
pointing results. Suddenly, as we drew nearer, I realized
that it was none other than my reverend friend himself. I
asked the driver to stop.

Rymer in the metropolis is a dude compared with Rymer
at Bagwick. As I walked towards him he was saluting me
with raised arm and sending up a welcoming wail of astonishment, tinctured with embarrassment—the raised arm
having a bad effect on the dog, at the same time exposing a
gaping armpit, the tattered tweed suggestive of the coarsely
hirsute.

The Rector of Bagwick was the village "bum" it seemed. In
sweet Auburn ugliest village of the Plain they had a scarecrow to preach to them! His attire was terrific. No mendicant
friar ever hobbled down a street in a more tatterdemalion
advertisement of poverty.

A brownish tweed that was so obsolete that it necessitated
a vertical patch the size of a folded newspaper in one place,
the sleeves of which had to terminate in cuffs of leather
three inches deep, and demanded to be reinforced with
leather at the collar line and to have two pocket tops bound
with pigskin, was already qualified to serve the tramp-co-
median in his act. Particolored patches practically everywhere
had plainly been selected for their effect. Only that could
explain the mighty patch placarding his left side: for did

it have to be *black*? It was a piece of "the Cloth" called into service—perhaps cut off what was left of the trousers he wore as a curate. Oh, Rymer—*cabotin*! [6]—almighty clown! That was my *first* reaction to the Rector *chez lui*.[7]

The flabby and sagging droop dawdled nearer, with his high-pitched cry: "Why didn't you telephone, you should have telephoned: I'd have fetched you." Then his big smiling face, ruggedly handsome and anxiously sweet, came up. I took him by a small corduroy patch upon his sleeve and said "Greetings, your reverence!" And he said 'I *am* glad to see you!" But the reverend gentleman moved away to pick up a stone. He bent down and oh what a vast expanse he had for sitting purposes! which now presented itself—lingeringly while he picked his stone. A small fluffy hole halfway up the left posterior for which a darning needle would soon be imperative—was this a declaration of independence on the part of a proud parson, or had he not noticed when a nail had torn his trouser seat? He stood up, and with placatory absence of passion he cast the stone (discovering a ragged elbow). The stone however struck the dog. "Oh, did I hit you, Jacko?" he called with patronizing contrition. "I am sorry, I'll bring you a bone, honest injun. Tomorrow!" But the dog as was evident held strongish views on the throwing of stones. He had retired out of range to denounce Rymer with a deeper note of warning to whom it might concern.

Reactions on my side continued to be uncomplimentary to such playing at the down-and-out as I regarded it in my shortsightedness. How would this big fat baby like to be homeless, his stipend what he could pick up on the street? He read my thoughts and flapped deliberately the black patch of obvious clerical origin, which seemed to be coming unstuck at the bottom. The dog interpreting this as an insult rushed towards us his teeth bared like a Hollywood glamor girl. Rymer flapped it again, and I expected to see one of his patches ripped off and with luck a bit of the flesh behind it. I thought Jacko would try for the big black one—or failing that go off with the blue strip on one of the knees. But the dog was petrified by a piercing cry as a gaunt villager flew out of a lane. "Jacko!" the woman shrieked, and the voice had the effect of the radar wave said to stop ducks in mid-flight. "Come here, do you hear me, Jacko!" She

6 strolling player, mummer
7 at home

yapped as she flew and the dog fell to the ground as if he had been shot, his ears glued against his head and his belly scraping the street.

The woman's eyes as she ran darted at Rymer; where to her mind the blame lay was plain enough and she would have told him so I thought if I had not been there.

"Ah, Mrs. Rossiter, thank you for saving my life!" In a high-pitched yell he musically greeted his savior. "Very kind of you, Jacko is unusually naughty this morning. I must bring him another bone—a nice big *bone*!"

Driving Jacko before her, his tail stuck tight between his legs, Mrs. Rossiter retired swiftly into the lane out of which she had come, with a rather dangerous growl followed by a spit.

We looked at one another.

"Exit Jacko. Quite a dog!" said I. Rymer, ruffled more by Mrs. Rossiter than by Jacko, agreed that the latter was *just all dog*.

"Mrs. Rossiter's a nice woman really," he observed.

"I thought she was nice," I told him.

"It's very sad, she lost her husband a year ago, he was killed by one of Jack Cox's bulls."

"Oh dear."

"Yes, it's very sad. Jacko's all she's got." He looked at me.

"I *see*!" I said. "Of course. . . ."

"He does that every time I come this way. He never seems to get used to me."

"It must be difficult for you to come into Bagwick," I observed. "Why don't you carry a stick?"

"I can't do that," he answered shortly.

Then he gazed at me with polite enthusiasm, welcoming me to Bagwick.

"Well, I *am* glad to see you," he exclaimed, "but why didn't you *telephone*? Shall we go up to the house? You must be hungry aren't you? My wife will be delighted to see you—come along."

Pointing to the "Lord Salisbury" I inquired: "Can't I get something at that pub?" I had to say something. "Will you come with me? A nice mousetrap sandwich and a glass of ale." But he of course said "Nonsense," so we drove to the Rectory, a few rat-like heads poking out of doors, watching us depart.

"What a jolly little village," I said.

"Yes, it is rather nice," he responded modestly.

As we drove along I took back the terms *cabotin* and *clown* which naturally at first I had hurled at him *sotto voce* —at the tatterdemalion Rector of Bagwick doubtless on his morning tour of duty, showing himself to his parishioners. Then I recognized I had been quite wrong. First of all, at Oxford he had enough money no doubt to dress the part of a young gentleman, but, of course, bar the patches, he must have looked much as he does at present. For a fashion of stylistic shabbiness (which he would seek to outstrip if I know my Rymer) would have turned him away from what "a young gentleman ought to look like" to "what in practice he *does* look like."

Today, however, he really had not the means to buy new clothes. A good suit costs forty pounds odd, a bad one twenty. The Oxford training would lead him to make a great big comic virtue of necessity. That was the first, and negative, side of it.

Next, what could he wear? In his circumstances, and with his beliefs, should he have adopted the overalls of the laborer? The Cathedral would have disapproved. To the petty, brushed-up-till-it-shone, shabby-genteel he objected. He preferred to satirize his poverty, to clown, rather than to conceal. Indeed there was protest in his getup. He preferred to parade the streets of his parish in rags—to go up to London and buy a drawing costing as much as a new suit—I looked at the bobbling black patch with appreciation. I actually had his check in my pocket. Noticing my glance, he wobbled his patch at me. He had once said he would like to be the Bishop's Fool, I remembered.

We entered the Rectory drive, the car poked at by the wild overplus of vegetation which was certainly not that of a normal garden. Such coarse-tongued plants as put in their appearance where there is no finer life or competitive human culture, were visible out of the window of the car. The car described an arc around an island that was a miniature wilderness, a dusty jungle growing to a considerable height above the gravel, upon which it dropped unidentifiable vegetable matter. When I left the car, I found that the Rectory was hemmed in by the same nameless growths, swarming up its walls with an ugly vigor.

"Polygonum," said Rymer, giving a name to what I was looking at. "It's rather nice stuff unless it gets out of hand." He paused. "It has got out of hand."

"It does look slightly like a riot. Why don't you grow roses?"

"Why don't I grow roses?" Rymer looked at the savage scene facing his front door. "Oh, I don't know: snakeweed is just as good. This stuff is rather nice: when it doesn't get out of hand."

The Rectory was unexpectedly tall, this was even apparent above the eruption of polygonum threatening it on all sides. A roomy house, it had been built to contain the bulging families which the Victorian clergy regularly produced between evening and morning prayers.

The place had a big parched lonely look. Nothing grew upon its pale brick face. But since it is an Ark which obviously for a long time has ridden the wastes, no emblem of stability, like ivy, would be likely to attach itself to this mansion meant for the Deluge. So it is as bare as when it was built, except for dust, droppings, or the kind of warts that neglected houses have.

Although, without, the scene was so savage, the Rectory within, excepting the hall which was a little wild, was otherwise like the popular idea of a rectory. Rymer had acquired a few other small pictures besides mine, the radio put the Rymers in touch with the intellectual giants of Britain on the Third Program, and of course all programs supplied buckets full of music. A piano enabled them to perform themselves. His wife is charming: he is for her a big willful schoolboy. Thus he was peremptorily dispatched as soon as we arrived to put on his London suit. For his son, too, whom I met on another occasion, Rymer is a bit of a youthful terror. That very grave and severe young man is at Oxford, though how he got there Heaven knows. A scholarship I suppose from the local grammar school. Both Eleanor and son Robert love him, but are strangers to his exuberances. Therefore even in his home he is alone with his excess of imagination, his poet's passion. All that is most serious to him seems like play to his family: his pastel, his politics, his pride in his poverty. This is not to say that his family are wanting in taste or vitality, only that he has *too much*—for a life passed on the poverty line. Indeed he is like a domesticated troll who having fallen in love with Eleanor had consented to live as humans do—and I have seen Eleanor stare at him with puzzled affection and he waggle his black patch at her and give a merry clerical whinny. For of course he is *not* a goblin but a born clergyman.

The living quarters are in the back of the house. Out of the drawing room windows however it is the same as out of the front door. Nature coarsely proliferates, and man does nothing to check her: she throws up her low-grade creations. No one in the house has the energy to go out and cut the stuff down and burn it up. Let it grow all over the building, let it do what it likes, so long as we can get in and out, so long as it is not inside!

Such is the response I think of the inmates, exhausted by petty hardships, harassed with taxation, worn out with wars, threatened with expulsion—it was their answer to an existence to which they had not been born or bred, in the golden aftermath of the Victorian era. But gazing out of one of the windows, I dismally responded to the scene of squalid vegetable fecundity, the solid sea of snakeweed, polygonum, or whatever it was, nettles and dock leaves of course adding themselves to this chaos. An inglorious duck pond appeared in the near distance—it is forced upon one whenever one looks out of one of the vicarage windows, how this man exists upon the frontiers of a vacuum of a new sort. The well-furnished room, with its gouache horsemen and its piano, is an advance post: there is the no-man's-land between our age and the darkness to come. He is the last of a species (to which we all belong) and in him in travail—and there are none of us do not experience the travail too—is another species.

Dressed in garments literally dropping to pieces he moves around his parish, among people who dread and loathe poverty and want. And he stands in spite of himself for poverty and for want. He is one of the first English clergymen to stand for poverty and want. And as he moves around, from house to house, the doors quickly shut at his approach as if he were infected with some complaint which no one was particularly anxious to have; and out of rags tacked together his "Oxford accent" issues with incongruous patronage; his encyclopedic affectations exasperate, his great-heartedness abashes—for there is no *cash* only credit in Heaven, the currency of religion, no longer legal tender. The majority of the shopkeepers and laborers' wives of Bagwick have given up "the opiate of the People," they are no longer addicts. Does Rymer at times wish he had another drug to peddle? I have often wondered. And as to Sundays, in patched surplice (it can hardly be whole, to judge from the remainder of his wardrobe) he goes through a majestic liturgy accompanied on a small harmonium, before a congregation usually of the odd villager plus the family.

On this occasion it was that he took me over to see his church, situated a couple of hundred yards down the road. The building was not large but it was absurdly lofty, like a thin slice of a cathedral. The vault near the entrance, for it grew to its greatest height at the farthest point from the altar, would not have been out of place at Canterbury. The font was so high it was not possible to use it without placing blocks of wood against it. I had no difficulty in understanding, as soon as I saw it, what had happened when first Rymer took up his duties at Bagwick. He saw the towering arches; his imagination, to his undoing, got to work. He made the great original mistake out of which all his subsequent miseries issued.

I had heard, almost in the first half hour of our earliest intimacies, about the beautiful reredos purchased by him for Bagwick. The protests and intrigues it had brought down on his head were things, one saw, of obsessional dimensions, looming up behind his unemotional narrative, when he spoke of the days when he first went to Bagwick. The extravagance had revealed to the village, it was easy to understand, the order of man that had come among them. They glimpsed the big troll I have spoken of. Promptly they started to gang up. No ordinary sensible man would be so lacking in judgment as to import the side of a house into a small village church! Some distant cousin of Don Quixote was in their midst—soon he might mistake them for the Saracens and begin cutting them down. Their faces hardened, not soft at the best of times north of The Wash, their tongues wagged. There was a village cabal at "The Marquess of Salisbury." Finally after years of bickering, the reredos had to be disposed of, sold at a crushing loss, and it was he who incurred it, not the village.

Our luncheon, I am ashamed to say, was excellent. There was, I am sure, the week's meat ration, also the week's bones in the nourishing well-peppered soup. More than half the week's rations were accounted for in this chivalrous hospitality. From a small farmer Rymer received certain favors. But this big arrogant man in rags, who always knew everybody's business better than they did themselves, would be a protégé that not everyone would choose. I can see some farmer giving him a half-dozen intact eggs and a few cracked ones *once*, but not making a habit of it. Much food for nothing, or at its market value, he would not get, and he has not the money to pay the black-market price for things, nor would it be wise to do so if he had.

Soon all clergymen in this country will have vows of poverty thrust upon them as I have already suggested, and a new type of ministry will come into being. Quite probably it is the *only* way to secure a truly Christian Church. It may after all be God's will. In His great wisdom it would not be likely to escape Him that a penniless clergyman is better than one who rides to hounds. Then the country people will have to bring gifts of food—a fowl, bread, pickles, a tin of sardines, pig's-trotters, apricots and greengages in season, as the moujiks once would do to their holy men. Otherwise the clergy quite literally will die out. An unpleasant transition is at present in progress. But people have so little sense of the future. The majority are completely defective in this sense. They fail to realize the significance of a process until life is suddenly quite different to what it was. They then adjust themselves at a disadvantage. The clergy should prepare themselves for penury; else quite unprepared they will find themselves the poorest class of men. Fasts would not be amiss. And they should accustom their parishioners to the idea that their sacred calling must reduce them to great poverty.

In the meantime we find Rymer, for a start, without clothes to his back, or only a travesty of clothes; and there is no other class of man that must go in rags, except the vagabond. I told him that I should come down in a year or so and discover him walking through Bagwick in a loincloth: what would Jacko say to that? How would Mrs. Rossiter react? It is one of those cracks that have an uncomfortably prophetic ring. Heaven avert the omen. Rymer still feels too much "the gentleman," of course, as his forebears were fine parsons in plump livings. He is a *master* type, of his own accord he will never go *the whole way* to the new model, to the country-clergyman-in-the-loincloth: soliciting alms in the name of God, or sitting near the altar of his church as people lay their gifts on the steps—sleeping on a camp bed in the vestry—I am not saying that will happen tomorrow: and Rymer was heroic, in the way a prophet is, as clothed in tatters he went poker-faced to meet his fate and that of all his kind. For the village dogs will not care much for the New Model man-of-God and the villagers not improbably may stone them.

That Rymer has the seeds of heroism I hope by now is plain. If need be he would sit naked at the foot of the Cross (though it might be with the superior glint of the *Have-not* in his glazing eye) and die if he was not fed.

3.

DURING lunch food—or its absence—was not discussed as invariably it is at any mealtime in England today. One felt that something vaguely was the matter. Then one realized what is was: a *certain topic* was conspicuously absent.

One soon discovered, however, that the difficulty of getting enough to eat was only one of a large class of topics under an interdict. Eleanor Rymer happened to refer to the difficulty of obtaining a proper supply of reading matter—of books. But at the word *difficulty* Rymer blustered into action, with that inimitable imitation of automatism of his, which his large wooden poker-face facilitated.

"Difficulty? Nonsense. There is no more difficulty today than five, ten, or fifteen, years ago."

"How about the petrol, in the first place?" Eleanor retorted with a show of fight, which of course was indispensable. "I cannot get books at Bagwick."

He pounced on *petrol* like a cat on an unwary tomtit.

"Petrol? There is all the petrol that *I* can see." (He might have added *can afford*.) "There's plenty of petrol."

"Excuse me . . ." his wife began, laughing.

But he swiftly intervened.

"I know what you are going to say," he told her, "that you haven't got all the petrol that *you* can use. Before the war you took out the car once a fortnight at the outside. Now you feel you want it every day. You never went to Cockridge unless you could help it. *Now* you are always thinking of things in Cockridge or in Storby that you must have this minute." He turned to me. "Because there is a *ration,* a limit, people imagine they are short of something they never had so much of before, or perhaps never *heard* of before. To hear them talk you would think that formerly they covered hundreds of miles every day in their car, ate enormous porterhouse steaks daily, chain-smoked from the time they got out of bed to the time they got into it again, bought a box of chocolates every morning after breakfast and another just before tea."

"I know a number of people just like that," Eleanor agreed.

But I felt Rymer must not be allowed to get away with everything.

"There are shortages," I remarked.

"Shortages," he retorted, "yes, if you want the earth. People today have as much food as is good for them—some, more than is good for them. People are putting on fat. I am. They have as many cigarettes or as much tobacco, as much beer as is necessary."

"As many clothes?" I inquired.

He stopped and eyed me blankly for a few seconds, as if holding a conference behind his poker-face.

"Clothes," he said slowly, "are not rationed."

Had he been dressed in the less formal of his two suits he would, I felt, at this point have stroked his black patch.

His wife was intelligent as well as beautiful, and addressed herself to the consumption of her piece of offal. (Why should the butcher, or, rather, the Food Office, employ this ghastly word?) She was accustomed, it was obvious, to being halted, turned back, and admonished upon the threshold of certain topics. Rymer would allow no one to grumble. No criticism of conditions under socialism passed unchallenged. He did not demand the quality of the bacon to be extolled (just eat it, would be the idea, and think of something else, such as how happy our grandchildren would be in a world from which *all* capital—small as well as great, had been banished): he did not require ecstasies at the mention of the Purchase Tax (some day there won't be much left to purchase, so there won't be any *tax*)—no, all Rymer exacted was *silence* about conditions under socialism. The Government are at war with Capital, it is total war: war conditions naturally prevail. Therefore, silence! Shut that great gap! Enemy ears are listening! All criticism aids capitalism.

Even Rymer would deny the existence of any obstacles in the path of socialism-in-our-time: his view of the socialist government's prospects are blindingly sunny. When he is foretelling an unprecedented export boom, if (in the interests of sanity) one should mention the fact that the United States can supply itself with everything it requires, which it manufactures far more efficiently than any other country is capable of doing (*vide* Mr. Lippmann), Rymer pooh-poohs such a statement. He describes it as ridiculous. American goods, he will assert, are of very poor quality: the Americans would be jolly glad to get ours if they had a chance. We market our stuff badly over there to begin with. "But believe me once our industry is on its feet again our exports will soar, you see if they don't." Rymer had never been to the United States and has not the remotest idea what American goods are like, so he is not cramped in these patriotic flights by firsthand knowledge. His boundless optimism is firmly based in the most blissful ignorance. Should you speak anxiously of Great Britain's situation, living as she does upon a massive dole from the United States, he will say that *that* is our fault for having anything to do with the U.S., with Wall Street. Were we to arrange to receive a dole from Russia instead—say a billion or two, marrying the pound sterling to the ruble—we should soon be out of the wood! If we had the guts to cut ourselves loose from the Yankee capitalists, stopped spending money on an army which we didn't need, and had a pact with Russia, we should be as right as rain.

Eleanor now brusquely changed the subject. She selected one quite free of political entanglements. The unprecedented, the sumptuous summer weather—that had nothing to do with a planned economy or the redistribution of wealth. No one was to blame if the weather was bad, no one had to be thanked except God if it was fine. And then she went on to say how perfect the weather had been up in London, where she had been on a visit to relatives. She thought nostalgically of London, and I asked her if she had been to any shows. No, she said, no: *just shops*. But she continued—with great inadvertence—to complain how difficult it had been to shop. There were such dense herds of people. Where on earth did they all come from!

Rymer waited until she had finished, and then he struck: "Where do *you* come from, my dear, there is always that." The slightly Johnsonian answer to her conundrum his wife received with a wry smile, having detected her *faux pas* too late. "Those people are the masses of women. . . ."

"They weren't all women!" she laughed.

"Women," he said firmly. "They come in their millions from the suburbs and the slums and the slums and suburbs of other cities. The pavements are impassable. It is like cutting one's way through a dense and rubbery undergrowth."

"What an excellent description!" his wife exclaimed.

"I agree they are *dense*," he went on. "Of course they are. For the first time in their lives they have sufficient time and money to go shopping in the most luxurious stores—where they could not go before."

Here I joined in with alacrity.

"Could not go," I said, "because of their *class*—without being followed around by store detectives, stared out of countenance by shopgirls from behind counters, asked every minute by a shop walker what articles they required. Any charlady now can go in, try on a mink coat or two, then fling them down and say she thinks she'll wait till next season when they may have a better assortment. Harrods is jammed with charladies. The working-class throng Selfridges like Woolworths at Christmastime. That really *is* socialism. Observe that in Moscow the slums are barred from any but the slum shops."

We returned to the drawing room after we had eaten and sat talking for a long time; it is a very peaceful spot, but in Rymer there is no peace. My hostess was washing up the dishes. She was absent at least and there was no one else in the house. The knuckly proliferation of the polygonum waved beyond the window sill, the yellow leaves tumbled past from a tree, a wasp appeared on his way from the larder where he had been able to find no jam, no honey—nothing sweet, because the English had won the war and consequently are not allowed to grow sugar in their West Indian islands, and there is not enough beet sugar to go round. Also I noticed a sick-looking bird. The crumbs put out for it were, of course, full of bran and chalk. I suppose it was constipated. It should have pecked off as much corn as it wanted before it was cut, making a rule to touch no human food. The corn gone, why not fly off to some more sensible country? What are wings for?

I think that politics and poetry are what interest Rymer almost exclusively. At that moment politics were uppermost in his mind because the question of communism (at his instigation) was coming up the following week at the diocesan conference, and he was of course to speak, or hoped he would be able to. Communism is with him something quite unreal, for he certainly is not a communist. He is of the generation of the great fellow travelers of the twenties, who painted the universities pink. But it was a solemn rag, a generational badge, and meant no more than a painter's stunt, painting for a little *all red* or *all blue,* to make a "period" with. Rymer, like scores of thousands of others, had had his "pink period." It shocked all the aunts of the time terribly, and scandalized his clergyman father. It was revolt—it symbolized *Youth*—his most glamorous moments had been pink.

Youth past, these *redmen* of the Oxford and Cambridge Colleges forgot all about it—real life began, dressing up was at an end, the minarets of Moscow faded on the horizon. And in any case Soviet Russia had proved a somewhat tough and embarrassing comrade to "travel" with. On the other hand, because Rymer had been buried in the depths of the country ever since Oxford he lived in the past a lot, and continued to potter around with Karl Marx, like a mascot of his youth rather, and he still got a kick out of it. That was *part* of the story of Rymer and the Kremlin. The rest of it was traceable to professional religion: the frivolous sizar and the fakir must be mixed.

When I asked him what he was going to say next week to the crowd of clergymen he said he would point out that in the contemporary world communism, or marxism, was, because of the huge development of Soviet Russia, too great a factor in world affairs for the Church to ignore, as it had been disposed to do up to now. "Let us put aside our prejudices," he would invite them, "let us examine this controversial theory of the state, and let us ask ourselves if there is anything in it which we as Christians should endorse." He and Herbert Stoner, the "red" Storby parson, had succeeded in "winning over" several of their colleagues. He named others who would have nothing to do with it—who asserted that the Church should set its face against "this atheistic creed" and all its works. These were he told me the "place-seekers," clergymen on the climb, who dreamed of deaneries and bishoprics. The only imaginable consideration which would impel clergymen to feel other than sympathetic towards communism was self-interest. Such was his extraordinary view. As this was absurd I thought I would help him to dispel from his mind so foolish an error.

"Ordinary people," I explained to him, "find it difficult to reconcile with their conscience anything short of censure of the methods employed by the Russian leaders. I do for instance. I see what is good in the theory, but I cannot swallow the practice."

To this he made no reply. He could have argued, for instance (for even the worst cause is polemically defensible) that barbarity had marked the regimes which the revolutionary governments had supplanted, in Russia and elsewhere. He even could have instanced the cruelties still inflicted

upon people daily by the operation of the capitalist economy, or any existing economy, or spoken of "poverty in
the midst of plenty": to which of course there are answers,
too, for a good debater. There are plenty of answers to the
criticism of *any* policy. He is not interested in being an
advocate however. He just enjoys pushing under people's
noses something they detest. He does not want to find himself in the role of *selling* it to them, of being too serious
about it. And, as I have said, he is genuinely no Red.

Where politics are concerned Rymer is not, as I have also
said, merely what-is-left of a 'twenties undergraduate fellow
traveler. What *does* conspicuously remain, it must be confessed, is the juvenile impulse to *épater le bourgeois*.[8] But
behind the exhibitionism is an authentic issue, that of the
priest inheriting a rotted religion from his laodicean fox-
hunting ancestors which he would naturally desire to rein-
vigorate. That he should borrow a little reality from politics
and pump it into the decayed tissues of the Church is an
obvious proceeding, more especially as his instinct must
inform him that what he would be borrowing had, in the
first instance, been stolen from his religion. That that *instinct,*
alone, is involved was proved by Rymer's reception of my
subsequent identification of socialism with Christianity.

Whatever is at work behind the mask has the character of
a religious experience: i.e., *he knows.* With any cause that
he embraced, it would not be a civil marriage. Meanwhile
he is as tightly sealed-up as a clam. In his secretiveness (that
of the priest, resembling the woman's) he sees no point in
exposing what he *knows,* or intuits, to the crude processes
of the human reason. So he remains very reticent and his
manner is aloof and also casual. "Here it is. What do you
think of it?" That kind of thing. Then he will turn his back
and saunter away: *never* get into a serious argument if he
can help it, though he is willing enough to argue provided
you do not show signs of pressing matters too far.

If socialism, instead of Christianity, were an official cult,
and he its bonze, he would teach from the absolutist angle—
carelessly, almost disdainfully, without "proofs." He would
deal in mystical fiats, allowing of no argument. But socialism is *not* his religion. He probably regards it as a reflection, upon an inferior (a political) plane, of Christianity.
Or he would so regard it if he were going to be rational

8 shock the bourgeois

and orderly about it, and come out of his muscular mist.

Of course Rymer is quite explicit about a number of things. He asserted for instance on this occasion that "whenever Christianity and communism have been confronted, Christianity has won the day." But his reason for making this assertion was not in order to arrive at some objective certainty, but in order to sway opinion. From this it would follow, if I interpret him correctly, that Christians need not fear to hobnob with communists, for the communists would all succumb to the superior medicine and become Christians —or, the only alternative, take to their heels. If communism, like any other form of socialism, were in fact only Christianity on a lower and mundane level, then (1) in close contact and association with Christianity it would naturally be elevated and in the end rise to the Christian level: and, further (2) there is an obligation to protect socialism against the wicked world. He did not push on into all these implications of what he said, though I have done so. His policy was to lead the mind in that direction—though I was never quite certain what he explicitly proposed.

Russia, he observed, must be regarded as "a great missionary field." "Ah, you mean to effect conversations, do you, among the reds?" I asked. "You propose to convert Stalin to Christianity?"

He looked down, then said shortly and cheekily: "Yes— p'raps."

He knew he was talking nonsense, but he didn't care.

After this absurd conversation I felt discouraged. Sitting a little while in front of Rymer's poker-face makes one feel that way as a matter of course. That socialism was something that needed defending against the wicked world was a proposition with which I was in agreement—provided it was the Western variety. But these were propositions existing in isolation from reality. For socialism could be taken over by the worldly, and then who or what was it required protecting? The worldly are never so dangerous as when they masquerade as idealists.

I have been building up an inductive Rymer which has some coherence: but that is not at all what transpires on the outside. He was dishing out to me the kind of rigmarole he had prepared for the conference. The diocesan conference was going to be a grisly affair.

But I then decided to see if I could break into this absurd reserve, by enlarging upon the whole question of

Christianity and communism. I thought I would explain
something about it, and see if I could tempt this cleric out
of his shell. It was a passing *énervement,* [9] no doubt,
but at that moment the large, blank, harassed, formality of
the mask in front of me was a challenge. The reserve
struck me as insolent and stupid. Why is this silly fellow
playing a part with *me!* is what I was disposed to ask. It is
the way one is bound to react in the end, before a shut door.
This is particularly the case, if from behind the shut door
comes a constant stream of words, all vetted for public consumption. Anyhow—verbally—I charged at the shut door.

"It has always been obvious to me," I began, "that the
Christianity of the Sermon on the Mount plays a major
role in the history of socialism."

"Not the Sermon on the Mount," Rymer, a little sullenly,
but lazily, objected.

"Oh, I see: not the Sermon on the Mount," I said.

"Well, why that?" he asked.

"I understand perfectly, as a matter of fact, your objection
to that. Contemporary socialism is so phenomenally tough
that you would rather not have the Sermon on the Mount
mentioned in connection with 'purges, faked trials, and labor
camps.' "

Rymer said nothing.

"The idea that socialism is unthinkable without Christianity
does not appeal to you. Yet was it not fundamentally a
Christian impulse that moved the Western intellectuals (even
though no longer Christians) to champion the cause of the
oppressed and 'underprivileged,' the underdog?"

He neglected the second member of this compound question, answering the first. "Socialism," he said, "is not unthinkable without Christianity."

"In that case you differ entirely from the present socialist
administration."

"Do I?" he sang, amusedly musical.

"So it appears. One of their brain trusters is my authority."
And I produced a cutting from among some papers in my
pocket. "Here is a cutting from the Paris *Herald Tribune.*"

It would be impossible for Samuel Rymer to scowl, he
is really too gentle in spite of his brutal dimensions but he
made an effort to do so. At the mention of anything to do
with the United States he reacted violently. The United

[9] enervation, distraction

States, in spite of its weaknesses, I like, so this is of his idiosyncrasies the one that appeals to me least. He drawled, in a bored and withering voice:

"Do you read the *Herald Tribune*?"

"Sometimes. But listen. The headline reads 'Ex-Adviser of Attlee Attacks U.S. Capitalism as Immoral.' "

"I'm glad Americans are being told what their capitalists are like," he breathed guardedly. "That's good."

"So you are prepared to accept a *moral* basis for the indictment?"

He blinked and let that pass.

"Well, listen now." (*I read.*)

"American capitalism was attacked as immoral and producing a neurosis with 'the stature of a national disease,' in a long article in *Fortune* magazine by Francis Williams . . . former public relations adviser to Prime Minister Clement R. Attlee.

"Mr. Williams called his article 'The Moral Case for Socialism'. . . .

" 'I am a socialist,' wrote Mr. Williams, 'because I believe that only within a socialist society can human rights be assured. . . .'

". . . Mr. Williams said it is no accident that many early leaders of British socialism were drawn from the churches and nonconformist chapels. 'It was not personal economic interest but ethical compulsion that drove men like Attlee, Cripps and others to try to build a more moral society,' he wrote . . ."

(*I stop reading.*)

"Finally we are told that Mr. Williams speaks of the 'great American tradition of *freedom* and *democracy*'."

Rymer's response was instantaneous. "Which is utter nonsense, the Americans have never known what freedom is. It is funny to hear freedom spoken of in the same breath with the lynchers and witch-hunters."

"You are interested in *freedom* now?"

"Of course I am." He was aggressively bland and blank.

I sighed. "Freedom, reverend sir, is what socialism takes even less interest in than does monopoly-capital. A socialist sympathizer must learn to be very guarded where *freedom* is concerned. Alas, there are far more political prisoners and concentration camps—far less freedom of movement, less freedom of speech, in the Soviet Union than in the United

States. Socialist England is far more regimented already than is the United States."

Rymer muttered something about the "third degree" and "prohibition." We were now approaching that invisible line, dividing the terms on which he was prepared to discuss something, from the terms on which he was not prepared to do so.

"But once we begin to discuss *freedom* . . . ! *Cela n'en finirait plus*.[10] Let us say that Christianity and socialism is our subject. Would you object if, instead of leaving this question of the religious origins of socialism floating about in the clouds, I brought it down to earth and attached it to a few hard facts from which it could not escape?"

"Why should I mind," he smiled, "if you regard it as important?"

"Our conscience must be *clear*. A muddy conscience is a bad conscience. But how can the conscience be clear unless we *see* clearly? Our conscience has no rest, nor has for years, it is being appealed to all the time by the contemporary politician. But before the conscience can function properly, or be of any service at all, we must *see clearly*. The politicians have a policy to sell us: let us get the clearest view of it we can—and of the politician! It may be a genuine moral article: or of course it may only be baited with a big moral appeal. No moral judgment is possible without a sharp image of the thing at issue."

"An almost cartesian desire for clarity!" Rymer smiled tolerantly.

"Appeals to the conscience seldom fail especially with the English. The fact that it is the *conscience* to which appeal has been made is so reassuring, too! A political party so appealing must be a peculiarly *moral* party! One takes for granted that a man appealing to one's good feeling, to one's humanity, must surely himself be a good humane man— the majority at least are apt to draw this conclusion."

"You are saying I suppose that socialists are attempting to secure power disguised as men engaged in a moral mission?"

"I am saying nothing of the sort. Nothing should be taken for granted. It is advisable to gain a *clear* idea of what is actually proposed, lest the conscience, working in the dark, mislead one. That is all."

"Are you saying," Rymer enquired, "that a stupid person cannot possess a conscience?"

[10] We'll never get to the end.

"Obviously not so good a one as a wise man."

"Oh!" howled Rymer.

"When a matter is beyond their understanding people cannot judge it morally any more than in any other way. But that is what I wanted to discuss. I am not as clear as I would like to be myself upon a number of points. But this is really a side issue."

"No it isn't," he interrupted. "Your case stands or falls upon that."

"My own conscience feels clear, as I am quite sure yours does. I would like to check up on its functioning however. The way to do that is to test the validity of one or more of the main beliefs responsible for the clear feeling. I always suspect a clear conscience, don't you?"

"Yes."

"In giving my own conscience this overhaul I may assist you to discover whether *your* conscience is as sound and as clear as you think."

"Speak for your own conscience. Mine is all right."

"You *think* so. You may be mistaken. People often buy things in a shop and when they get them home find they do not like them at all."

"Shortsighted people usually."

"Why, exactly. What they *thought* they saw in the shop has changed into something else: into its real self. They have bought something they did not bargain for. Now the kind of socialism which people, in their woolly and hazy way, have fastened on their back, may be one of those things that look very different later on to what at first it seemed. As an indication of what I have in mind, there have been many things to cause misgivings in socialist behavior (especially in the official class) since the Welfare State took over from free enterprise. In a word, those who have come to rescue us from Power have themselves displayed too patent an appetite for power. The old bosses are being economically liquidated. Too often it seems that Bossiness has come in their place. As this state power grows more absolute, will not these disquieting symptoms develop? English socialism as we know it today is complex: in it what is desirable and what is undesirable do battle."

"Because a few officials misbehave . . ." Rymer waved his hand to dismiss such insignificant blemishes.

"There should be an extremely searching debate upon the type of new society—'collective,' as it is called—being thrust upon everyone in England with practically no debate—such as a parliamentary Opposition is supposed to provide. I am not against that new society: I am against the way it is being adopted. To confer such unheard-of powers (such as no feudal king in England has ever possessed) upon a group of politicians just because they say they are 'socialist,' is absurd. In the mind of the majority 'socialist' signifies a selfless person dedicated to the welfare of mankind. Somebody may not *like* socialists, because he thinks they are too good and moral to suit him. But the *moral* status is taken for granted."

"Are you disputing the bonafides of socialism?" he asked me.

"No," I answered. "It is frightfully important that that moral essence of socialism should be a reality, that is all, and even more that it should *stop* a reality. I believe that some machinery should be invented to make certain that it does so stop. Finally there should be no blank check."

"You are too distrustful."

"You are too authoritarian. Are we for Authority, however corrupt or callous it may become? My conscience cries out for checks."

"That conscience of yours is dreadfully overdeveloped, isn't it. I don't remember ever hearing of one like it." His face was furrowed in mock concern.

"I think it is yours that is underdeveloped," I told him. "If it is as modest in size as I suspect, mine must, of course, seem enormous."

"An enlarged conscience is pathologic," was how that bout ended, he nodding his head admonitorily as he spoke. "It is nothing to be proud of; I should keep it quiet if I were you."

We laughed humorlessly.

4.

IN this talk we were having it was my idea to say just enough to oblige him to forsake some of his romantic conventions and to adopt a more realistic attitude: *or* come out and defend his obscurantist absolute. "I have been speaking," I went on, *"of socialism by consent.* It is an odd phenomenon to occur in a country like England. But the English voted themselves into 'Labor' (which promptly transformed itself into 'socialism,' of the toughest, the 'total,' type). They would have voted themselves into anything that promised speedy demobilization. Six years of Churchillean Tory heroics had been too much. They knew Labor would turn them back into civilians much quicker than Churchill would. That was Aneurin Bevan's explanation of the Labor landslide. It was, I think, the right one, in the main."

"You think that is all—an overlong war?" Rymer breathed a little crossly and sleepily.

"Something the long war precipitated. The background was a hundred years of Liberalism. A hundred years rushed down in the 1945 landslide. The history of the nineteenth century in Great Britain recalls the thousand small steps of a Mayan pyramid, each step a liberation for some depressed class. So Britain mounted to the present pinnacle, a real live working-class Government, with teeth in it like an alligator. From Chartism to the Steel Bill is a long purposeful *moral* ascent. It is the moral foundation, deriving directly from the teaching of the Gospels, of this monumental progress culminating, in 1945, in the mass acceptance of ethical politics—it is this which is to be my theme."

"You will be preaching to the converted," Rymer threw in.

"The nature of the dynamism is obvious. That the working class played a part is a political fairy tale of course."

"Oh!"

"The British working class is the reverse of socially ambitious. Always it has been the despair of the agitator, a mass as difficult to ignite as a rain-soaked mackintosh. It has been content to be an animal, fond of beer and of football, not envious of the well-to-do because it would only be envious in terms of beer and football and Château-Yquem and golf fails to stir its pulse. It has been terribly easy to exploit and to 'keep in its place.' It is unnecessary to add that ethics is not its strong point. The *moral ascent* in question was a middle-class phenomenon. The progressive levitation of the mass of manual workers is one of the miracles of Christ. It is on a spectacular scale the Raising of Lazarus."

Rymer was tying up his shoe. "Rot" was all he said.

"The mere mass, the numbers, of the working class could have produced no such result. To argue that it could is like saying that a mountain must merely, because it is so large, submerge a village at its foot. And so it might if someone placed so tremendous an atomic charge within it as to blow it up."

"The working class is not inanimate," Rymer growled.

"You must have something more than mass, than numbers.

The way workers have extricated themselves from underneath the middle-class is often likened to the manner in which the latter supplanted the aristocracy. There is in fact no analogy whatever. The vast colonial expansion of Great Britain and temporary industrial monopoly enriched and expanded so much the class of bankers, merchants, industrialists, that that class wrested the leadership from the landed society. What was responsible for this revolution was something with an action equivalent to atomic fission, namely money."

"The aristocracy were only businessmen. Money was nothing to do with it," Rymer heckled automatically.

"Now strangely enough the rise to power of the working class was only made possible by money too: not its own money for it has none, nor for its thirst for power, for it was not interested in power. It was a purely middle-class money which has caused the artificial elevation of the working class at the expense of the middle class."

"How on earth do you make that out!" Rymer expostulated, lazily.

"You see, even all the agitators, from the creator of Marxian socialism onwards, belong to the middle class. Lenin, for instance. Our Fabians, the Webbs, Shaw, or Cripps, have been typically of the middle class. H. G. Wells, who came from the working class, protested at the revolutionary zeal of his 'betters'."

"Where does the *money* come in?"

"Have you ever thought of the immense sum involved, in this century alone, on socialist propaganda? Money has always been forthcoming—millions and millions of it—to advertise the beauties of the Left Wing. It all came out of bourgeois bank accounts, where it was not straight political subsidy."

"Why should the middle class or any section of it spend so much money in order to have the middle class supplanted by the working class? Was it economic suicide?" Rymer was wearily withering.

"Various explanations of this curious fact have been advanced. There may, of course, be several secondary interests involved. I am concerned exclusively with the major and essential impulse."

"Good! *Gooood!*" sang Rymer with bantering patronage.

"The *complete* emergence of the working class from underneath the possessing class (which it abolishes—or which is abolished for it) is perhaps meaningless. Fifty, or a hundred million people cannot rule. What would they rule? They can only be *told* that they are ruling, which is another matter: and meanwhile of course they go on laboring just the same as before. The people who *tell* them they are ruling, those people are in fact the rulers. As we see in Russia, the majority must always toil. It is an age in which paper takes the place of bullion, and the verbal of the physical."

"It is a different thing working for yourself and being exploited by some boss," Rymer interjected. "That is solid enough."

"There is always a boss. They have a different line of talk, that is all. And the abolition of the middle class is a disservice to the working class, it seems to me. The classless society has been proved a myth. If *class* we must have, then a trinity of classes is preferable to two classes. The natural class-arrangement is to have a middle class, involving the perpetual *individual* emergence and ascent of manual workers, passing into the middle sphere, the reverse constantly occurring too, duds dropping out of the middle class into the working class. This *individual* emergence should be facilitated. Complete 'emancipation' would signify everybody being relieved of the necessity to work, when they could divide their time between the football field, the dog track, and the cinema: which is absurd. In the last analysis, for one man to be slaving down in a coal mine, and another man to be passing his time between august Downing Street and luxurious Checquers, is unjust: which is emotionally true but otherwise absurd.

"The present theoretic eminence of the working class is a piece of illusionism. It is pure Maskelyne and Devant. The situation today speaks for itself. Workers' wages, after spectacular rises, are frozen in order to enable the devalued pound to push up the cost of living, so that the workers will be economically where they started, before the honeymoon. In the end all they will have gained is millions of free dental plates and pairs of spectacles. Even these retrospectively they will be made to pay for."

Rymer cleared his throat, and the new National Health Service dental plate stirred indignantly about. "The working class is no better off than it ever was then?" said he with mild derision.

"I did not say that. The Socialists have not improved upon the Liberal achievement, that is the point."

"Give them time. And besides the advance has in fact been enormous. Ask them!"

"A bogus inflationary advance, and a supply of ideologic stimulants. But the idea of a Glorious Working Class World has to be paid for and it costs billions of pounds. The *actual* workman has to pay for the advertisement of his imaginary self."

"The view of most people of course," said Rymer, "is that the working man is overprivileged, is spoiled."

"Everybody, not only the manual worker, is taken in by the advertising, that is all. His prestige but not his pocket has benefited. It is the same as with Culture and the Arts. So much money is spent in advertising how artistic and cultivated we are that there is no money left for artists or for *real* culture. All the money goes in the salaries of officials, public relations men, promoters, and in official publications, large buildings, educational activities, entertainment, and so on. There are now millions of political administrative parasites on the back of the working class, and their numbers multiply hourly. Every working man has a *petit bourgeois* appointee on his back."

"How about the parasites that were there before?" came from Rymer in a sardonic shout.

"The Liberal dream of 'the just' and 'the fair' and the right to liberty and the pursuit of happiness, people will live to regret in the rigors of the 'total' society."

"I thought utilitarian thinking had been sufficiently discredited," Rymer broke in again. "Men are great idealists. That is what you forget. The negative satisfactions of 'peace and plenty' do not appeal to them."

"Etcetera!" I answered him a little sharply. "Every power-thirsty Führer endorses those arguments and is clamorously in favor of 'heroism,' 'living dangerously,' plain living (a little 'mouse-trap' cheese and a glass of watery bitter beer). That shows a splendid spirit, they think. That people should be prepared to endure hardships makes them ever so enthusiastic —those who aspire to be their tyrants."

Rymer began tearing up a piece of paper into smaller and smaller fragments.

"Then think—war after war: what could be more utterly unutilitarian than that—and the consequent debt that is heaped upon the unprotesting nations—more crushing debts at each fresh massacre. No greatest happiness of the greatest number there! England is finished, tomorrow America will be finished, riddled with war debts, rotted with inflation. All this accepted without a murmur! What *heroes* we are! What idealists! The wars of our time are the means by which men are being pushed towards total servitude."

"Or towards a free world."

"Certainly not that. Such freedom as many may enjoy is perhaps all in the past."

"Freedom to exploit!" heckled Rymer.

"In any event, historians—unless such irresponsible snoopers into the past have to shut up shop—will marvel at the twelve decades in which the 'liberal' ferment was at work in English life. From such early steps up as the Cotton Factory Regulation Act they will see it at work, through thousands of measures of Christian legislation, up to such a climax as Lloyd George's National Insurance Act. The present socialist government is, then, the most spectacular achievement of a truly idealizing cult—and it will be its last. The moralist politics of Protestant Christianity was violently anti-authoritarian, in contrast with the Catholic philosophy. This is its last Protest, as it were."

"Why its last?" asked Rymer dully.

"Because it has given birth, now, to its opposite: to something tough and authoritarian. It must mean it is exhausted. Or perhaps, after all, it has achieved its end. Jesus said, you may recall, 'The first shall be last, and the last shall be first'."

"I remember that."

"Nietzsche who described Christianity as a 'slave religion' . . . "

"That I remember too!"

". . . could have opened his argument by quoting those words. Today the first are becoming the last and the last are loudly advertised as being the First. Liberalism has done its work? What do you say?"

"What are your politics?" he inquired.

"Liberal, really," I laughed. "Liberal, yes."

"Oh. I never would have thought of you as a liberal."

"No? I experience some anxiety as to whither my idealism may lead us. It is my conscience. My liberal conscience."

He sighed. "That conscience again! How long have you suffered from conscience? However, it does not obtrude in everyday life; in fact, no one would know you had one."

"You are less fortunate," I told him. "Its absence is all too apparent with you."

A cat at this point appeared from somewhere and rubbed itself against my leg. It was a thin cat, I could feel its ribs as it pressed its body against my trousers.

"Fond of cats?" I asked.

Rymer shook his head.

"Not very. Pussy is antisocial."

I am not fond of cats, either, but I scratched its bony, independent head.

"Having," I said, "put my hand to the plough, I will just finish the furrow. The evidence is abundant and conclusive. That the *sentimental conditioning* of the English public by constant injections of a Christian ethical-political preparation is responsible for *all* we see. Without having soaked themselves (or been soaked, which shall we say?) as no other nation has, in burning sympathy for the oppressed, no surrender of India or Egypt—no sentimental enthusiasm for the 'great Russian experiment' (we should have noticed long ago it was an ugly despotism)—no conservative Opposition so full of trimmers as to make it appear merely a socialist right wing. No mythical British 'kindliness,' therefore, but Reformation Christianity in its Victorian and Edwardian swan song laid the foundations of the Welfare State.

"The tough institutionalism of Rome has naturally seen to it that the Latin countries are provided with a class that has *some* resistance to set a limit to professional indiscipline or red excesses. In France or in Italy communism is more open, not 'crypto' as with the English. The declared communist is easy to check. It is instructive to speculate what a purely Catholic Europe would be like at this time. In all likelihood a practical and orderly society would be there, instead of a feverish ideological patchwork, the rabid indiscipline of parties. With the fearful deterrents to revolt, or even to criticism, at the disposal of a twentieth century ruler, where there was any real authority the agitator would not exist. In Russia today he would be instantly *liquidated,* as we know in any non-Christian society that is what would happen."

"You believe in bumping off everyone who disagrees with you?" was my listener's comment: comments usually made in the form of a question, but hardly anticipating an answer, though on this occasion receiving one.

"No. I am in fact conducting a polemic, among other things, against absolutist methods."

"Stupid of me. Sorry."

"In my last remarks, for I have been indecently long and

must finish, there is the evidence I must not omit, of how the rich have taken their squeezing to death by the State."

"They had no choice. They had no option."

"The average coarse illiterate tycoon, banker, or manufacturer one might expect to defend his property with savage desperation. But he does not do that, in these islands at least. He hands it over like an apologetic sheep, who has taken more than his share and knows it."

"Not in this county!"

"No, they are as if spellbound, 'like somnambulistic cattle.' This is the result of the long *conditioning*. It is, otherwise, undeniably our nature as men to put up a fight to protect our property. I should myself defend, with gun if necessary, my typewriter, let us say, against a nocturnal intruder. I have no right to such a possession, except for that nine-tenths of the law possession takes with it. I just *have* it, have worked for it, and should defend it. If a man entered my flat, laid his hand upon my typewriter crying, 'Property is a theft,' I should answer, 'Get out, you thief!' If he did not leave, I should take steps (however violent) to prevent my typewriter from being removed and passing into his hands."

"Oh, wouldn't you let him have it? I should." Rymer pretended to look astonished at my possessiveness.

"But you haven't got anything!" I indignantly pointed out. "It's easy for you to talk. You haven't got a typewriter. I am speaking of normal property-owning people, who perhaps have a nice overcoat they do not want to lose: and of course the normal possessing class in a free enterprise society, with whom it would be, only greatly magnified, the case of my typewriter."

"Yes, I see the sort of people you are talking about—whose mobile police would machine-gun strikers and jail their leaders."

"That, more or less, is the normal behavior. Our life is animal. What I mean is that we have the most house-trained set of magnates here on record."

"They had no choice," said Rymer dully.

"The Russian communists, to return to that, deal with dissent as a Bengal tiger would. This—once more—is because they have rooted Christianity out of their system. They are 'sincere': they are an ideologic tiger. They are dangerous, unless you feel like joining them."

"But what are you driving at?" There was a new note. Rymer, my Chorus, was showing signs of returning to personal life, and ceasing to be a mere heckler. "I see what you want to prove. But what then? Supposing I say, 'Very well. Socialism is a product of Christianity.' What happens next? Why should you wish to convince me of that?"

"I can clear that up for you at once," I told him. "The way things have gone has involved for us a terrible dilemma —for us ex-Christian liberals. The Third War approaches. That deepens the dilemma; since it will be a war between a liberal principle, and an anti-liberal principle."

"What war is this? What war are you talking about?"

"Soviet Russia has never been socialist according to Western ideas (and *Western* connotes Liberal). In the same way the communists misuse the term democracy, as we understand it. But the twentieth century Left Wingers repudiated the Western norm: totalitarian socialism they regarded as just an up-to-date model—extreme perhaps but authentic. The Left Wing, of course, shades off into Liberalism where Mr. Attlee stands. And much muddy thinking develops: terms originating in the West, implicit in them the backgrounds of the Western mind with its roots in Aristotle or in Plato, come to be used to describe their opposite. Terms like Democracy and Liberty are stood on their head, or turned inside out. Verhovenski, and William Morris or Mr. Herbert Morrison, are supposed to stand for the same thing. Meanwhile the old men at present in control in England are good if confused men. All are hospital cases, however. Bevin's doctor accompanied him everywhere: Bevin has dropped out. Cripps, the strongest of the Christian-socialist leaders, has dropped out too, though still alive. Attlee was in hospital for some time and it was believed he would have to lay down the premiership. Morrison was many months in hospital, his complaint phlebitis. None of them can survive the wear and tear of office for more than a few years. Who will it be then? How long will our rulers go to Church? How long will they understand, like Mr. Attlee, that socialism was born out of Christianity? The natural twentieth century drift must be towards the eventual repudiation of Christianity, or its sentimental political puritan hangover. We see that occurring everywhere, do we not? In a word, the danger is that in its hour of triumph socialism will forget, ignore, or violently discard, the ethics by means of which it was able to gain acceptance and to mount to power: indeed that it may strip away all our civilized Christian freedoms and thrust us back into a system of villeinage and worse. Socialism without ethics is a terrible thing."

Stopping as if it were a book I had finished reading and was now closing with a snap, I looked over at Rymer. I saw that he was deeply upset. It might take him a half hour to recover. I have explained how his is the religious approach: what he enjoys teaching he wishes to see treated as a sacred text. A hint that this fabric of salvation *could* have a fatal flaw was highly distasteful to him: the view that the very basis of socialism in Christian ethics might be its weak spot must have distressed him deeply. For when Christianity vanished, all socialism's angelic credentials, as being so obviously unselfish that the power of Ghenghis Khan might be entrusted to it with absolute safety, would vanish too.

That all such credentials would become worthless, was an odious suggestion to a man who would not even allow his wife to discuss the No-Food Minister's Monkey Nut Scheme. So poor Rymer was miserable, had been sealing himself up with sealing-wax for fear he might burst, and I should have to break the wax.

But I thought I would round off my discourse; so bending a stern eye upon him, I said:

"As a priest yours is a great responsibility."

"Oh, really?"

"Yes. To advocate socialism, as you do, is perhaps natural for a Protestant clergyman. It is good Christianity. But surely it is your duty to be critical and if necessary to denounce tendencies on the part of political extremists, to transform a basically Western theory into its illiberal opposite, subsituting a violent caricature of the Hegelian State for the City of God."

"Well, no one can say," said Rymer, with his brashest smile, "if I neglect to do my duty, that I did not know what it was."

Unexpectedly the tension relaxed. He shook himself and smiled sweetly. "Very interesting," he told me in a most affable way, "although supposing you decided that socialism is too dangerous to go on with I do not see what you would do about it."

I shook my head and shrugged my shoulders.

"That was not the point. I neither wish, nor should I be able, of course, to take any action. We were talking about *you*—about official Christianity. Your natural enthusiasm for the triumph of the Christian ethic in the triumph of socialism should be tempered by the thought that the political expression of the Christian ethic is administered by ambitious men who might betray it. The Church, a rejuvenated Church, should be on the bandwagon and seek to function as the conscience of the politician. It is surely the Church's privilege to do this: it is after all its ethic that has been used."

"The Church consists largely of ambitious men also," Rymer pointed out sedately.

"You must get a new Church for the new socialist society," was my answer to that.

"Are you a socialist, would you say?" he asked, sitting up. This was the counterattack.

"I belong to no party, seeing that, if you do, the only truth you are allowed is a partisan truth. Your judgment then must function only pragmatically. I prefer to concern myself with a nonpragmatical truth. A literature at the service of propaganda ceases to be an art: it becomes an agent of intoxication and of deception."

"Not a socialist," he summed up laconically. "He says he's *not* a socialist," as it were to himself.

"That's not quite true, either," I objected. "You have assured me, Rymer, that it is not necessary for your parishioners to come to church on Sunday. They can be equally good Christians by stopping at home: is that correct?"

"Yes," he answered with a shade of defiance.

"Well, as a good nonchurchgoing Christian man I cannot help being, to some degree, a socialist. Socialism is lay-Christianity. I am what a good socialist ought to be."

Getting up, I went over and looked out at the waving jungle. "My conscience compels me—unofficially and not as a party man—to approve of the idea of socialism, which I understand as an attempt to realize the brotherhood of man."

The savage vegetation waved hysterically as a gust from the sky blew on it. " 'Socialism' is a term that covers very different state forms. Some are like primitive communism, some like highly organized capitalism. 'If there were dreams to sell, which would you buy?' "

I returned from the window. Rymer is physically a slothful man. He was still huddled in his chair.

"Please show me," I said, "those new poems of yours. Those epigrams and things you spoke about in your letter. Let us forget the Sermon on the Mount and turn to the Song of Solomon."

"Would you really like to see them?"

He had them wedged in a book at his side. So we passed over into the other compartment of his mind. I took one after the other verses of half a dozen lines perhaps, each emptied of anything possessing weight. Most feelings had to be excluded, ideas were his enemies.

His lines drifted across the mind like a shadow of a bird. Some were deliberately concrete: say a feather out of a white cloud. But it was visibly dissolving as you held the paper. What he set out to fashion were words that melted as the eye rested on them. His heaviest words had come to rest on the page like the whispering leaf of a canary bush falling like a shadow upon the emerald lawn of a Persian miniature. He did not always succeed. Several were far heavier than air, and one contained an idea: it had slipped in somehow. Then he had written quite different verses, but now they were apparently always like this. As he drifted heavily through Bagwick in the costume of the Bishop's Fool, he was, I expect, lightening a line, or looking for a word that would fall like a snowflake, a silent self-effacing word.

I picked up the last of these pieces; even the paper on which he got the schoolmistress in Cockridge to type his verses, was the flimsiest available. He sat in a shapeless huddle in his chair, as though there were no bones inside his clothes, but a great jellyfish. His face was as careworn as that of a Chinese sage, umber-faced, umber-eyed, every furrow at its sharpest and with the expression of a miserable malefactor—one who knew that he had murdered a violet or been guilty of weighting with too ponderous a dew the rose upon the grave of his friend.

As I lifted the sheet of paper there was a thumping in the hall and a ringing: immediately Eleanor came in to announce the Storby car. It was a little windy outside. As Rymer drooped like a dejected porpoise over the sash of the car window I warmly shook the poet's hand. He cheered up as I shook him and as I drove off he was singing his good-byes. I heard Eleanor's firmer note and agitated my hat out of the window.

5.

I NEVER had such a good visit again to Bagwick. Either there were young people there or Rymer was preoccupied by the worries of his *cure*, connected mainly with the hostile activities of the young farmer. But when he came up to London he was in better spirits. He returned to the excitements of his youth: he would have been to see a new Italian film which reminded him of the early Russian ones when he was an undergraduate. Another time he would have been to see a socialist curate in an East End parish who reported packed churches of slum dwellers, to listen to a sensational mixture of inflammatory social doctrine and tawdry mysticism.

Two months or more after my visit I sent him a postcard message as follows:

> "Recalling my discourse socialism and Christianity. Have just seen something written or said by David Low, the famous Cartoonist. Here it is.
>
> " 'If any man come to you from the Right or the Left and promise you economic security on condition that you first surrender your personal and political liberty, kick him downstairs. You won't get the security and what is more having surrendered your liberty, you will then be in no position whatever to argue about it.'
>
> "I fear that Low will have lost an admirer in Bagwick."

Whenever I saw Rymer I made a point of inquiring if any new moves had been made, by his enemies in the parish, to have his living taken away from him. I got the impression that they had given it up as a bad job. He did not say so, but that is what I gathered was his view.

Then one day in January, while a young Italian workman was "hacking out and reglazing" one of our hall windows, the icy wind from Siberia still blowing in, there was a knock at the front door. The young Italian went on hacking. Mr. Rushbottom, my old man of errands, my washer-up and guardian of the street-door key was standing hat in hand, counting with difficulty his silver. "Shall I see who it is, sir?" he inquired. I asked him to do so, and he went out into the hall. A moment later he returned, practically walking backwards with his customary exaggerated deference. He was followed by the massive form of Rymer, limping, and with a large black patch over his left eye. The Rymer that looked at me out of the other eye was a stranger.

"Rymer, of all unexpected visitors!"

"I'm sorry," the stranger said.

"Aren't you cold? Come over here and sit by the fire."

"I'm not cold," said the stranger.

"Sit down," I repeated. "Have you hurt yourself?"

"No. I have not hurt myself."

"No? And you are limping, too. Bad luck. One moment, I will settle with Mr. Rushbottom."

I accelerated Mr. Rushbottom's ritual of the-change-out-of-a-pound, dismissed him with old-world courtesy on both sides—a bow from Mr. Rushbottom at the door towards the ominous vault of Rymer's back. That finished, I returned to the fire, facing my visitor.

"You look as if you had been fighting," I observed.

"I have," said the stranger.

Gradually I grew accustomed to the lonely eye, staring at me with a new expression. It was not the eye of the Bishop's Fool. Samuel Hartley Rymer was there, as he had begun: the parson that was underneath the rags and patches—which he was not wearing today: the man who played the Bishop's Fool for my entertainment. Even the poet had deserted this forlorn figure.

All those attributes removed, the personality was as it were undressed. However, this sort of psychological nudity was presented to me with dramatic satisfaction, so the old Rymer was there after all, peering at me dully out of his one eye.

There was a long silence. Rymer looked down at the floor. The "hacking and glazing" the other side of the door filled the room with violent sound. Rymer turned towards the door.

"Who is that?" he enquired.

"Why, that is an Italian workman," I told him, "putting in a new pane of glass. He cannot speak, nor can he understand, the English language."

A silence ensued.

"See this?" He pointed to the black patch obscuring his left eye.

"I do," I nodded.

"The farmer did that," he told me, panting a little.

"I am sorry, Rymer. How disgusting."

"Yes, I've come up to see a lawyer. And a doctor."

There was a short deep silence.

Several deep groans broke from him like successive belches. He took out his handkerchief and wiped his uninjured eye.

"Will this lead to anything tiresome?" I asked him.

"Lead to anything! I have been told to pack. I am to move into rooms in Storby. The Archdeacon came over last night. I was still in bed, he came into the room and told me no other course was open to them, I must go *at once*. I asked him what

I had done. I have done nothing, people have done things *to me*. It is not I who should move away from the neighborhood, it is Jack Cox. But they are such liars, a lot of people have come forward to testify that I . . . *was drunk*."

"You *drunk*!"

"*Drunk*. They say that I *stank* of whiskey. I never drink anything at all; even if I have people to lunch or to dinner and buy a little of wine for them at the grocer's in Cockridge I never have any myself."

This I was able to confirm.

"I noticed," I said, "when you brought a bottle of claret back for lunch one day, that you drank nothing yourself. Here, I have offered you everything from beer to burgundy— certainly you do not *drink*. You're the driest man I ever met."

"No, I don't drink. But they say I do and that's all that matters."

"A beastly situation! How did it all come to pass? You seem to have a lovely black eye."

He told me then how he had been trapped. Knowing him as I do it was not difficult to reconstruct the scene. I could see him as clearly as if I had been there, attempting to extricate himself. But a clergyman is a very easy prey, and this one perhaps especially so. He was a most unpractical man and at the same time overconfident in himself. His was so subjective a temperament that he was disposed to feel he could subdue to his will the most resistant fact. He behaved often as though the objective world were clay to be fashioned —not rock to negotiate. If a solid fact came into collision with him, as in this case for instance with his eye, he would be nonplussed.

How things began was as follows. A married woman in the village in whom his wife and he had taken an interest (I suppose because she was a bad hat) had got herself in a fix. She had stolen something in a shop in Storby, and the presence of the stolen article in the house had led to difficulties—the details are immaterial. He wanted to ask his wife to come down and see this woman, and he went into "The Marquess of Salisbury" to telephone to the Rectory.

The public telephone was situated at the far end of a passage, and in order to reach it one passed the two doors leading into, first, the public bar, and, next, the saloon bar. It was Saturday afternoon about two o'clock and there were people in both bars. As he passed the second door, which was open, he saw Jack Cox at the bar with two other farmers. He telephoned, and, having done so, as he turned around he found Jack Cox was standing there in the narrow passage looking at him.

"Ah, hallo, Jack. I thought I saw you inside with Joliffe."

But Cox did not speak. What was more, he did not move and there was no room to pass him.

Rymer is the most pacific and friendly of men, for all his arrogance, and I honor him for it, I cannot imagine him speaking roughly to anybody. Cox was plainly barring his way out and it might be assumed that he had been drinking enough for his ego to have swollen. There was probably nothing to be done but to push him out of the way. But English clergymen are not supposed to push human obstacles out of the way.

"Hello, Jack," said Rymer, as if addressing an awkward child. He rested his shoulder against the wall and crossed one leg over the other, as though settling down for a chat. "How is the farm? I must run up there and pay you a visit. I've been intending to for some time."

"I shouldn't," said Cox.

"Oh, why not, Jack?" he sang musically, with a teasing note, as if Jack was being a little silly.

"Because I'll kick you out of it on your bloody neck. That's why."

"But *why*? That's nonsense, Jack. Aren't we friends?"

At this point the most pacific clergyman should have taken steps to bring this colloquy to an end. Not so Rymer. No, he would charm this enraged animal into docility.

"Jack," he coaxed, "you've got this all wrong you know. You are not pleased with me, of course I know that, but you've got the wrong idea about me. Let's talk it over, Jack! Shall I come up and see you tomorrow?"

"Yes, come and convert me to communism. You've tried it on all the men who work for me. Come up and try it on me. But first of all take *that*."

With which he hit Rymer, the blow breaking two of the new set of Health teeth. Rymer straightened himself in a bound, putting his arms up in front of him—not pugilistically but to create an obstacle, and advancing at the same time: but Cox sprang to one side and shot in a second blow which brought the blood out of his nose.

Jack Cox, whom I have seen, is half Rymer's size, a little legginged English yeoman with a reddish bullet head. Although much older, I should suppose the larger could have annihilated the smaller had he wanted to. In this case the annihilation took a different form. With a great roar of "Jaaack!" which echoed all over "The Marquess of Salisbury," the Man of God, as if in an access of love, flung himself upon Jack Cox and folded him in an ardent maternal embrace. Dropping blood all over Jack's face and shoulders —when they caught sight of them people got the impression that Cox had been half murdered—Rymer practically carried him out of the public house.

"Now, Jack Cox! Will you behave yourself," he croaked huskily and breathlessly in Jack's ear, as he hugged him under the inn sign of a bearded man, ostentatiously plastered with stars and medals.

Those in the bars had come out into the street and people had come out of their houses, men, women and children, so that by now most of Bagwick was watching him. They did not watch in silence. The greater part of the men were Cox's laborers. Rymer was surprised at the hostility toward himself. He had always believed himself popular and several of the hostile faces he could see as he struggled with his foully cursing prisoner belonged to men with whom only recently he had had most friendly conversations about labor conditions. But apparently they hated him! He thought inevitably of Christ and the Jewish populace.

His tattered suit, under the strain of this violent encounter, was showing signs of disintegrating. Several patches had been torn off by Cox and he could hear a man derisively shouting: "Hi, sir, ye 'comin' onstuck! Why don't ee get t'misses to sew ee together!" But voices on all sides gave him very little comfort—the great tattered bleeding clergyman, hugging and heaving this way and that the little farmer, who was spitting insults up into his face like a little geyser of wrath, was not the sort of man to appeal to Hodge. He heard them cry: "Let him go! You coward, stand up to him!" "Trip him up, Jack! Kick him, Jack, he'll drop yer then!" "Murder! Parson's murdering Jack Cox!" There were no counter-cries to these. All were against him.

Then Bill Crockett, the village "red," arrived on the scene. Rymer could hear him coming and his heart sank. It only needed Bill Crockett to consummate the scandal. It would become a political issue, that man could be guaranteed to make political capital out of a dogfight. The "red's" voice could be heard in raucous argument not far away, though there was so much noise he could not hear what he was saying. Rymer for the first time began to despair—this was just what Cox wanted. "Go away, Bill Crockett!" he called. But he had loosened his hold a little in order to expand his chest to shout, and Cox managed to jab him under the rib. Suddenly Crockett was shouting in his ear, "Squeeze the life out of the dirty little exploiter, Mr. Rymer. Teach him to soak the poor!" "Go away, Bill, for Heaven's sake!" Rymer panted. But Crockett was kicking Cox on the shin-bone in his ideological enthusiasm. There was an indignant roar from Cox's chorus, and out of the corner of his eye Rymer could see Bill Crockett exchanging blows with one of Cox's men.

Rymer became more depressed, confused and obsessed with the dread of the consequences every minute. "This is a bad dream. It cannot be *happening!*" was the semi-comforting idea that helped to sustain him.

Releasing Jack Cox, and stepping back, he said:

"Jack, let us put a stop to this disgraceful scene. You see what is going on. It does credit to neither of us. Do be sensible, Jack, and stop striking me. I am a clergyman, you know I cannot strike you back. It is cowardly to attack me."

Cox's little eyes shone with malice as he stood listening and his little fists were tightly clenched. One of his little fists flew up into Rymer's face. That is how he got his "shiner." This nearly sent him to the ground; it also made him angry. He sprang at his enemy before the little fists could be used again and this time pinned him to the wall of the inn—holding him as before in his arms but up against the brick wall. That way it was less hard work, the wall assisting. Not of course that Cox remained just a bundle in his arms; he kicked, jerked this way and that, and stamped on Rymer's toes. Nor, of course, did the people round them give him any peace and they might suddenly intervene in favor of their boss. Bleeding, perspiring, panting, he rode his little nightmare in a chaos of shouts, oaths, kicks, and chatter. The shrill voices of women pierced the murky fever of his mind. Mrs. Rossiter's voice was the nearest and shrillest. His left eye was closing up now, so what happened to the right of him (the brick wall being in front) was less in his field of vision and less distinct.

He could see no issue to this but, as a final absurdity, a stand-up fight with the farmer—for as he struggled in a hot blur his mind darted about seeking a means of escape. He saw the headlines in the Storby papers, "Fighting Parson. Riot in Bagwick. Farmer Cox's story." For more than a decade this man had been his enemy and it was most unlikely that he would let him off with anything short of the extremity of humiliation and scandal. His appeals to "Jack" he saw had been absurd. There was always Providence—it even passed through his mind that the Archdeacon might pass that way. He ran through all the most unlikely visitants before reaching his wife. But Eleanor had said on the telephone that she would run down in the car almost at once, so it was after all in her that the best hope of intervention lay. He would hold this little rat pinioned to the wall until Eleanor stopped the car a few yards away, jumped out and hurried over to "The Marquess of Salisbury." She would of course be horrified. "My poor darling!" she would cry when she saw his face, which was in a bit of a mess. And when she noticed Jack Cox was unmarked wouldn't she just give Jack a piece of her mind when he richly deserved—and these brutes too, standing around here and allowing their Rector . . . well, he *was* their Rector!

So in a sense he became numbed to outer sensations, he no longer heard the invective directed at him by his captive, he prosecuted the locking up of the little fists of Cox as an automaton. His mind supplied a feverish daydream to distract him as he rocked about on top of Cox. It ran on like a clockwork producing consoling images.

But Jack Cox began to wriggle and to sink—he was slipping down all the time. Rymer tried to pull him up, but he had got down almost on his knees. Rymer at last was obliged to slip after him until *he* was on his knees too. It was impossible to hold him like that. He had to throw him over on his back, an operation he found none too easy. He did at last get him over, receiving a nasty punch or two in the process, and he then lay on top of him. Perhaps the earth would help him to hold Jack Cox better than the wall had.

Meanwhile this was psychologically a less satisfactory position. He would have looked, to anyone suddenly arriving on the scene, more like an *aggressor*—lying there on top of a man as if he were a victorious wrestler, than he would have while they were both on their feet, and he obviously pinioning Cox's arms, in the way a quite gentle police constable might. That, Heaven knows, was not a pretty picture: but this was a *worse* picture—should the Bishop happen at that moment to drive through Bagwick. He shuddered as he thought of the Bishop's reaction on finding one of his clergy-men lying on top of a man in the street, surrounded by a jeering crowd.

He panted on top of Cox and it was much more difficult in this position to immobilize him. Their bodies lay parallel to the houses so he looked up at the road before him, in the direction of the Rectory. Eleanor was taking her time!—or had something made it difficult for her to get away? (He refused to say *impossible*: difficult, perhaps.) Then, with a howl of pain, he leaped off Cox as if suddenly a bar of red-hot iron was there in place of Farmer Cox. He rushed away doubled up, in a crouching run. There was no longer any question of *holding* Cox. Without thinking, a wounded animal scuttling blindly for safety, he bolted from Cox as if that harmless-looking little countryman were possessed of some malignant property, fatal to life. He did not look back; he looked nowhere, heard nothing. Crouching and scuttling up the road he made for the Rectory.

Jeering laughter followed him. Everyone was laughing and chattering, great hilarity prevailed in Bagwick as their Rector ran away from it screaming with pain. "Take it to y'missus, parson, she 'ull fix it for ee," one of them called after him, a gust of fresh laughter beginning before the jeer ended. But the malice of Bagwick took a more tangible form. Mrs. Rossiter's Jacko, from the start at his heels, now ran level with him, and, to round off the whole performance, plunged his teeth into Rymer's calf. "First Jack—then Jacko!" as I said when he told me of the payment of that long-outstanding debt—pulling up his trousers and pants and showing me the relevant bandage.

Eleanor appeared almost at once, he saw her red tam-o'-shanter. As she drew near to the crouching figure, smeared with blood, disheveled, his patches gaping and fluttering, she could scarcely believe her eyes. As she stopped the car and sprang out she exclaimed "My poor darling!" just as she had done in his fevered daydream upon Cox's breast. But the villagers began to move back into their houses as they saw her approaching, and Jack Cox had already gone back into "The Marquess of Salisbury," so it was too late for the telling-off even had he not been suffering such atrocious pain. In the middle of the road was the inanimate form of Bill Crockett—who at first Eleanor had supposed must have been her husband's victim.

But Rymer was, it seems, practically inarticulate and she

helped him tenderly into the car, saying, "My *poor* darling!" again as she did so. One of the many thuggish tricks included in commando training had been utilized by the farmer (who had been exempted from military service because of his farm but who had learnt a few of the best thug tricks for use in civil life). All the facts were sorted out afterwards; Eleanor saw it was no time to ask questions. She turned the car round and with all speed made for home.

His story greatly shocked me. I felt sorry about him as I should with a child. The majority of men are so cunning and practical, such little strategists. *They* would have known exactly what to do. They would in any case never have found themselves with a drunken farmer in their arms outside a public house.

Rymer's departure from my flat was rather sudden. He recalled the hospital hours: I offered to go with him but he would not allow me to do that. He hobbled past the Italian workman who was still glazing though he had stopped hacking. Rymer's back went slowly along the corridor; that was more than six months ago and it is the last I have seen or heard of him. I have written several times but received no reply. I am beginning to wonder whether Rymer exists or whether he is not, rather, a figment of my imagination.

My Disciple

LETTERS that I receive from unknown correspondents, requesting an interview (mostly to do with other people's lives, not mine) I drop automatically in the wastepaper basket. Such letters are often those of a person who rates flattery very high among the stock baits—a person who fancies himself as a trapper. (An "eminent" man must be a vain man, otherwise—so obviously the unknown argues—he would never have sweated his way up to eminence.)

I have experience of what happens if one does *not* treat these letters as wastepaper. It does the correspondent no good to see him—it is just as humane therefore not to do so. Besides, I do not happen to be vain.

Mr. Walter Gartsides' communication lay before me, I looked down at it as I lighted a cigarette: and it was not a half-dozen lines before I reached "I have haunted the cocktail parties in the hope of meeting you." Of course at this point I prepared to get rid of it. As I gripped it to tear it in half I saw the word *Rochdale*. Mr. Gartsides (the sweet euphonious name—I could see it was hideous though the signature was only partly legible) was "taking up an appointment," I read, "as art director." It was in connection with this that Rochdale came to be mentioned; that was where he was going.

Rochdale I had seen ten days before. In a railway train after puffing your way through the Pennines, gazing with indolent sadness at those hill villages of chilly charm—for they force you to think of England before it began to dig in its black entrails and cover its pretty little face with soot—after the Pennine interlude you reenter the bleak huddle of this mass-day, the factories of Rochdale. Would Mr. Gartsides' job take him up where it is still beautiful in the hills, or on towards the metropolis of soot, mighty Manchester? "A few miles from Rochdale," could mean either: but there can be no "colleges" in the Pennines. . . .

To discuss with me the policy he proposed to pursue at this college, such was Mr. Gartsides' wish. At present he taught in Bermondsey: he picked ugly neighborhoods, did this man with the ugly name. I pictured him as a big seedy earnest man. The letter was not badly written, was not embarrassing as some are, was unsmiling, was just cordial enough to be agreeable.

An aversion to humanity is not what makes me difficult of access, only an aversion to painters or poets. There are so many thousands of individuals wasting their time at the game of "self-expression"; brooding over some midget talent in some dirty little room, with some dirty little woman. After a great war they are found to have alarmingly multiplied. Were it the tinker or the tailor who wanted a conference, or the local builder, tobacconist, or publican, that would be different. I am uncommonly sociable. It was undoubtedly the fact that Mr. Gartsides lived in so underprivileged a neighborhood as Bermondsey that decided me to write and ask him to come to tea the following week. Owing to great pressure of work I regretted that about an hour was all I should be able to spare. There is no pretentiousness, I may add here, in being particular about time, I am short of time. It is the government makes me short of time, or the penury of the country.

On the appointed day, and, with great precision, at the appointed hour, this knock was heard: loud—firm—short. Upon opening the door I had a surprise, which was apparently reciprocated. In such cases embarrassment is usual on the visitor's part, whereas the rules prescribe that the grantor of the interview should be bursting with self-importance—or if he is not bursting with it, is weary with the weight of it, or most "graciously" waives it—or perhaps moves circumspectly like a man with something sensational on his person—say a bomb. Mr. Gartsides, though for some reason surprised, was in no way embarrassed.

My visitor was a rawboned man of thirty-nine, not to say forty, an age to which I do not think he had in fact attained. He carried a khaki raincoat over his arm, wore no hat, his reddish hair was rough but thinning; he was short, brisk, poker-faced, a man who had never been a great many feet above the gutter. I should expect to see him in a strike picket, and his hard voice was like one coming out of a picket too.

Whatever it was had halted my visitor was effective for perhaps the one tick-tock of a clock: then his underdone pink face, rationed as regards expression, admitted what I assume was his party look, and his harsh voice rasped quietly out my name. He marched straight in without much invitation. "Be seated, Mr. Gartsides," I said, and was glad the letter had been answered, and I had got something more primitive than I had asked for, and he sat down at once in my best and largest armchair, and gave my room and belongings a resolute look or two. It was not a *stare* for his aggressiveness was quiet and reserved. He sat up red and alert and silent. But his redness was not that he colored, it was always there, and no one who lives in a classroom keeps such a face.

"I was not able to read your signature," I told him.

"No? I am sorry."

"But I am glad my letter reached you. In addressing the envelope as I could not make out the name I imitated the shapes, and put Esquire after them."

He smiled—probably he thought I was being superior about his handwriting.

"What *is* your name however!" I politely laughed. "Your handwriting is beautifully clear, but, like many people, when you write your *name* you become illegible!"

"Gartsides," he barked back, making the name sound even harsher than it is.

"An uncommon name," I said.

"Not in Durham where I come from."

"Indeed."

"Yes, Gartsides is a name you often hear."

"I can see how that might be, it sounds as if it could have belonged to a collector of the Danegelt."

To put an end to these trivialities Mr. Gartsides announced, "I have read your books, Mr. Lewis, at least some books. I am very glad we could meet. I have haunted parties and shows in the hope of meeting you."

I gave him a reproachful look and hastily changed the subject.

"How do you come to live," I enquired, "in Bermondsey, Mr. Gartsides. You teach, you said in your letter."

"Yes, that's right, in an Elementary School."

"You dispense elementary education to those whose parents were insufficiently acquisitive and so had not the cash to send their kids to more classy places."

"Yes. I went to one like that myself too. Elementary—that's all I got."

This was given out coldly, as an indifferent fact, but he was laying bare an injury that society had inflicted upon him. It had given him a clown's equipment, and a clown's tongue.

"Token instruction. It's disgusting!" I protested. "Does it not worry you; to help perpetuate this system?"

Mr. Gartsides looked politely blank. Sympathy, or "understanding," was a commodity the bona fides of which he doubted, and for which he had no use anyway.

"But it is art I teach," he explained. "Sometimes in *art* the elementary is the best."

"*Sometimes!*" I conceded with extreme dryness.

Tea arrived, and some of the lardless, sugarless, eggless cakes of Great Britain, 1949. The tea had suddenly improved about Christmastime, before which it had no taste whatever, having deteriorated during months in the warehouse. As he drank he remarked: "Good tea. Darjeeling and China. I always bought that": he laughed—"when I could get it."

His laughter was the public enjoyment of a private joke, and I was impelled to ask him:

"Have you always taught art in elementary schools?"

He gave a short laugh at that. "Oh, no," he answered. "Only for a year. I was a soldier."

"During the war—but before that——"

"No, I was a regular. I was seventeen years in India."

India, with its mosques and temples, its solar topees, polo ponies—seventeen years of it violently expelled the image of Bermondsey as the background for this little figure. It was with a new eye that I focused him. It was literally as if he had confessed to a prison sentence.

"What was your rank?" I asked.

"Sergeant."

"Quarter-bloke?" I suggested.

"No, just sergeant. I trained the boys for jungle warfare. Blackett's boys."

I digested this.

"I'm an old man," he said harshly. "I know I have not much time. I have to be quick."

He spoke as a man with a mission. But I had not been prepared for a long-service sergeant—that was one of the half-dozen things for which I was totally unprepared.

It was not the ranker—my class-bar works in reverse: but this is a Briton who comes out of a mold manufactured at the same period as the footman. On retirement, if personable, old soldiers became Commissionaires, or such up to now has been the case: prison warder, police constables or what not. With domestics they traditionally have shared a necessary obliquity, unshakeable appetite for tips, a philosophy of sloth. Following the mass training of citizens for the first world war the type had suffered a change—but in such cases a type is apt to keep the worst of the old while incorporating the worst of the new. Finally, it is not a creative occupation, and cannot but be a servile one, so long as the old disciplines hold.

In "total war" the first regular sergeants had left no over-all pleasant impression upon me. On the other hand, there was this: I could not imagine any of them, by any stretch of the imagination, becoming art teachers. So we stared at one another, at this point, blankly and bleakly—for no more than the interval decreed by punctuation by its colon sign —he, reddened by the sun that "never set" on the Empire that is no more, I paled by electricity, under which I labor nightly to distinguish myself and attract ex-sergeants: he who —in his sergeants' mess in Hindustan—so he was to tell me, would listen to some ex-service minstrel who, for a drink or two, would give the sergeants "The Road to Mandalay" (where the old flotilla lay)—a year or two before the English "hurled themselves"—to use an American columnist's phrase—"out of" Kipling's India—and *I* who—(to find a minstrel for myself) once listened to an American minstrel who read a lay of his own, which he had called *The Waste Land*, while the ink was scarcely dry on it. That was after Western civilization had committed suicide in a blood bath. The second decade of this ill-starred century had just banged its way off the stage.

The sergeant revealed a brand-new set of state teeth—first fruits of the famous Health Act, falsely white and symbolically of a deadly uniformity. His smile advertised polite satisfaction at the effect produced by his words.

"Well all right, so you're a soldier," I began, with ostentatious finality.

"I *was* a soldier," he mildly corrected.

"How does it come about though that you teach art?"

He seemed surprised at the question. It appeared the most natural thing in the world that he should teach art.

"Oh, I see," I said.

But he proceeded to open my eyes still further—relished the operation, it was quite plain. Upon leaving the army he had at first no idea what to do with himself. As regards the length of this blank interlude I know nothing, but it cannot have been long. Mentioning the problem one day to a chance-met man, he heard how soldiers were being turned into teachers (not of art—that came later). The idea appealed: he fancied himself as a teacher. Sergeants develop an appetite for the imparting of knowledge.

Of course in fact he had had a wide choice of callings. Upon demobilization he could have become almost anything from a Harley Street consultant to an Anglican clergyman, by means of a Government grant: to the mind of the politician, who is anticraft, the notion that it takes a long time to become anything worth the being is repugnant. The politician, like the journalist, is a professional amateur. The only thing there was no grant for was to learn how to be a politician. The laziest of the ex-servicemen naturally chose the fine arts. The nation's money was drained off on oil paints, palettes, mahlsticks, six-foot lay-figures, poppy oil and sable brushes —and of course studio rents. Sculpture was not so popular, it sounded too much like work.

Gartsides was sent to an emergency training center. In one year he would have qualified as a teacher in an elementary school. Shortly, however, he discovered that there was no obstacle to his transferring, if he so desired, and training to be an art teacher. So he changed over (he probably found arithmetic a bit of a sweat): whether remaining in the same training center or not I forget. On the completion of a brief period of art training, he blossomed forth as art teacher, was appointed to a slum school. The other teachers there, of whatever kind, were "certificated"—which meant they had matriculated and spent some years in procuring their licence to teach. It seems he was not a popular figure, even before he showed what stuff he was made of. But it was no time at all before he did that. He quite literally painted the school red.

A thigh thrown over a desk, an arm akimbo, his utility shoe dangling, the children were addressed by Gartsides: and their fidgety little eyes popped out of their curly little heads. They were told that what was *spontaneous* was best. Spontaneous meaning what *spurts* up, free and uncontrolled, not fed out by a nasty *tap*. The freest expression—the most *innocent* release—of their personalities was what he was there to teach. They would get no *direction* from him, his role was that of a helpful looker-on. Ready to give a hand, that was all. (He conveyed a very vivid impersonation of these transactions I am obliged naturally to abridge). Art was *doing what they liked*. It was not doing what *he* liked. They must pay no attention to him or to anyone else—it did not matter a hoot what *anyone* thought. He waved a rebellious eye over toward the office of the superintendent. He could teach them nothing. What can one person teach another except to be himself, as if he lived on a little island all by himself? They all lived on little islands all by themselves. No, he was simply there in the capacity of a wet nurse, to assist them to be their little selves, and to bring forth—to create—whatever was inside them!

The children—typical Giles-like gnomes from the neighboring sooty alleys and crapulous crescents—were of course alarmed and excited. Then he appeared one morning with a number of tins of house-painters' colors and a couple of dozen suitable brushes (and he was very proud of introducing house-painters' colors into the teaching of art). He pointed dramatically to the walls of the classroom crying: "Here's paints and brushes and there's the old wall. Atta boy! Paint me some pitchers on it."

His petrified class suddenly saw the light. With squeaks of rapture they went to work. Soon the walls, part of the ceiling, as well as the cupboards and doors and even some areas of the floor of the classroom were as rich with crude imagery as the walls of a public lavatory. Some of the children were smeared from head to foot with paint.

After this his popularity suffered a further decline among the teaching staff. Next the school inspectors arrived one morning and "nearly threw a fit" when they saw his classroom. He played the simpleton. He grimaced with a wooden jaw, hanging open an idiot lip and goggled with his eyes, to show me how smart he could be. It seems that the inspectors were satisfied that he was practically imbecilic. Of course they recognized that this was the type of man called for to teach art. They bullied the children, however, a little, for obviously *they* should have had more sense.

After the paint he obtained some plasticine.

"What do you think they did with it?" he asked me.

I shook my head, to indicate my inability to guess what might supervene if their personalities were left alone with so malleable a substance as plasticine.

"Well, they all made the same sort of thing," he told me.

"Indeed. How curious."

"Yes," he agreed. "They stood their piece of plasticine up on end like this." And he stood a safety match upright on the table. He smiled at me. "I asked them what it was," he said. "They told me a lighthouse."

"Ah, yes. That lighthouse rescue probably. It was in all the papers: I suppose it was that."

"No," he said, obviously disappointed in me. "It was—well, a phallus. Phallic."

"I beg your pardon," I said. "I see, of course. How amusing. Their personalities vanished momentarily. They became one—the primeval child."

He looked at me with surprise.

"No," he objected. "Each did a different lighthouse."

I laughed at that. "I wonder," I asked him, "if you have read Herbert Read's *Education of the Child?*" For his goofy goings on, without looking any further, might be the response to some such stimulus.

"Oh, yes." In a lightly drawling tone of voice which dismissed my suggestion as irrelevant. "The book that has had most influence on me, Mr. Lewis"—and he bent his gaze upon me as if I were showing a little ingratitude—"is your *Caliph's Design*. I have got more fun from that book than any other and I was meaning to speak to you about it."

My consternation may easily be imagined. My *amour pro-pre* [1] reeled at the impact of such approbation. *The Caliph's Design,* with for sub-title *Architects Where is Your Vortex?* was my earliest pamphlet. It is to do with the fine arts, with especial reference to the case of the architect. The human shell, dwelling or public building, should be demolished, I protested, no city should be spared or time wasted, and our architects should construct upon the *tabula rasa* thus created, a novel, a brilliant city.

The teaching of this book is violently opposed, surely, to the emotional "personality"-world of Mr. Gartsides and his true master Mr. Read. I put pressure upon my memory to produce some passage, or perhaps chapter, which would give aid and comfort to my "admirer." But my memory of my own work is imperfect and I abandoned the attempt.

"*The Caliph's Design?*" I asked coldly.

"Yes. It's a book that ought to be reissued."

I blinked.

"Do you still think the same as you did when you wrote it?" he asked me.

"Just the same." But I began to understand. "That the out-dated dingy shells in which we live—indeed everything, you mean, should be razed to the ground and a national city re-place it? Dazzlingly white in place of blackened brick and dirty stucco? That the sordid antiquated apology for a city in which we dwell disappear as if by sorcery, and a new city stand there suddenly where it was—of hard white logic?"

He nodded.

"Well, I want that now as I did then. The only difference is I know I shall not get it!"

"Why not?" he retorted, with a touch of what was for him almost heat. He became guarded at once. "It's worth trying for, anyway."

"Oh, yes. However, since you have expressed such interest in that. . . . When writing *The Caliph's Design* I was superb-ly ignorant of the difficulties."

"Of course there are difficulties," he agreed airily.

"Firstly, the obstacles which stand in the way of pulling down, or of building, a single house, let alone a street—or a city."

"Property rights."

"That is so. But there are factors more fundamental." I

[1] self-love

got up and passed him to fetch a box of matches. Back again I said. "I was not a social revolutionary."

"I know you were not." He was prompt and businesslike. "You had the vision t..ough. You saw what should be done to the *outside*—to house the new society."

"Very well—I had a vision, like my Caliph—but suppose for a moment that I had found a social revolutionary, Mr. Gartsides, to act upon my vision. What would he have done with my vision? Naturally what Hollywood does with a literary masterpiece. He would have diluted, vulgarized, and betrayed it. It is no use going into partnership with a violent reformist philistine. Yet to realize your 'vision' you require capital: and in this case the capital required is *action*."

Gartsides jerked himself over from the right arm of the chair to the left. He stroked his raw face as if it hurt. "The man of action," he murmured lazily, "is not always a philistine though."

"Well, we won't have to parade as Men of Action! How I see it, and you came to me as to an oracle, is this. All the dilemmas of the creative mind seeking to function socially center upon the nature of action; upon the necessity of crude action, of calling in the barbarian to build a civilization. The result is as disconcerting as what is unmasked at the basis of the structure of the human reason—I mean the antinomies."

That was my longest speech, in this access of volubility. I lay back and smoked. Then I said: "A penny for your thoughts, Mr. Gartsides!"

"My mind is a perfect blank!" He smiled the smile of the smart.

As a result of our conversation so far I understood, of course, that art was the last, not the first thing that weighed with Mr. Gartsides, whose interests were political or sociological. Like most astute men of this type he had no time for private feelings, he did not take too seriously the non-political character of my mind—especially as I was not hostile but only had not trained myself to think of the human being as a power unit.

But I think he felt this was becoming a stalemate, or we had drifted away from the fiery purpose that had brought him to see me. Sitting up, he again mounted his savage hobby horse.

"So you still think like that—that's good, Mr. Lewis. I'm glad. That's how I think. It is why I came to see you. I can make people enthusiastic," he assured me brightly, "I can make them see what I see." This he repeated later several times. He regarded it as his *raison d'être* [2]—to be an intoxicator of innocents, with big brash phony phrases. "You remember what you said in your book about the artist and the engineer?"

"That they should cooperate?" I looked at the clock.

"That's right. That's what I am going to do up in the college—make the engineers art conscious. They never think about art. I want to make them see they can use art in their work."

"I see." I looked at the clock: but I was unable to make him time conscious. I had not his power to make people see what I saw—at least not when it was a timepiece.

"Why don't you go out, Mr. Lewis, and make people enthusiastic, make people see what you see?"

"My way of doing that is to paint pictures," I told him. "I paint pictures of a world that will never be seen anywhere except in pictures."

"You don't think so? But the day of the easel picture is over."

"Then there will not even be that pale reflection of something more intelligent."

"No one sees what the artist does in his studio."

"You mean that like the Borough Group he should take his canvases into the Public Gardens so that the dormant responses of the common man may be stimulated? Or the way artists stick their things up in an alley near Washington Square, New York?"

"Why not?" he said. "The artist is wasting his time doing easel pictures. What he puts into the easel picture he should put into the world outside. Spread his vision around—in things that people can touch—eat out of—*live* in! Their houses, their clothes."

He was all set evidently to intoxicate *me*. I resorted to the grin, which is all that it is necessary to do when people like Mr. Gartsides who cannot paint easel pictures, and understand nothing about the art of painting, condemn the easel picture: or the novel or indeed any of the other so-called individualist art forms the destruction of which they are apt to predict if not to urge, basing the abolition upon some utilitarian moral.

[2] reason for being

"You could make people enthusiastic!" How right was the eighteenth century, I reflected as I listened, in its deep distaste for "enthusiasm."

But he proceeded to enlarge upon the novel functions involved in his job of "art director," and explained the purpose of the new colleges invented by the socialist administration. (In the field of Education they are not seen at their best.) He had gone up to Rochdale and was accepted on the spot. The director had said: "You're the only one who took the trouble to come up and have a look. You shall have the job." What would his "art direction" consist of, I wanted to know. Would he sit down the engineers-in-the-making this college had been created to train and make them copy plaster casts? He laughed away all plaster casts. Or the nude model? I inquired. He smiled away the nude.

He was not evasive. He made no difficulty about explaining that what he would do was just to *inspire* and *enthuse*.

"How do you mean," I persisted. "You will in the morning leave your quarters charged with enthusiasm. You will walk around the workbenches or rooms where young men are bent over blueprints, and spout art as one would spray some intoxicant into the air? Will you get these young men to paint the college walls and ceilings?"

"Certainly that is the form their enthusiasm might take," he answered. "I don't know what form it will take however. I am here to discuss that with you."

"There would be no work on pieces of paper or canvas—which might lead eventually to . . . the easel picture?"

"No, of course not that. What's the use of that?"

"What indeed. Do you paint yourself, Mr. Gartsides?"

At this he was convulsed a little.

"Oh, I shouldn't like you to see any of my pictures"—he gulped down a self-deriding laugh at the mere thought of the feebleness of his own "creative" efforts.

"Are they not good?" I asked.

"No, they're rotten," he assured me.

"Your activities are mainly destructive"—I assumed the air of one musing.

"No, I am creative. I can fill people with enthusiasm."

"For what?"

"For art."

It was six o'clock and I stood up. He had had his sixty minutes—and so had I.

But I rather liked Mr. Gartsides. I even secretly wished

him luck. This remarkable sergeant naturally regarded art as an uproarious racket. In that, however, he was by no means alone. Many dignified gentlemen, who draw fat salaries as—*directors* just like Gartsides only on a far bigger scale, regard art in precisely the same way. The parasites that art attracts are legion. What I liked about Gartsides was the way he had jumped into it with military alacrity, out of the farmyard or the Barrack Square. He had taken Time by the forelock. He had swung himself up on to the tremendous bandwagon. If we were going to live with nonsense, rather Gartsides and his "enthusiasm" than the higher-up impostors—the "stripe-pants" of the art racket.

I took a fancy to Gartsides. From that day to this I have breathlessly followed his career. He has grown to be a somewhat different person: but he retains, to the full, his fine rough artlessness. If only he could learn to paint, he might do for the Army what Rousseau did for the Douane.[3]

---

[3] customs

PART II

the first world war

In 1947, Lewis published the first installment of his auto-biography, *Blasting and Bombardiering,* which covers the years from 1914 to 1926 and describes the beginnings of his activity as a writer and painter, his association with T. S. Eliot, T. E. Hulme, Ezra Pound and James Joyce, his editorship of the avant-garde magazine, *Blast,* and, above all, his experiences as an artillery officer in the British army on the Western Front.

"The War," he said, "is such a tremendous landmark that locally it imposes itself upon our computations of time like the birth of Christ. We say 'pre-war' and 'post-war,' rather as we say B. C. or A. D. . . . You will be astonished to find out how like art is to war, I mean 'modernist' art . . . . It is somewhat depressing to consider how as an artist one is always holding the mirror up to politics without knowing it. My picture called 'The Plan of War' painted six months before the Great War 'broke out,' as we say, depresses me. A prophet is a most unoriginal person: all he is doing is imitating something that is not there, but soon will be. With me war and art have been mixed up from the start. It is still. I wish I could get away from war. This book is perhaps an attempt to do so. Writing about war may be the best way to shake the accursed thing off, by putting it in its place, as an unseemly joke."

As John Holloway pointed out in a perceptive article,

Lewis' concern with the elements of war made him more contemporary, so to speak, than any of his artistic colleagues, most of whom were only obliquely affected by the First World War. His fascination with and revulsion from violence gave him a subject that, with the years, has become perhaps the most urgent subject in both modern art and modern political life. What Lewis once said about Nietzsche can well be applied to himself: "It may have been because this very complex and sensitive man was so responsive to the claims of violence—because he had made it so much his own—that he understood its opposite as well as he did. The notion of domination, and of the struggle for domination, obsessed him. But he was also obsessed by the refinements of the intellect which cannot coexist with the struggle for existence."

from BLASTING AND BOMBARDIERING

Bombardiering

"In the life-order advances are made to me from all sides in order to free me from the claims to selfhood or self-expression."
K. JASPERS

As a bombardier, at Menstham Camp, I was instructing a squad in one corner of the enormous field, while other bombardiers were instructing other squads in other corners. Our martial voices rang out. Rifles rattled down to the right foot, hands smote the reverberant body of the rifle. The camp adjutant, placid little peacetime major, with South African War ribbons, entered the field, accompanied by a sergeant major. He looked about him, the sergeant pointed in my direction, and both of them advanced toward me.

For some time the adjutant stood behind me, first of all

having said "Carry on, Bombardier." I shouted myself hoarse
in attempting to get the rifles smartly off the lubbardly
shoulders and down onto terra firma with something like one
blended bang, and then up again to something like respectable *pre-sent*! For I wished this adjutant to recommend me
for a commission at the Artillery Cadet School at Exeter (to
which I subsequently was sent) and my impeccable parade-
ground manner was imperfectly seconded by the massive but
slow-moving miners I had to drill. The presence of the
adjutant alarmed them, and one or two lost control of their
rifles, which whirled about in an uncanny way, or even
flew out of their hands and dropped with a disgraceful and
unmartial clatter upon the ground.

"Or—der UMMS!" I bellowed.

Down rattled the butts with a discouraging haphazard
one-after-the-otherness, anything but trim and all together.
And anyone who could have snapshotted me at that moment, my right eye somewhat more open than my left, and
flashing with indignation, would have put me down as a
deep-dyed martinet.

"Bombardier!" called out the sergeant major who accompanied the adjutant—rudely I thought. I instantly wheeled
with the precision of a well-constructed top; and with the
tread of an irresistible automaton I bore down swiftly and
steadily upon the adjutant; I brought my heels together with
a resounding spank, gave my rifle a well-deserved slap, and
stood looking over the adjutant's head: it was impossible
for me to do otherwise, as he was the best part of a foot
shorter than myself. I knew what was coming, or I thought
I knew. My squad and its instructor were to be held up to
obloquy.

"Bombardier," said the adjutant, "what is all this Futurism
about?"

I blinked, but did not move.

"Are you serious when you call your picture 'Break of
Day—Marengo?' Or are you pulling the Public's leg?"

I did not move a muscle. I lowered my eye, as he was
speaking, and fixed it sternly upon the guncarriage wheel
upon his cap. He seemed a little nervous, I thought. I was
deeply surprised at the subject matter of his remarks and
could not decide offhand if this boded ill for me or the
reverse, in the military context. And it was at the moment
the military context, decidedly, that mattered. I knew that a
photograph had appeared in the *Daily Sketch* that morning,

showing an abstract oil painting named "Break of Day—Marengo" from my hand. So I saw what had happened, at least.

"No, sir," I said. "Not the Public's leg."

I glanced out of the corner of one eye at the sergeant major—whom I had had to carry into the camp the night before through a hole in the hedge, having picked him out of a ditch full of stertorous Anzacs, who had succumbed in a welter of alcohol.

"They say—these newspaper wallahs that is write—that—er—one has to look at these things you do as if one was *inside* them instead of outside them."

The sergeant major permitted himself a discreet chuckle.

"Am I mad, Bombardier, or are these fellahs mad, that's what I want to know? It must be one or the other."

"It is the other sir," I reassured him. "I will answer for that."

"Then what they say is all poppycock?" he said, with evident relief.

"Undoubtedly, sir. They have no understanding of the art they are reporting. You must pay no attention to them."

"I am glad to know that, very glad, Bombardier."

Standing in this hieratic attitude, rifle on shoulder and heels together, I hoped that I might not have to pursue this absurd dialogue for too long. This Jack-in-office had no right really to catch me in that attitude—seeing it was an attitude I could not abandon and that it was wholly unsuited for expounding the mysteries of an esoteric technique. It was as brutal as surprising a Court Chamberlain in his socks and pants: my private life should have been respected—the parade ground was a place of arms, not a forum for civic discussion. That was how I felt about it. I stood there stock-still before this officer, my calves bulging beneath my puttees. I understood what it must feel like to be a butler, and to be inopinely cross-questioned about his sexual life or the conditions of his bowels by a snobbish master.

"Very well. Carry on, Bombardier," said the adjutant apparently satisfied that he was not irretrievably batty. I stamped angrily, about-turned, and marched back to my lines of drooping coal miners, shouting fiercely as I reached them—

"Squ—a—ad! Ab—out *turn*! Quick—*March*!"

I was far more professional than when I had left them. And I marched them off as far away from the adjutant as possible, and roared and blustered at them for full ten minutes until their arms ached from heaving their firearms about from side to side and up and down.

I have said my "Private life." But of course in the last two years I had become a public figure. I had shot into fame as the editor of *Blast,* the first number of which had appeared in the six months preceding the declaration of war. I was the arch-futurist. It was generally called "futurism," what I did, though this was a misnomer. My anonymity was gone forever at all events. This I had not thoroughly grasped. For no sooner had I become famous, or rather notorious, than the War came with a crash, and with it, when I joined the army, I was in a sense plunged back into anonymity once more. This I by no means objected to. I quite easily felt anonymous. I like the sensation: "bombardier" was after all a romantic incognito. And since I had been in the army the brief spell of sudden celebrity became a dream I had dreamed, of no particular moment.

My career as an artist and writer was a private matter, something not public but private as I saw it. Not of course ashamed of it, nevertheless I did not relish its being unearthed, since it was irrelevant. I preferred to forget it. I had said "good-bye to all that," when I first put that uniform on. My mind was, in fact, so constructed, that I must resume what I had been before I was a "lion," and regain my anonymity, in order to confront death. There was no point in meeting death on the battlefield, if that was what was in store for me, as Mr. Wyndham Lewis. In a word, this existence—that of a soldier—was another existence: not the same one, continued, in a change of scene and circumstances merely.

The adjutant seems to have been grateful for having his confidence in his reason restored to him. We had no more talks, on or off parade, about futurist pictures. But when my battery paraded shortly after that for service in France, I was called out of the ranks and told by the adjutant to go to my hut. From a window looking on to the parade ground I watched it march away and was attached to its successor. In this way I saw two more batteries depart. This was something depressing. I was not dying to fly at the throat of the Hun or to massacre the Boche, and so make the world safe for Democracy. But I did find that I readily developed *esprit de corps* of sorts. I experienced a healthy affection for my rough, pathetic, shambling companions.

As a noncommissioned officer it was one of my duties to

stand beside the medical officer when the men queued up
for vaccination. As the biggest and most bull-like of these
new recruits exposed their arms above the elbow, as often as
not the blood fled from their foreheads and they swayed a
little. As the knife touched their skin they were apt to just
roll up their eyes and sink to the ground, and the bigger
they were the more likely was this to happen. It was one of
my duties to catch these big babies as they fell and to remove them after they had fallen. And I reflected as I did so
that as regards mind and matter, mind was as it were matter's
heart, and that when a small, feeble, and immature mind
was put to function in such a disproportionately large body,
it had uphill work all right.

These casualties of the vaccination parade seemed in some
way symbolical. Why did these big fellows collapse? I thought
of Bombardier Wells, I was reminded of Joe Beckett; our
"horizontal champions." The latter I had seen (or was to see)
put to sleep inside a minute by Carpentier. I wondered what
all this meant.

England was of course much like any other country, sound
as a bell. But England had always fought its wars with
pressed men, "crimps," criminals and such like. Wellington
indignantly inquired when it was proposed to abolish flog-
ging in the British Army, how he was expected to win battles with such material if he could not flog it into shape.

England was not "militarist," even it had always disliked
its military. "It's thank you Mr. Atkins, when the band begins to play," croaked that bitter "militarist," Kipling, but at
other times Tommy was not much appreciated. A desperado
personnel of "Foreign Legion" type, plus a martial aristocracy, accounted for Waterloo and Blenheim. Slave armies,
in the first feudal days, and then "crimp" armies had built
up the great military reputation of an island of freemen enjoying "a degree of liberty which approached to licentious-
ness," one of whose dearest boasts had become the right *not*
to bear arms.

Kings had had to tussle with a stiff-necked Parliament for
even small accretions to a miniature standing army. Are we
not informed by de Lolme that "another very great advantage attending the remarkable stability of the English government, is, that the same is affected without the assistance of
an armed standing force: the constant expedient this of all
other governments." And "all the monarchs who ever existed,

in any part of the world, were never able to maintain their ground without the assistance of regular forces at their constant command," whereas the English kings had not "a guard of more than a few scores of men," although their power was equal to that of "the most absolute Roman emperors." But they naturally often desired to have a "regular" force, like other non-English kings, so as to go abroad and enjoy the Sport of Kings.

So here was the first citizen army of unmilitary Englishmen: and though a fair proportion of Bulldog Drummonds were to be found amongst them, they were anything but lovers of martial exercises. Britain had unexpectedly gone continental, to carry out the dictates of the deadly Entente Cordiale, and of secret military pacts, entered into behind its back by its Government. A new epoch in the history of England had begun.

Meanwhile I dashed water in the faces of this highly strung cannon-fodder of ours, quiet chaps mostly, like large inoffensive cattle, so helpless in the hands of all these doctors, drill sergeants, padres and "officers." It is for that reason that I referred to them as "pathetic."

The pathos got worse as one watched them month after month at the Front—telling themselves that this was a war-to-end-war, and that was why the free Britisher was in it: otherwise it would have been unthinkable. Just *this once* all the heirs of Magna Carta and the Bill of Rights were behaving like the conscript herds of less favored nations, and dying too in unheard-of numbers. They wrote to their missus "Keep Smiling," or "Are we downhearted!" As an officer at the Front I took my turn at censoring their correspondence, a melancholy occupation.

These freemen had certainly been properly entrapped and were cowed and worried, though they shed their historic "rights" overnight like philosophers. Sophists of the school of Bairnsfather! Of course that was a wretched hypocritical philosophy, but in this sudden emergency it was all they had.

I knew that that *anonymity* I have spoken of would have best served their turn. That was the true solution of all the troubles that infested their old kit-bags. Actually discipline was the secret, if they only knew it. But it was a solution that all their traditions would have repudiated.

The faultless bravery of the Japanese is the child of Shinto, of an iron racial culture directed to the confusion of the ego; and of the Barrack Square, at last. But how on earth should these spoiled children of Anglo-Saxon Democracy, who had turned their back upon the disciplines of the Church into the bargain, acquire the notion of a saving *discipline*? Discipline, of all things!—that was the last thing that they could be taught: almost the only thing that reconciled them to military rigors was the thought that they were banded together to destroy forever all discipline in Western Europe.

Yet unquestionably the A.B.C. of their difficulties, of those of any man similarly placed, was to be found in the extinction of self—of the self in order to retain which they were dying in this ridiculous shambles! Naturally there was no one to tell them anything of this, since Democracy with a capital D was ostensibly the threatened principle, and whatever else Democracy may be, it is not a philosophy of the extinction of self or the merging of it in a greater organism. The training of the *Mensur*,[1] or of its proletarian opposite number, was not for these democratic volunteers: no one had ever dreamed of suggesting to such men that they should take a stern and pessimistic view of their destiny and stand and allow the blood to course down their cheeks from a slash received in a sham fight, to harden themselves against inevitable hemorrhage. Theirs were not Samurai backgrounds: they had inherited as great a "respect for human life" as others had cultivated a disrespect for it.

So when the little knife of the doctor with his smallpox serum started to scrape their cuticles, they did an ignominious quit—they just closed their eyes and withdrew in a swoon from all this spectacle of suffering.

But here *was* a new world beginning for this sheltered people and its "free" institutions. They would have to get used to many things that the Nineteenth Century Englishman would not have believed possible. I was present—I dimly recognized—at the passage of an entire people out of one system into another. I could not but, in consequence, discharge my question marks in their bloodless faces, as these men lay there, put out of action so early in the day. And I of course was one of them, in this most awkward of fixes, shoulder to shoulder; I too was being translated from a relaxed system to a far more stringent one: I was experiencing my full share of perplexity at finding myself assisting at the assassination of Democracy: I put just as much value on my

---

[1] ritual duel, test

skin as they did on theirs, I was as exigent on the score of my privileges as an individual; I too was born to Habeas Corpus. I differed from my brothers-in-arms only in a scepticism regarding the reality of this Democracy which had bestowed upon me such a high opinion of my skin, and experienced an inability to accept the theory that I was making the world any more "safe" by my present activities. Everything that I was doing seemed to me to be making it very much the reverse.

There was another way in which we differed, I and my brothers-in-arms: namely, in what fundamentally was my attitude to "militarism." For I was less averse to Mars and all his works than they were. My aristocratic training accounted for this a little I suppose—the Army Class it had been my intention to enter as a schoolboy, my period as a student in Germany, the influence of a peculiarly martial father. The career of arms, at all events, as such, did not scandalize me. Perhaps I had a touch of the Junker, I do not know.

I took no great interest in war: but that was nothing. Who was the king, surely a Teuton, who disliked war, because, he said, it was so bad for the army—undoing in a few weeks what it had taken years of intensive parades to accomplish? How right that king was! If I had had my way we should have militarized ourselves out of all recognition—but never gone to war. Everyone would have been afraid anyway of going to war with such martial looking chaps.

Somewhere Frederick Nietzsche—you may recall the name, he was a Hun philosopher who was a power-maniac, with bristling Polish mustaches—somewhere this Nietzsche describes his emotions of unquestioning response at the spectacle of martial power. A regiment of Prussian horse guards crashed past him, with all their cuirasses, drums and eagles —at the time he was a young doctor, "doing his bit" in the Franco-Prussian War. Though not going so far as that perhaps, for after all I am not a Prussian, nevertheless things military do not outrage me. They do not throw me into pacifist tantrums, or bring to my lips a Huxleyish sneer. If I do not burst into a great mystical *Yea!* on the pattern of that fire-eating Prussian professor, I yet do not fall into the furibund *Nay!* of the Anglosaxon man of Peace (of Collective Peace). Had I been at Rolica in 1808, where the English wore for the last time their pigtails and powder, the smell of guncotton and the stains of rice-powder upon the scarlet tunics would have appeared as natural to me as the nails on our fingers and the battle of our phagocytes in the blood: I should not have examined too closely the "intelligence" of our behavior. Indeed it would never have occurred to me to suppose that it was intelligent: for if I had examined it, I should probably have concluded that since this was an impossibly clumsy and wrong-headed universe, public brawls, in powder and pigtails, were no worse than private brawls, in which words and "mental cruelty" take the place of round-shot and physical violence.

At this training camp in Dorsetshire I behaved in all respects like other Bombardiers. The evenings were passed bombardiering in the public bars, or secret upstairs parlors, of the neighboring port. One of my bottle companions was the sergeant-major to whom I have already had occasion to refer. In the company of this dignitary and that of the "quarter-bloke," I would march down into our seaport most nights after supper to the "house" favored by the S.M. I remember that on one occasion, this having happened as usual, we were almost trapped in a police raid.

Sitting upstairs in the seclusion of a curtained parlor, a pianola pedaling away for us, we sang drunkenly in mawkish ragtime. The "quarter-bloke," his tunic open at the neck, his hair ruffled by the fingers of a pub houri, periodically turned to me, as we sat side by side on the sofa and exclaimed "I say, do you think we shall *win!*" or "I say, what a gime! Eh? *What a gime!*" And I would turn to the sergeant-major and hiss: "I say, Sergeant-Major. Do you think we shall win?" At which the sergeant-major would reply, "I think so, don't *you!*" And I would answer, "I feel we shall. I feel we shall!"

But the S.M. had his rank to think about. He was not a bird to be caught in an ordinary police trap. Springing up, after cocking his ear for a moment, he was out of the door like a startled stoat. "Jump to it. It's the M.P.s! Police!" he called back to us as he disappeared. Not many paces behind him I stumbled out into the pitch-black yard at the rear of the public house, and at once fell headlong over the prostrate bodies of a sailor and one of the daughters of the house. They lay parallel with the door. All the nice girls love a tar—but I cursed and was scrambling to my feet when the quarter-bloke came cannonading over the handyman and his momentary consort, horridly indifferent to the military "busies" blasting their way into the inner premises.

Down I went a second time. When the quarter-bloke and myself emerged in the dark and empty street, the S.M. was half-down it, his cane glued into his armpit, his rather stiff straddle taking him off into safety with commendable celerity. When we caught him up, he looked grave. The threat to his rank had scared and sobered him. Then, hardly recovered from this, when we reached the bridge across the estuary, a searchlight burst out of the street we had just left. The S.M. ordered us to take cover, and we all went over the side of the bridge as one man, and crouched out of sight till the car had passed. It was driven by a soldier and contained officers: good little S.M.'s, as all other ranks short of the starry commissioned one, should have been in bed and asleep. Another narrow squeak for the S.M. crown on his sleeve. We entered the camp as usual, not by the gate where a sentry stood, but by a gap in the hedge. This was the recognized backdoor and invariably used by those out after hours.

After the departure for France of these earliest boon companions I continued to bellow in the field where the recruits were instructed in the elements of infantry drill. Then at last I was told that I had been recommended for a commission and left for the Field Artillery Cadet School at Exeter.

We did not correspond, the S.M. and myself: we were ships that passed in the night. But later on in France I met a member of my original unit. My attachment to this human group was manifested by my meticulous inquiries regarding the fate of its individual members. It was then that I heard that the Sergeant Major had been killed within a fortnight of his arrival at the Front.

It appeared that the S.M. had died giving utterance to a torrent of expletives. The O.C. Battery was the principal target for his dying tirade; for they had been in disagreement regarding the site selected for the battery position, which the S.M. regarded as too exposed. It was the usual battle between the old army, represented by the S.M., and the transmogrified bank manager, the temporary officer and gentleman, who was in command of the unit. The pig-headed incompetence of this little jumped-up amateur had cost the life of a better man than himself, such was the burden of my old friend's swan-song. The ill-conceived position chosen, especially for the dugouts, had accounted for a direct hit being registered with such promptitude upon the sumptous rat-hole of the S.M., which, in spite of all the logs

and sandbags heaped on it under the direction of its occupant, could not withstand an ordinary 5.9, much less an
H.E. or high-explosive shell.

This man was in reality a quartermaster in the old army,
in appearance more like a prosperous tradesman than a
warrior. He was a tall, corpulent man, with a slight stoop.
On more than one occasion he remarked to me: "I can tell
you one thing, *this* child doesn't intend to get killed and
that's that!" An ill-omened boastfulness on the part of this
ill-starred S.M.

The Romance of War

ARRIVAL at "the Front" for us was not unlike arrival at a
big Boxing Match, or at a Blackshirt Rally at Olympia. The
same sinister expectancy, but more sinister and more
electric, the same restless taciturnity of stern-faced persons
assembling for a sensational and bloody event, their hearts
set on a knockout. Somebody else's, of course.

We arrived at railhead at night and a battle was in progress.
For a long time, as we moved slowly forward in our dark-
ened coaches, the sound of guns had been getting louder and
nearer. There was no moon or stars—all lights had been
turned down for the performance. Only the unseen orchestra
thundered away, before an unseen stage. We had to imagine
the actors which we knew were there, crouching in their
sticky labyrinths.

From the crowded carriage windows, at last, sudden bursts
of dull light could be discerned, and last of all an authentic
flash had been visible, but still far away—angry and red, like
a match struck and blown out again immediately.

We left the train, and finally reached, I forget how, the
fringes of this battle. We reached it unexpectedly. We were
collected upon a road, I seem to think. Perhaps we were
waiting for lorries to take us to billets—for we of course
were not going into action then. We were not for this battle.
We had no guns either. They could not be made quickly

enough. We were just the *personnel* of a battery, with no guns, who had come to stand by, or be parceled out as reinforcements.

With great suddenness—as we stood, very impressed as newcomers in the midst of this pandemonium—in a neighboring field a battery of large howitzers began firing. After this particular picture I can remember nothing at all. It is so distinct everything in its neighborhood is obliterated. I can only remember that in the air full of violent sound, very suddenly there was a flash near at hand, followed by further flashes, and I could see the gunners moving about as they loaded again. They appeared to be 11-inch guns—very big. Out of their throats had sprung a dramatic flame, they had roared, they had moved back. You could see them, lighted from their mouths, as they hurled into the air their great projectile, and sank back as they did it. In the middle of the monotonous percussion, which had never slackened for a moment, the tom-toming of interminable artillery, for miles round, going on in the darkness, it was as if someone had exclaimed in your ear, or something you had supposed inanimate had come to life, when the battery whose presence we had not suspected went into action.

So we plunged immediately into the romance of battle. But all henceforth was romance. All this culminated of course in the scenery of the battlefields, like desolate lunar panoramas. That matched the first glimpses of the Pacific, as seen by the earliest circumnavigators.

Need I say that there is nothing so romantic as war? If you are "a romantic," you have not lived if you have not been present at a battle, of that I can assure you.

I am very sorry to have to say this. Only a care for truth compels me to avow it. I am not a romantic—though I perfectly understand romance. And I do not like war. It is under compulsion that I stress the exceedingly romantic character of all the scenes I am about to describe.

If your mind is of a romantic cast, there is nothing for it, I am afraid. The likelihood that you will get your head blown off cannot weigh with you for a moment. You must not miss a war, if one is going! You cannot afford to miss that experience.

It is commonly remarked that "there is no romance in modern war." That is absurd, I am sorry to have to say.

It has frequently been contended that Agincourt, or even Waterloo with its "thin red line" and its Old Guard of

Napoleonic veterans, was "spectacular": whereas modern war is "drab and unromantic." Alas! that is nonsense. To say that is entirely to misunderstand the nature of romance. It is like saying that love can only be romantic when a figure as socially eminent and beautiful as Helen of Troy is involved. That, of course, has nothing to do with it whatever! It is most unfortunate: but men are indifferent to physical beauty or obvious physical splendor, where their emotions are romantically stimulated. Yes, romance is the enemy of beauty. That hag, War, carries it every time over Helen of Troy.

The truth is, of course, that it is not what you *see*, at all, that makes an event romantic to you, but what you *feel*. And in war, as you might expect, you feel with considerable intensity.

The misunderstanding goes even deeper than that, however. Knights in armor, with plumes and lances, are not, even in the visual sense, the most *romantic* subject matter for a romantic painter.

You only have to think a moment: the dark night, with the fearful flashing of a monstrous cannonade—all the things that do not come into the picture, which *are not seen*, in other words, but which are suggested in its darkest shadows— what could be more technically "romantic" than that, if it is romance that we must talk about?

But even if the pictorial subject matter were insignificant, it would still be the same thing.

Romance is partly what you see but it is much more what you feel. I mean that *you* are the romance, far more than the romantic object. By definition, romance is always inside and not outside. It is, as we say, subjective. It is the material of magic. It partakes of the action of a drug.

Place a man upon the highest passes of the Andes, and what he *sees* is always what he feels. But when *on joue sa vie,* [1] it is not so much the grandeur of the spectacle of destruction, or the chivalrous splendor of the appointments, as the agitation in the mental field within, of the organism marked down to be destroyed, that is impressive. It is that that produces "the light that never was on land or sea," which we describe as "romance." *Anything* upon which that coloration falls is at once transfigured. And the source of light is within your own belly.

[1] one stakes one's life

Of course it would be impossible to overstate the contribution of the guns to these great romantic effects. Even in such an essentially romantic context as war, they are startlingly "romantic" accessories, and help to heighten the effect.

It is they who provide the orchestral accompaniment. It is they who plow up the ground till it looks literally "like nothing on earth." It is they who transform a smart little modern township, inside an hour, into a romantic ruin, worthy of the great Robert himself, or of Claude Lorrain. They are likewise the purveyors of "shell shock," that most dramatic of ailments. And lastly, they give the most romantic and spectacular wounds of all—a bullet wound, even a dum-dum, is child's play to a wound inflicted by a shell splinter.

I have slept soundly through scores of full-dress bombardments. It is very few people who don't, in a war of positions, where bombardments are almost continuous. Through a long artillery preparation for an Attack—a hoped-for "breakthrough," with the enemy retaliating at full blast—in the very thick of the hubbub, with things whizzing and roaring all round—I have slept for hours together as peacefully as if I were in a London garden suburb.

Rapidly one ceases to notice this orchestra. But although one forgets about it, one would miss it if it were not there. These are the kettledrums of death that you are hearing. And you would soon know the difference if they stopped.

Howitzers

WE had been hanging about some time, when I was posted to a battery to replace casualties. It was a "six-inch How" battery, not far from Bailleul. My own battery disappeared: later on I joined it, in another part of the Line.

I arrived at the battery mess and made the acquaintance of the other officers. Our "battery position," that is, where the guns were, was only a short distance away from our sleeping quarters and the officers' Mess. There was not a great abundance of dugouts. I was given bed room in the dugout of another junior officer. It was very small but he took me in temporarily. And it was with him that I received what would have been called in the old days of war my baptism of fire. This is how it occurred. It happened straight away, on my first night.

We went to our dugout and got into our respective camp beds. My brother officer was in a very nervous condition I thought, and he unburdened himself to me on the subject of a certain observation post, which was very much on his mind. Twice in the last week he had passed a couple of very unpleasant days in it. "I *dread* going up to that O-Pip do you know—I dread it! It's the most bloody awful death trap. You wait till you see it!" he told me with a commendable frankness, though I believe he could not help himself. And after he had described the sort of health resort it was, I confess that I felt in no hurry to visit it myself. However, he was very exhausted, and soon he turned over to address himself to sleep.

No sooner had he done this, than something unpleasant began to happen. There was the unmistakable sound of a shell, which I then heard for the first time, and the explosion followed, not far away outside our dugout, I took it to be.

"They've started shelling again." he groaned in disgust, moving restlessly in his bed. "This happens every night. They shelled us for an hour the night before last. They've spotted us, I think—they'll never let us alone now."

No sooner had he uttered his complaint, than a second shell came over. As he heard the sound start, of its whooping approach, his bed gave a violent creak. I watched him heel over on one side. As the shell descended—with its strange parabolic whooping onrush—an anal whistle answered it, from the neighboring bed. This response was forced out of him, by unrestrained dismay.

That was my first encounter with "wind-up," as it was my first experience of shelling. In fact, it was the most perfect specimen of wind-up that it would be possible to find I think. And at each successive shell-swoop it was repeated. He raised himself slightly; and he answered the frightening onrush of the cylinder of metal with his humble gaseous discharge. He did not seem to mind at all my seeing this. I suppose he thought I would put it down to indigestion.

After a few shells had come over, we sat up in bed, and he gave me his opinion of the architecture of our dugouts.

I was glad, as it seemed to take his mind off the shells.

"This dugout is a joke!" he told me. "It wouldn't stop an india-rubber ball! These dugouts are washouts."

"Are they?" I said, glancing up with considerable uneasiness at the mud roof a foot or two away from my head.

Like most military novices I had innocently supposed that a dugout—any dugout—was there to keep out shell-fire, and was reasonably secure. I had felt as safe as houses in this earthen igloo. But he rapidly disabused me.

"A five-nine would go through this as if it was paper!" he assured me. "If one of those shells happens to hit this dugout—well, it's all up with us. We should both of us be dead within a second."

As he spoke another shell plunged down outside, very much nearer this time. Indeed it seemed to me that it had come down a few feet off—for at first it is very difficult to judge the distance of a "burst," from the sound, if you do not see it but only hear it.

"That was pretty near wasn't it?" I asked.

"No, they most of them fall in the next field. But it's quite near enough."

"Quite," I said. "Oughtn't we to go out and see what's happening?"

"Nothing's happening," he said. "This goes on all the time. This might stop a splinter. But *a direct hit!* Then we're for it!"

I saw if we went outside we should be inviting a splinter. I supposed the chances of a direct hit were so much less that he was wise to stop where he was.

He went on instructing me in the futility of dugouts, however—especially *our* dugouts. They were champion death traps for unlucky subalterns.

"There's nothing on top here," pointing up over his head, "but a little loose earth. Just a few shovelsful of loose earth and a log or two."

"Is that all?" I muttered indignantly.

"That's all. What's the use of that? There's a piece of corrugated iron."

"Is there?" I asked, looking up with expectation.

"Somewhere I expect. A lot of use *that* is! The sandbags at the side are a foot thick, if that. A shell goes through that like butter. It likes sandbags. Shells like making holes in sandbags."

I tossed up my head, in scandalized silence.

"I don't know why they take the trouble to make them. They're useless. We might just as well be sleeping in a Mission hut. It doesn't even keep the rain out. It drips on my face when it rains."

"I suppose," I said for the sake of something to say, "there is a slight chance. The logs might interfere with the burst."

"Don't you believe it! It would come clean through and burst in our faces. We'd be full of splinters inside a second."

I found subsequently that he was quite correct. As regards the surface dugouts, of sandbags, baulks, and earth, they were useless. Later on I was given a bed chamber of my own. It was a shack of corrugated iron, without any pretentions to being a parabellum. It was even a less desirable residence than the sandbagged one, seeing that it was most conveniently placed upon the edge of a road. And whatever else is shelled or not shelled, a road is *always* shelled. It had a further thing to recommend it, namely its position immediately behind a battery of big heavies. These naturally attracted the enemy fire, apart from the banging that they kept up all night.

As time went on, I found that there was one situation in which I did not at all enjoy finding myself. I did not like to be subjected to indiscriminate shell fire when undressed. Lay me to rest in a flea-bag and I jib at shelling. Most of the shelling was at night. In view of the particular position of my sleeping shack I never knew, when it started, whether it was (1) the road that was being shelled, or (2) the gun in front of me, or (3) our dugouts behind me. Not that it mattered a great deal, from my point of view. But if it was the gun in front, my companions behind would regard it as no business of theirs (though it was of mine—seeing the eclectic nature of my position): whereas if it happened to be *us* who were to be bombarded, then it was our habit (the officers) to collect in the officers' Mess and have a whiskey and a smoke. What the men did was somewhat their own affair.

The men's quarters were big and of course unsafe dugouts. Life in them cannot have been pleasant. In my own battery —which as I have said I joined later—there was a gunner whom I had noticed before we came out to France. He was very "nicely spoken"—much too nicely spoken to be comfortable in such a class-conscious country as England, and seeing that none of the officers were particularly nicely spoken except myself. Later on in France he became the victim of panic. He nursed a shell shock. Huddled at night in the men's quarters, in a position that was constantly shelled, the other men complained that he kept them awake at night by his shivering. They said his tin hat rattled against his dickie all night long. At last he had to be sent back to England.

The disadvantage of these conditions of the siege-gunner's service is obvious. He was always "in the Line," he had no spells of rest "behind the Line." Where he slept, often for a year on end, was in the midst of nests of batteries which were one of the main objectives of the enemy shelling.

Of course my tin house—rather like a suburban garden coal cellar—was a palace in comparison with what I should have got as a gunner. When it had been stuck together, the O.C. remarked casually that it was awkwardly placed. I said that was all right: one place was much the same as another.

When the first shell would come over, I would roll swiftly out of the flea-bag and pull on my trenchboots. That is really all I worried about. I think *the whole* of his feet are man's "Achilles heel." I would hate to face a firing squad in my stocking feet! Clothing and its part in the psychology of war is a neglected subject. I would have braved an eleven-inch shell in my trenchboots, but would have declined an encounter with a pipsqueak in my bare feet.

From my standpoint the worst shelling here was road-shelling, since I was more or less *in* the road. I preferred a bad shelling of the dugouts at my back, when we were assembled in the mess, which was more matey. It doesn't matter a bit if *everybody's* being shelled.

This battery had among its officers—he was I believe second-in-command—an eminent young mathematician. I knew he was a good mathematician because he was unable to do a simple addition sum, and as to the august operations of subtraction and division, they were entirely beyond him.

While I was reading in my flea-bag by the light of a candle one night—it was the *Chartreuse de Parme* I had just begun, and I was for the second time upon the field of Waterloo—down came the shells, and there was no mistake that this time it was *us* they were after. All were going back of my shack. As I made for the mess I came upon the mathematician. Shells were coming over pretty fast, but he had placed himself in as exposed a position as possible, and was watching them narrowly, as they arrived. With a look of eager surprise he was darting his head round as one fell behind him, and back again to the front as one fell ahead. Something was amiss in his calculations, it seemed, and the position of the bursts was profoundly puzzling, if not unsatisfactory. I could not imagine what he was doing. The laws of probability, or something of that sort, were at stake, I deduced. Nature was behaving eccentrically, affronting, perhaps, laws with which I was totally unacquainted. *Something* was undoubtedly wrong; for he ought by all the rules to have been hit by this time, as a shell splinter had nearly hit me, and I had only just arrived.

The mess was a long open dugout, high enough to stand up in, and was reputed to be a *good* dugout; the only good one we had. I don't know why it was supposed to be good, but we were all persuaded that it could be hit by a five-nine with impunity. (The "five-nine" shell was the German equivalent of the six-inch English. And practically all the shelling we had to expect was from the five-nines.)

After a bit the mathematician came slowly in, looking very disquieted, sat down and rolled a cigarette. I did not like to question him, though I saw that the shells had been falling in a very unorthodox sequence; and I longed to ask him why a shell *never* hit the Mess. That was what puzzled *me*. Indeed they never hit a dugout. They made holes all round them, but never got a bull's-eye. But I suppose it is like a game of darts in a pub.

A Day of Attack

IT was a Day of Attack—"somewhere in France," and the O.C. Battery had himself decided to go to an observation post, and observe a bit of what was going forward. He took me with him. It was a reasonably distant one, and we saw what we had come to see without too much interference. We saw the battle: there had been no breakthrough, but a push-back. When it was evident that *something* had happened, and that the new front line would not be where the old front line had been, he turned to me and said:

"Well, that's that. I'm going down there, to find out where the new front line is now. Would you like to come with me?"

I expressed my desire to find myself at the side of my commanding officer.

"We shall have to fix on a new O. Pip."

That, I agreed, would undoubtedly be one of the disagreeable things we should have to do.

"Yes, I think I'll go and see what's happening. Besides, I should like to have a look!"

"I should, too," I answered.

"You're sure you'd like to come? God knows what it's like. There may *be* no Front Line."

"In that case we shan't be able to find it," said I, circumspectly.

"If there's one *there* I'll find it!" said he with great soldierly resolution, as he got up. So we started off, first returning to the battery to explain what we intended to do.

This O.C. was more alive than most—a small commercial gent (perhaps a garage proprietor, I thought, or employee in a Shipping Office) blossomed suddenly into a Major, R.A. Slight in build, about thirty, lightly mustached, he was able and very collected when other people were the reverse. I concluded from what I saw of him that he had set his mind upon taking back a Military Cross to Balham. I was under the impression that he would deserve it, if he could extract it from the donors of such things. Not exactly the man for an unambitious subaltern, more interested in blasting than in bombardiering—and whose most coveted crosses were not military—to go hunting for the Front Line with, in a new No Man's Land, upon a morning of attack!

But I laid it down for myself that two principles should coexist for me, in my conduct of this war game. As a "crowd-master," it was my business not to succumb to the lure of a transitory military laurel: it was on the other hand my business to observe at firsthand all of war's bag-of-tricks. Therefore I allowed myself a pinch of inquisitive pleasure at the prospect of a trip to this problematical place of battle.

Going through the lines of "the Field" the shelling was heavy—though on the whole there was every evidence that the enemy were not replying with their customary aggressiveness. Their artillery was being moved back.

A Field Battery beside which we were making our way was having a rough time, however. There were several casualties while we were passing its guns, but my little O.C. might have been taking a walk with his dog for all the notice he took. Good boy, I thought! He knew his stuff.

But at this point civilization ended. At least so far, we could be sure of our bearings. Beyond this battery was a short stretch of shell-pitted nothingness—for we had entered upon that arid and blistering vacuum; the lunar landscape, so often described in the war novels and represented by dozens of painters and draftsmen, myself among them, but the particular quality of which it is so difficult to convey. Those grinning skeletons in field-gray, the skull still protected by the metal helmet: those festoons of mud-caked wire, those miniature mountain ranges of saffron earth, and trees like gibbets—these were the properties only of those titanic casts of dying and shell-shocked actors, who charged this stage with a romantic electricity.

Picking our way across the first hundred yards of rugged wilderness, we reached a little ridge and stopped. What had we expected to see? Something, at all events. Whereas we gazed out over a solitary and uninhabited steppe. There was nothing. It was entirely empty and silent, except for a slight movement away to our left in the middle distance and the occasional door-banging effect of a shell burst.

The battery behind us clamored, as in duty bound. The thunder of the hammering artillery never stopped at our backs, and for miles on either hand. But before us stretched, terrible in its emptiness, the land we had come to explore.

What we were standing on the edge of was in the nature of a hollow, of cratered nothingness. For it was a hillside, terminating eventually in another ridge, which, with the ridge on which we stood, shut it in, whereas immediately in front of us the ground fell away somewhat. So it was a sort of one-sided valley.

From beyond the opposite ridge came the distant banging of the German artillery. Otherwise this was the most thrilling solitude that the most particular of explorers could have wished for. No valley in a tropical steppe could have been better, from that point of view. The inner fastnesses of the Sahara could not have developed a more inaccessible air of unearthly remoteness. Give this wilderness a palm, and make believe that the artillery outside was some strange mirage effect of desert thunder—an aural in place of an optical phenomenon—and this could have been the bleak center of Africa.

But the O.C. battery pointed a little way ahead of us.

"Our old Front Line," he said.

"Where is our new one?" I asked him, for I knew he wanted me to ask that.

"God knows!" he answered. "Let's see if we can find it. There's a barrage on that ridge. It's somewhere there I expect."

Some distance to our right, upon the skyline, there was a succession of shell bursts. That would doubtless be it.

For some time we stumbled and leaped, advancing into this extremely debatable ruin of what was until an hour or two before an underground fortress, under a rain of shells. We crossed what had been our own Front Line and entered the German. It was profusely lined with fresh corpses. We picked our way amid scores of green-clad bodies. Newspapers in Gothic type were a feature of this scene, and I put one into my pocket, to see what Berlin said about these events.

We got out of this—I hated all these bodies, but put that impression away, to be pondered at a later time—and were hurrying forward when my companion dropped into a trench with the suddenness of a collapsing Jack-in-the-box. Simultaneously I heard a sharp tap-tapping—unfamiliar then, but I guessed its import: and I dropped too, with a creditable celerity.

"Machine guns," he said, as we hurried along—keeping for some time now to the trenches. "They've left machine-gun posts I expect, or perhaps redoubts. They always do that. I doubt if we've got a proper line yet."

We continued our breathless and sweaty tramp, always along the abandoned German trench system, bearing to our right all the time. We were moving over till we got before the line of bursts upon the ridge, a matter of a quarter of a mile. At last my leader stopped. He mopped his brow, and I mopped mine. Then we came once more to the surface and looked round. No machine gun chattered at us this time. We were at the foot of the gradient which led up to the line of bursts.

Now we were in the heart of this sinister little desert. Despite the angry hammering from the world of batteries we had left, and that from the world of batteries whose frontiers lay not so far ahead, but still not near enough to sound very loud—in spite of that agitated framework to our "mystery land," nothing could have been more solitary. I should not have been surprised to see an Atlas vulture or some desiccated African goat. For it was definitely a red desert, more African than lunar in appearance.

Most of the explorers who have trod those deserts have either left their bones there, or if they have come back to tell the tale, never have told it. For in restrospect they mostly have believed that they must have been dreaming. But a new war is probably near at hand. A new generation will be setting out for that Never-never Land. So it is that these dreams become topical, alas!

To make a reconstruction of this landscape for a millionaire sightseer, say, would be impossible. The sightseer would be the difficulty—for the reasons I have given already in my dissection of romance. This is a museum of sensations, not a collection of objects. For your reconstruction you would have to admit Death there as well, and he would never put in an appearance, upon those terms. You would have to line the trenches with bodies guaranteed freshly killed that morning. No hospital could provide it. And unless people were mad they would not want—apart from the cost—to assemble the necessary ordnance, the engines required for this stunt of landscape gardening.—Except that they were mad, they would not have wanted ever to assemble it.

To obtain this parched, hollow, breathless desert you have to postulate madmen.—It was the hollow center of a madman's dream we had got into. As our feet struck the ground they seemed to be echoing faintly from end to end of this mysterious place of death.

Two men were brewing an inky coffee over a brazier— I have always regarded it as an odd occupation. They half-sat, half-crouched, behind a fragment of wall—a wall borrowed from that other system of domestic peace to be a stunted property of this inferno. The barrage began a few yards away from their blackened nook.

They were the only human beings we had encountered so far. In an exhausted lassitude they attended to their brazier. We had reached the summit of the incline. Along this crest or ridge went a road, terminating in this fragment of wall, behind which we now stood. For fifty yards the road was visible and every inch of it was being shelled.

There was no regular front line yet, the two men thought. There were Germans just the other side of the crest, or they thought there were. They'd heard a machine gun just now but to whom it belonged they didn't know. Meanwhile

Battalion Headquarters was a wee bit along the road. Yes, where that shell was bursting.

"I'm going to Battalion Headquarters," said the O.C. pointing toward the shell burst, but every two seconds others were coming down in between. "You stop here."

I obeyed. There was nothing I wanted this dark game could give, but my O.C. had his plans. He was not a romantic person. What he did was methodic and in pursuance I am sure of business—plus patriotism, that is understood. Every step of that walk he took was a gamble with death, and he was a hardy gambler to whom I wished luck.

I call it a walk, but it was quite different to a walk. No sooner had he stepped on what was left of the road, than a shell rushed at him, and only just in time he flung himself upon his face. He got another two or three yards at most, and down crashed two more; and down he went for the count. But he was only lying low and resting. I would see his alert little figure rise from the dust of one shell burst, step briskly along and disappear in the spouting of the next. At last with a rush he made what was apparently the entrance to the subterranean headquarters of some invisible battalion.

He stayed down there a while. I sat drowsily nodding in the lee of the fragment of wall, only half-conscious of the whooping and thumping of the shells. The two men and myself became a waxwork trio in this wilderness. I suppose they continued to brew their infernal chicory, at my back. Suddenly I became aware of the imminence of my commanding officer's return. I stood up and after a half-dozen imperative prostrations, and as many headlong rushes, there he was before me, as cool and collected as ever, pointing back over his shoulder.

"As soon as they've got the front line fixed, there's an old German dugout there," he pointed to the roadside, between us and the Battalion Headquarters, "which would make an excellent O. Pip. I'll come up tomorrow again with some signalers—there may be something better, but if not that will do."

Our return journey was less peaceful. More German batteries were firing now, and a number of shells intercepted us. We met an infantry party coming up, about ten men, with earthen faces and heads bowed, their eyes turned inward as it seemed, to shut out this too-familiar scene. As a shell came rushing down beside them, they did not notice it. There was no sidestepping death if this was where you *lived*. It was worth *our* while to prostrate ourselves, when death came overnear. We might escape, *in spite* of death. But *they* were its servants. Death would not tolerate that optimistic obeisance from them!

I heard that our commanding officer got into hot water about this expedition. He sent reports in at once, but they were ill-received. Artillery officers going down before the Front Line was organized—what next! What, to select observation posts before the "mopping-up" was over—before anyone knew where we were going to be, or where the Germans were going to be! Preposterous! Supposing, sir, you had run into a German counterattack! What then, sir!

One can imagine the dudgeon of the staff, at so much officious zeal, the true motives of which they would not be slow to detect.

Whether my O.C. got his M.C. in the end or not I do not know. He was a man it would be difficult to stop. He would probably have contrived to have me hit, and have carried me into the nearest approach to a front line he could find, if the two coffee makers had not been there.— But I daresay they gave him an M.C. anyway, just to keep him quiet.

Passschendaele

THE center of "the Salient" was where my battery next found itself. The Salient was the bulge, of course, round the romantic ruin of the town of Ypres. No Norman Keep in ivy-clad decay was ever so romantic as Ypres, literally swarming with ghosts even at high noon (in the moonlight you could not tell which were the quick and which the dead) and looking as if Time, that does not hurry when making a ruin as a rule, had telescoped itself to make this one, Death having lent it a hand.

The famous Salient was a *stupid* bulge, but one of which

the high command were inordinately proud; not because it was of any strategic importance, but because a great many men had been killed in its creation. It is obvious why a "salient" is an unsatisfactory place for the men who are in it. They can be shelled from three sides, more or less, instead of one. But this Salient was sacrosanct. It was *the* Salient. It was as great as it was costly as a feat of arms, to hold it. So it was kept intact, as a monument of "doggedness." At the time I thought it was stupid to have a salient. Since I have found it was even more stupid than I had suspected.

Our forward position was up the Menin Road, to the east of it. It was not far from yet another "Hellfire Corner," but we could not see this one as there was a rise in the ground that interrupted the view. All day long, however, we could observe the shambles on the Menin Road itself (the shouting for stretchers just reached us at our guns) which was chockablock at all times with A.S.C. and Anzac transport, ambulances and the rest of it.

The big Australian drivers, on their high seats, idly cracking their whips, moved up it at a leisurely pace, like characters of Callot's—again incredibly romantic, grandiose and scarecrow figures from another age: or out of a contemporary print, depicting the prairie wagons of indolent pioneers, pushing on lackadaisically into the Never-never, or the Back-of-Beyond. They displayed a superb indifference to the rushing deliveries of the mechanical war god. For shell after shell pounded down without intermission upon this central artery of the battlefront. But these great sunburned plainsmen refused to recognize the machine age as in being—as any more than a thunderstorm, if as bad as that, for at least it was not *wet*. Its crashing shells were just particularly troublesome thunderbolts. They were in greater number, certainly, than were usually seen. That was all.—But for them the power involved still was *nature*. These children of nature imparted an air of natural happening, of an elemental disturbance, to all the mechanical "planning" of our latterday Clausewitzes upon the other side of the Line, and their understudies on our side of it.

But the Anzacs turned the field of battle itself into a less sinister locality, with their open-air habits and free and easy ways. I have seen them walking about after an attack in the empty space behind the Front Line, as unconcernedly as if they had been out duck shooting—potting the German airmen as they came over, contemptuous of the retaliatory barrage, while we, with more discretion, remained down in the captured trenches. They could not be prevented from doing that, although the relations between the officers and men was such that there was no question of interfering with this sport.

These colonial habits, however, invaded our dull battery, in the person of a spirited overseas officer. We had attached to us a lot of West Indian negroes, principally for purposes of shell humping. In command of them came to us one Kamper, if I remember, from Jamaica. If Kamper was asleep in his dugout, his black servant had the strictest orders to wake him, at the first sign of a German plane. Out he would rush, revolver in hand, spring on top of his dugout and empty his weapon into the air, waggling it about in the hope that one bullet, at least, would find its mark.

The great open spaces of Jamaica seemed to make him feel about these bogus birds much as it made his rugged colleagues from the Australian steppe. Fond as he was of his siesta—however much he might be lapped in a Caribbean calm within his fleabag, he would not miss Richtofen for anything. For he was persuaded it was Richtofen he was settling accounts with when he came flying out of his musty, rat-infested lair, his red hair tumbling over his face.

Nestling at the side of Ypres itself was our place of rest and relaxation, for we had one here at last. It was then that I made my only attempt to live undangerously and to furnish a little.

I was allotted a sandbag dugout (6 feet by 4) by the side of a battered rivulet. My clay room was upon its bank. My batman installed a shelf upon which I stood my dozen volumes in an orderly rank. All was set for a little picnic of the mind in this cell of a booted anchorite. "The wilderness were paradise enow," though I had no book of verses with me, but *Das Kapital* which was probably more suitable under the circumstances.

It was a smiling day when I moved in. But that night when I went to it I was promptly apprised as to what was to be the fly in this ointment. For making ready to follow Proudhon over into the pages of Karl Marx, his great opponent (and later, I found, mine) it became painfully apparent that the brook at night was stiff with pertinacious mosquitoes.

My light had to be put out immediately; my sleep was intermittent and my disappointment knew no bounds.

With a few quiet bombs dropping in the ruins of Ypres, and an occasional shell in the dump at our back, I should have made a pretty picture, burning the midnight oil, above my battered rivulet. As it was I was bitten to pieces and Karl Marx had to wait. I preferred sleeping at the battery position, though that was nightly plastered with high explosive. I would infinitely rather have had my garden coal cellar, allotted me in my first battery, where I got my trench fever, but had no malarial insects.

The climax of the war was approaching. Or rather our high command were meditating the conversion of the Salient into something still more magnificent—a *real* bulge, namely, indefinitely elastic. The Germans of course could read their thoughts like a book. And the Germans were explaining to them, as best they could, that this was *quite out of the question*. They did their best to show them that it was quite difficult enough to stop where they were, and that it was wholely unfeasible to wade forward through the bog that lay between us and our enemies, and so on to Berlin.

The Front Line and a half-mile behind had become a first class quagmire. The irrigation which normally, in these Low Countries, drains off the water, had for a long time not been practiced; and meanwhile every few yards shells had splashed down into the water, and mixed it and the earth into a sea of mud.

This great bog was traversed everywhere with duckboard tracks—otherwise gangways of wood, for people to walk in Indian file. Off the duckboard track, more often than not, conditions were frankly aquatic.

The preparations for Passchendaele were a poem in mud cum blood-and-thunder. The appetite of the Teuton for this odd game called war—in which a dum-dum bullet is a foul, but a gas bomb is O.K.—and British "doggedness" in the gentle art of "muddling through," when other nations misunderstand British kindliness and get tough, made a perfect combination. If the Germans and the English had not been there, all the others would long before that have run away and the war been over.

These two contrasted but as it were complementary types of *idée fixe* [1] found their most perfect expression on the

---

[1] fixed idea

battlefield, or battle-bog, of Passchendaele. The very name, with its suggestion of *splashiness* and of *passion* at once, was subtly appropriate. This nonsense could not have come to its full flower at any other place but at *Passchendaele*. It was preordained. The moment I saw the name on the trench map, intuitively I knew what was going to happen.

On the coast we had no O.Pip work, but now all the time one or other of us were going up to the front line with our parties of signalers. As I have said, I had not the slightest idea what was occurring, and since that time I have never cared to go back and investigate according to what logical system I was moved about upon this muddy board. There were "zero hours," for which we waited with our eyes on our wristwatches, there were days of attack, or rehearsals for attack, practice barrages, sudden alarms and excursions, which died down ten minutes after the first flare-up. I cannot tell you what any of these things were.

All that I know is that I moved hither and thither over this sea of mud and have since been told that it was a fool who was moving me. However, had it been the greatest Captain in the world it would have been all one to me. I am not interested in Great Captains. "Everything bores me except the philosophic man." There is for me no good war (*la bonne guerre*) and bad war. There is only *bad* war.

Ours, then, was an epic of mud. Mud was even one of our weapons—an alternative weapon. Once when two of the negroes had started a razor fight it devolved upon me to stop it. So to start with I seized them respectively by the shirt collar and opening my arms abruptly, as you open a pair of scissors, I flung them apart. One drooped to the right of me, one to the left of me: but only for a moment. I supposed I had ended hostilities: but then simultaneously each of them scooped up a handful of mud and discharged it across my face at his antagonist. And soon we were all three covered in liquid clay. Kamper appeared—revolver in hand—however, and as if by magic the two Blacks vanished and I found myself alone, straddling like a statue of clay, with only a razor at my feet to testify to the fact that I had not been dreaming!

I never got the right touch with the West Indian negro. At our Nieuport position one dark night the negroes were rolling shells up to the guns—very large ones, since the guns were outsize. This operation had to be effected without so much as a match struck, lest the German air patrols should spot us. A negro sergeant I noticed was not only stationary, and peculiarly idle, but actually obstructing the work of the dusky rollers. I spoke to him. He neither looked at me nor answered. I could scarcely see him—it was very dark, and he was very dark. I ordered him to do a little rolling. This was *a word of command*. It elicited no response from the dark shape. Whereupon I gave him a violent push. This propelled him through space for a short distance, but he immediately returned to where he had stood before. I gave him a second push. As if made of india rubber, he once more reintegrated the spot he had just left. After this I accepted him as a part of the landscape, and the shells had to be rolled round him, since they could not be rolled *through* him.

The "O. Pip" on the Ridge

I have often referred to O.Pips, or observation posts. Here are a few typical experiences of that type of amusement.— When I had to go up to the observation post I had to be woken—no easy matter: that was the first step. Upon this occasion, as usual the signaler N.C.O. woke me. It was the early hours of the morning and I cursed him. I had been sleeping in a stretcher upon the ground; the stretcher was two inches under water, so I had been slumbering in a bath. My underside was submerged. I flung off the heaviest sleep I have ever been stupefied with, which is saying a lot, for I sleep like a log. It must have been the effort required to sleep half under water.—I rose dripping to my feet and put on my tin hat. Then I drank a cup of tea and ate a biscuit.

It was an attack of sorts, infantry were moving up in the night, and it was important to do as much of the journey as possible before daybreak. We were late in starting. The O.Pip was a mile or two along the Line to our left. We crossed the Menin Road, and shortly afterwards, as the day was breaking, we found numbers of infantry held up beside the road we were to follow. A barrage had suddenly come down a short way ahead.

A couple of dozen yards from the road there were some empty dugouts, on a slight elevation, and I took my party there to wait. As I stood in the opening of a derelict Mess, my men inside, expecting nothing untoward, and still half-asleep, a shell whooped down at me. It was at *me* it undoubtedly had been aimed. It exploded two feet from my head, the top of the dugout wall was between my head and the burst. Without its crashing into your head, you could not be nearer to a shell than that, and I banged against the side of the opening and was then carried forward in a stampede of my trusty followers from within. We hastened away from this unfortunately chosen shelter, but the German battery meant business. We had to crouch as we ran, to allow the passage over our backs of the buzzing shell splinters from a series of five-nines.

Having rejoined the infantry, more time went by, people coming back reporting the continuance of the barrage. Therefore we set out to see if we could not walk round it, or find a way through it farther down.

Upon a duckboard track as we tramped forward, we came upon two Scottish privates; one was beheaded, and the leg of another lay near him, and this one's arm was gone as well. They had been killed that morning—a direct hit I suppose: the Scottish battalion to which they belonged having lost a number of men, I later heard, on the way up.

As we approached them my party left the duckboards and passed round the flank of this almost sardonically complete tableau of violent death. Averting their heads, the men circled round. Their attitude was that of dogs when they are offered some food which they don't much like the look of. But a moment later when a shell passed over us, to burst a fairish distance away, my party bowed itself, as it advanced, as if to avoid a blow, though ordinarily such shelling would have been disregarded.

We encountered the barrage, but negotiated it without mishap. Everywhere the enemy was bustling and aggressive however, and the entire front was in an uproar. At length we came out upon the last stretch, the empty approaches to the Front Line, and there to our great indignation were machine-gunned by a low-flying plane.

It was the first time any of us had met with this particular type of aeronautical caddishness. I even didn't know they could do it. I was intensely surprised. Now, of course, airmen think nothing of picking off shoppers in the streets of a city, or whisking past a window and spraying a woman with bullets in her bath. It is recognized as one of the most triumphant assertions of man's mastery over his biped handicap. And we're all very proud to think that our airmen can retaliate and pick off bipeds of discordant nationality. But at the time we all felt it was an uncalled-for interloping to say the least of it, on the part of a particularly vindictive type of flying Bosche.

In spite of the unexpectedness of this occurrence, we saw at once that this low-flying plane was upon some ungentlemanly errand. Of course it was a Bosche—no English plane was ever so near the Line as this. We sank into a shell hole with the rapidity of a well-drilled Music-hall troupe (dresses by Bairnsfather). "Don't show your faces!" said the corporal. I watched from under the peak of my cap the two men who were staring down at us as they approached, but we were not hit, only scandalized. With their staccato snapping superimposed on the roar of their engine, they went over our heads. But an infantry party going up the Line, the only other thing in sight, they successfully attacked, accounting for three of them, it seemed.

I forget the order of these events, but I believe this was the Broudsind Ridge period, preparatory to Passchendaele. Everything was perfectly vacant and quiet just here: it was the vacuum immediately behind the Line—a No Man's Land that had been left behind, and so was more No Man's Land than ever.

Upon the crest of the ridge ahead was our observation post. We had no difficulty whatever in locating it. No one, in fact, could miss it. For it had a cluster of shellbursts around it, rather as a mountain peak is crowned or ringed with cloud.

We were not far off the ridge when I was considerably startled by the sudden emergence from a trench of a dramatically perspiring Brigadier. He advanced toward me in a somewhat minatory fashion. Generals in such places as that were unusual. I saluted and he thrust out his finger, pointing at the crest of the ridge.

"You know the enemy is over there?" he asked me sternly.

"Yes sir," I answered humbly.

"You know you are under machine-gun fire as soon as you get to the top?"

I answered that I did—that I had been here before.

To satisfy this general officer I got my party into a trench, and we circuitously approached the tumultuous spot which it would be our task for the rest of the day to occupy. It was one thing to get to it, another matter to enter it. We were a suicide club, I and my signalers (at least that was my attitude). And having got within hailing distance of it, we halted. When we got into it we should merely be wasting our time. So we might as well humor the Brigadier, and watch our step. I lighted my pipe, and discussed the incidence of the bursts with the corporal.

The danger from machine-gun fire the Brigadier exaggerated. But that factor had to be taken into account in this last stage of the proceedings. The main thing, however, was to judge one's moment properly, with regard to the shellfire. Most of the shells went slightly beyond, sometimes they would lengthen, and there were periods when they eased off, though they never stopped entirely.

We waited about ten minutes in a trench, then I gave the signal and we rushed at it heads down. I was last in and just yanked my tail into the funk hole as a shell came down in the trench behind.

This observation post was the regulation German "pill box." There was room inside it for all of us. You may represent it to yourself as a monstrous Easter egg, its shell of four foot thick concrete, sunk in the earth. Its domed top protruded slightly above the level of the parapet, covered with a thick coat of caked oil. It was entered from a trench; and as it had been a German pill box in the first instance, its entrance faced the enemy. It was from this trench at its mouth that the "observing" had to be done, either by periscope or otherwise.

There were five of us, myself, the signaler corporal, and three signalers. We crowded down into it puffing and laughing. There was no floor, this was its only drawback; a miniature sheet of water was where there should have been. But this dark expanse of water—perhaps four feet across—had as it were a bank. It was on this shelf of clay that we sat or stood.

When we were not there our O.Pip was the home of a family of rats. They did not, however, leave it when we entered, but sensibly accepted our intrusion. They frequently were to be seen swimming in the water, and we would throw them pieces of cheese, when these rodents would indulge in a little fierce polo. The shells thudded upon the roof of this excellent concrete egg, and we, in our moments of relaxation, or when the shelling was so severe that it had driven us inside, fed the rats and smoked.

The German front-line trench was almost immediately beneath us—the two front lines were so close together here that we could almost look into it. It was very thinly held at this time. I sometimes thought there were no Germans there at all.

On another occasion I was in this observation post when a great barrage was laid upon the German trenches. A Field Artillery officer was up there with me and we waited down in the trench for the barrage zero hour. We got up just before the storm broke. Then, to the second, there was the muffled crash of massed artillery, and over came the barrage —every type of projectile, groaning, panting, bumbling, whistling and wheezing overhead. Down they plunged upon the German trench, a chain of every type of burst, and a screen of smoke and earth defined, as far as one could see on either hand, the German Line.

As we stood watching—there was no occasion to consider exposing ourselves to enemy fire, with such a tornado as this absorbing all his attention—the other officer clutched my arm and pointed his finger. "See that!" he said. I looked where he pointed, and saw something dark fly into the air, in the midst of the smoke. My companion said it was the leg of a Bosche, but I thought, though it looked rather like a boot and half a thigh, that it was in fact some less sensational object. It may all the same have been a German limb: and if so it was probably my strong feeling that there were no Germans there that made me incredulous.—Also I did not care whether it was a leg or not, there is always that.

It was from this observation post that I "registered" batteries upon the last vestiges of a village: and as I have said elsewhere, experienced a certain satisfaction at the thought that it was reputed to be empty. "Registering" merely means that a conventional point is selected on the map, and one or more batteries begins firing at it. You, through your field glasses—up in your observation post—observe the "burst." You telephone back to them (by field telephone) to "shorten" or "lengthen," according to whether the shell fell beyond, or short of, the object aimed at. (Same procedure, of course, if it is wireless instead of telephone.) This is called "bracketting." This conventional object, will be, of course, the *point d'appui* [1] for their other calculations, once they have hit it a time or two.

On this particular day little observation work could be done because the wires were incessantly being cut by the enemy fire, which was very heavy. The attack had not materialized—if it was to have been an attack—but the enemy were in a very irritable mood. No sooner would I get through to the battery, than bang the line would go—no more messages would come through. It was then the very disagreeable task of the signalers to go and follow the line back and mend it where it was broken.

That evening we evacuated our pillbox under a perfect fusillade of shells. I lost my pipe as we went steeplechasing in and out of trenches. In the distance I turned to look back at this obnoxious death trap, as one turns to look back at a mountain whose top one has just visited, once one is down below. The sunset had turned on its romantic dream light and what had been romantic enough before was now absolutely operatic. A darkening ridge, above a drift of saharan steppe, gouged and tossed into a monotonous disorder, in a word the war wilderness; not a flicker of life, not even a ration party—not even a skeleton: and upon the ridge the congeries of "bursts," to mark the spot where we had been. It was like the twitching of a chicken after its head has been chopped off. We turned away from this brainless bustle, going on all by itself, about an empty concrete Easter egg, in a stupid desert.

1 point of support

PART III

art in
transition

In 1919, Wyndham Lewis published a booklet entitled *The Caliph's Design: Architects! Where Is Your Vortex?*, which he later described as a painter's random notes. They are introduced by a parable: A Caliph commands his "most ingenious" architect and engineer to draw up the plans for a new and beautiful city. They are given one night to do so; if they fail, their heads will fall. Promptly, the next morning, the plans are ready.

The selections from this booklet reflect the then current feeling in avant-garde circles that the world should and could be entirely remade with the new techniques of modern art. The ugliness of the modern environment might in a curious and perverse way be stimulating to the artist, Lewis conceded, but for the ordinary man, who lives naively through his senses, it could only be productive of a soul-destroying vulgarity and deadness. Therefore, for the general social good, the artist must give up his tawdry toys and cooperate with the architect in building a more beautiful world.

Lewis' analysis of the inner motives of much of avant-garde art still has relevance today, when supposedly "new" movements such as "Pop Art" are founded on just the notions that Lewis ridiculed and exposed so many years ago. In this booklet we also see Lewis making his first attempts to come to terms with a major problem: the machine and its effects on life and art.

The next essay, "The Objective of Art In Our Time," appeared in the book, *Wyndham Lewis, the Artist*, published in 1939, and it presents perhaps the most thorough exposition of Lewis' theoretical approach to aesthetics and the plastic arts.

from THE CALIPH'S DESIGN

The Bull Sounds

WE are all agreed as to the deplorable nature of the form-content and color-content around us. But there agreement ceases.

What would Flaubert have done had France not bred Bouvards and Pécuchets with rabbit-like fecundity? Can nature ever be thanked enough for Sir Sampson Legend, Mantalini, Boswell's Johnson, Falstaff or any such types of Comedy, composed of the nastiest excrement and washiest imbecilities? No one would diminish by one ounce the meat of art that resides in folly or deformity; or see snobbery, gluttony or cruelty reduced by one single exemplaire, once his mind was fixed on the benefits that the aesthetic sense has received from their abundance in Nature!

A less self-indulgent satirist like Aristophanes, it is true, will attach a stink or some disgusting attribute to his absurd character, relying on the squeamishness of his audience, sending his characters about like skunks. But most authors are not so moral as to poison our pleasure with these gases. A stupid form is for the painter the same food as a stupid man for a writer like Gogol or Flaubert.

So it is very debatable whether without the stimulation of stupidity, or every bestial, ill-made, tasteless object that abounds in life today, the artist would be as well off and well nourished. Would he not be in the position of a satirist, like Flaubert, without a Bouvard, or of an artist like Boswell without his rich and very unusual dish? The irritation with the particular French folly that surrounded him, and that Flaubert ate every day as regularly as his breakfast; the consequent pessimism that became the favorite manure for his thoughts; we cannot see Flaubert without that, any more than we can conceive of Rousseau the Douanier without his squab little bourgeois, and blank, paunchy little villas.

The point rather lies in the *attitude* that was Flaubert's and that was the Douanier's. Flaubert hated Bouvard, and considered the vulgarity and idiocy that he witnessed a very sad and improper affair. The Douanier, on the other hand, probably admired his Bouvards very much. It was with a naively respectful eye, it may be assumed, that he surveyed the bourgeois on Sunday, and noted his peculiarities like a child, directly, without judging.

Shakespeare, it is true, must have relished the absurd or deformed more consciously; and Dickens made a cult of it. But with Shakespeare it was against a vast background of other matter, and as comic relief, or used in farces, and so labeled. It has never amounted to what has practically become, in our day, a *rejection* of anything as dull or useless unless it lends itself to our appetite for the comic or the "queer."

But Wilde's antithetic glitter, when used in journalism, may become the most wearisome thing on earth. We long, confronted by such a monotony of inversion as we get in Mr. G. K. Chesterton, for instance, for a plain "dull" statement. In the same way, if the villainous stupidity that has always been around every man since the world began (only he has belabored it with one hand while caressing it with the other) became something like the religion of the educated—such education, that is, as enabled you to enjoy it— and its pursuit and enjoyment the one topic and habit of life, should we not sigh for the old variety; the hero, the villain, the lovely lady and the Comic Relief? Should we not also, if embedded in some bric-a-brac of stuffed birds and wax flowers, and the languors of the "aesthetic period" of the article I cite later in this pamphlet, look toward Karnak, a plain French provincial town, or almost anywhere—with eyes of longing?

Surely all this sensibility of the "queer," the "amusing," the divinely ugly, the exquisitely vulgar, will date, and date very quickly.

There would today, in the "modern" section of the art

world, be as great an outcry if some philistine proposed that the lovely embellishments of our streets, colored signs, posters, beautiful police stations and bewitching tiled Tube stations should be pulled down, as there would have been formerly, and is still by the "beauty-loving public," when some "picturesque old bit" or decaying cottage is removed.

But, with men trying their hardest to eliminate ugliness, injustice, imbecility and so forth from the world, has there ever been any absence of these commodities for the sweet, or bitter, tooth of the artist? Is there ever likely to be? It is true that the artist can gorge himself today probably as never before. But is that the best thing for his talent?

If twenty Christs charged abreast anywhere in the world, you would still get in a remarkably short time, and within a half-hour's walk of their supercalvary, some such monument as the First Pyramid, the result of such a block of egotism as had never been seen before, to show you the weakness of the humane corrective. But I do not believe you would ever get a pyramid builder without Christian hysteria.

Even in order to appreciate the "banal" you must not have too much of it. And you must *pretend* you do not like it even if you are incapable of liking anything else. The reactionary Prussian theorists of war—good, beneficent war— tyranny, and so forth were less useful than the Pacifist, and less intelligent.

The arrangement seems to be that you spend half your time destroying the cheap, the foolish, the repellent; and the other half enjoying what is left over after your efforts! This evidently being how we are intended to live, there is no excuse for slackness in the carrying out of your unpleasant duty: that is to desire equity, mansuetude, in human relations, fight against violence, and work for formal beauty, significance and so forth, in the arrangement and aspect of life.

But to conclude. The great line, the creative line; the fine, exultant mass; the gaiety that snaps and clacks like a fine gut string; the sweep of great tragedy; the immense, the simple satisfaction of the surest, the completest art, you could not get if you succeeded in eliminating passion; nor if you crowned imbecility, or made an idol of the weak.

Whereas you can always get enough silliness, meaningless form, vulgar flavor to satisfy the most gargantuan or the most exquisite appetite.

The Politician's Apathy

WHAT is this ugliness, banality, and squalor to which we have been referring? It is simply what meets your eye as it travels up practically any street in London today, or wanders around any Hotel lounge or Restaurant, or delects itself along the wall of the official galleries at Burlington House. Next, what influences go to the making of this horrible form-content and color-content that we can either offer up a prayer of thankfulness for, take no notice of, or occupy ourselves with modifying, in our spare time? Exactly what set of circumstances, what lassitude or energy of mind working through millions of channels and multitudes of people, make the designs on match boxes (or the jokes on the back of some), the ornamental metal-work on the lamp posts, gates, knife handles, sepulchral enclosures, serviette rings, most posters, ornamented Menu cards, the scenery in our Musical spectacles, chapter headings and tailpieces, brooches, bangles, embossments on watches, clocks, carving knives, cruets, pendants in Asprey's, in Dobson's, in Hancock's windows in Bond Street; in fact, every stitch and scrap of art work that indefatigably spreads its blight all over a modern city, invading every nook, befouling the loveliest necks, waists, ears, and bosoms; defiling even the doormat—climbing up, even, and making absurd and vapid the chimney pot, which you would have thought was inaccessible and out of sight enough for Art not to reach; for the cheap modern thousand-headed devil of design not to find it worthwhile to spoil?

We are all perfectly agreed, are we not, that practically any house, railing, monument, wall, structure, thoroughfare, or lamp post in this city should be instantly pulled down, were it not for the "amusement" and stimulus that the painter gets out of it?

A complete reform (were it not for the needs of the painter who *must* have his bit of banality, bless his little heart!) of every notion or lack of notion on the significance of the appearance of the world should be instituted. A gusto, a consciousness should imbue the placing and the shaping of every brick. A central spectacle, as a street like Regent Street is, should be worked out in the smallest detail. It should not grow like a weed, without forethought, meaning, or any agency but the drifting and accident of commerce. A great thoroughfare like Regent Street develops and sluggishly gets on its ill-articulated legs, and blankly looks at us with its silly face. There are Bouvards and Pécuchets in brick and stone, or just dull cheerless photographs. There is no beautiful or significant relief, even, in this third-rate comic spectacle.

Do politicians understand so little the influence of the Scene of Life, or the effect of Nature, that they can be so indifferent to the capital of a wealthy and powerful community? Would not a more imaginative Cecil Rhodes have seen that the only way an Empire such as he imagined could impress itself on the consciousness of a people would be in some such way as all ambitious nations have taken to make the individual citizen aware of his privileges and his burden? Whether in the weight of a Rhetoric of buildings, or in the subtler ways of beauty signifying the delights and rewards of success won by toil and adventure; in a thousand ways the imagination of the multitude could be captured and fixed. But beyond the obvious policy of *not* having a mean and indolent surrounding for the capital of what sets out to be an "Empire," simply for human life at all, or what sets out to be human life—*to increase gusto and belief in that life*—it is of the first importance that the senses should be directed into such channels, appealed to in such ways, that this state of mind of relish, fullness and exultation should obtain.

It is life at which you must aim. Life, full life, is lived through the fancy, the senses, consciousness. These things must be stimulated and not depressed. The streets of a modern city are depressing. They are so aimless and so weak in their lines and their masses, that the mind and senses jog on their way like passengers in a train with blinds down in an overcrowded carriage.

This is worse, again, for the crowd than the luckier individual. The life of the crowd, of the common or garden man, is exterior. He can only live through others, outside himself. He, in a sense, *is* the houses, the railings, the bunting or absence of bunting. His beauty and justification is in a superficial exterior life. His health is there. He dwindles and grows restless, sick and troublesome when not given these opportunities to live and enjoy in the simple, communal crowd manner. He has just sense enough to know that he is living or not living. Give him a fine, well-fed type of life, a bit dashing and swanky, suitably clothed, with a glamor of adventure about it, to look at, and he is gladdened, if his own stomach is not too empty. Give him fine processions, and holidays, military display. Yes, but there is something you are going to omit. By the deepest paradox he knows that the plaster objects stuck up in Oxford Street outside Selfridges for Peace Day are not a symbol of anything but commerce; in which he equally, though not so successfully, is engaged himself. There is nothing there that he could not do himself, and they do not reach his imagination. Similarly, it is not such a tremendous critical flight as you would imagine for him to connect in some subtle way in his mind these banal plaster statues with the more careful but even more effusively mean Albert Memorial, or any other monument that meets his eye. Yet these he knows are the monuments that typify the society of which he is a unit. This putrid dullness, hopeless deadly stare of almost imbecile stupidity, that he is confronted with in the art offerings from those above, as in their persons, can hardly be expected to stimulate him, either to buoyancy, obedience, or anything but boredom.

So if there are a hundred reasons why Painters should oppose any modification of the appearance of our works, which is *Perfect* in the quaintness of its stupidity, there is no reason why the politician should feel obliged to protect it.

Machinery and Lions

THE Futurists had in their ideé fixe a great pull over the sentimental and sluggish eclecticism, deadness and preciosity of the artists working in Paris.

But they accept objective nature wholesale, or the objective world of mechanical industry. Their pæan to machinery is really a worship of a Panhard racing car, or a workshop where guns or Teddy bears are made, and not a deliberate and reasoned enthusiasm for the possibilities that lie in this new spectacle of machinery; of the *use* it can be put to in art. Machinery should be regarded as a new resource, as though it were a new mineral or oil, to be used and put to different uses than those for which it was originally intended. A machinery for making the parts of a 6 in. Mk. 19 gun should be regarded apart from its function. Absorbed into the asthetic consciousness it would no longer *make* so much as a popgun: its function thenceforward would change, and through its agency emotions would be manufactured, related, it is true, to its primitive efficiency, shinyness, swiftness or slowness, elegance or power, but its meaning transformed. It is of exactly the same importance, and in exactly the same category, as a wave on a screen by Korin, an Odalisque of Ingres, a beetle of a sculptor of the XVIII dynasty. Ingres lived in the midst of a great appetite for the pseudoclassic: the Egyptian sculptor lived in the presence of a great veneration for the beetle. Korin's contemporaries possessed a high susceptibility and sentiment for the objects of the natural world. Korin's formal wave line is the same impulse as Balla's Linea Andamentali: the Beetle and the Odalisque are both sleek and solid objects! Ingres probably did not believe in the Odalisque as an Odalisque, although realizing the admirable uses to which she could be put. The Egyptian probably found the beetle objectionable until transformed into stone. And there should be no obligation to supply veneration, or to behave like a religious fanatic about a sausage machine or a locomotive: other people can supply that, indeed should do so about something or other. If the world *would only build temples to Machinery* in the abstract then everything would be perfect. The painter and sculptor would have plenty to do, and could, in complete peace and suitably honored, pursue their trade without further trouble. Else what is the use of taking all the useful Gods and Goddesses away, and leaving the artist with no role in the social machine, except that of an entertainer, or a businessman?

Imagine Koyetzu, Signorelli, or the sculptor who carved the head of Akhenaton or of the wife of the Sheik-el-Beled, alive painting and carving, today. They would have been in the profoundest sense the same artists. But just as a painter may use one medium one day and another the next; so far more than simply traces of the fact that they had seen the machines that play such a part in our existence would be found in their inventions. Just as the sculptors of Nineveh put the lions that were such immediate objects in their life, to good use in their reliefs; or the painters of the Sung period the birds and landscapes found by them in their wilfully secluded lives; so it was inevitable today that artists should get into their inventions (figures, landscapes, or abstraction) something of the lineaments and character of machinery. An artist could excel, no doubt, who never suggested in his pictures acquaintance with anything more ferreous than a mushroom. But you would not be liable, I suppose, to pick a quarrel with the artists of Asshur because they used the lions at their door?

This ground has to be gone over, and thus much reasserted, for the purposes of the new adjustments I propose.

The Artist Older than the Fish

THE artist goes back to the fish. The few centuries that separate him from the savage are a mere flea bite to the distance his memory must stretch if it is to strike the fundamental slime of creation. And it is the condition, the very first gusto of creation in this scale of life in which we are set, that he must reach, before he, in his turn, can create!

The creation of a work of art is an act of the same description as the evolution of wings on the sides of a fish, the feathering of its fins; or the invention of a weapon within the body of a hymenopter to enable it to meet the terrible needs of its life. The ghostly and burning growths, the walking twigs and flying stones, the two anguished notes that are the voice of a being, the vapid twitter, the bellows of age-long insurrection and discontent, the complacent screech, all may be considered as types of art, all equally perfect, but not all equally desirable.

The attitude of instructed people as regards "the artist"

has changed. It is mixed up with, and depends a good deal on, the exactitude of their application of this term. With the grotesque prostitution of the word Artist, and its loose, indeed very loose and paltry meaning in this country, I will deal in a separate section. A German philosopher, living in the heyday of last century German music, accepted the theory of an æsthetic justification of the universe. Many people play with this notion, just as they play with Art. But we should have to disembarrass "art" of a good deal of cheap adhesive matter, and cheap and pretty adhesive people, before it could appear a justification for anything at all; much less for such a gigantic and, from every point of view, dubious concern as the Universe!

The artist's function is to create—to make something; and *not* to *make something pretty,* as dowagers, dreamers, and dealers here suppose. In any synthesis of the universe, the harsh, the hirsute, the enemies of the rose, must be built in for the purposes as much of a fine æsthetic, as of a fine logical, structure. And having removed the sentimental gulf that often has, in the course of their checkered career, kept Sense and Beauty apart, we may at this stage of the proceedings even refer to their purposes as one.

Fabre describes the creative capabilities of certain beetles, realizable on their own bodies; beasts with a record capacity for turning their form and color impulses into living flesh. These beetles can convert their faces into hideously carved and detestable masks, can grow out of their bodies menacing spikes, and throw up on top of their heads sinister headdresses, overnight. Such changes in their personal appearance, conceived to work on the psychology of their adversaries, is possibly not a very profound or useful invention, but it is surely a considerable feat. Any art worth the name is, at the least, a feat of this description. The New Guinea barred and whitewashed masks are an obvious parallel. But any invention or fantasy in painting or carving is such. As to the wing mechanism that first lifted a creature off the ground, and set it spinning or floating through the air, you must call Shakespeare in to compete with it. Ma Yuan we can consider, roughly speaking, as the creator of the first tree; or substitute for him the best artist, who has painted the best tree, that you can remember.

The more sensible we grow about the world, the more sensible we grow about the artist. We are really more in sympathy with a bird or a fish today than we have been for a considerable time. And while people at large are being forced, by snobbery, into a less anthropomorphic mood, they find, with some awakening of respect, traces and odd indications of the artist's presence everywhere they go beyond their simian pale. The artist, we all agree, was the first scientist! His "inhumanity" is so old that he looks with considerable contempt on the upstart and fashionable growth that the last twenty years has produced!

We have got out of our anthropomorphism, then, to this extent: that it is today in reality as respectable to be a fish, as it was in the latter part of the last century to be a savage. The Robert Louis Stevenson, George Borrow, "back to Nature" Englishman (not an artist type at all) is as dead as a doornail. It is the artist type, even, that has prevailed in the philosopher's mind, its dogmatism correcting itself by a careful liaison with the spirit of the artist.

We no longer dream about earlier communities, knowing more about them, or long for some pristine animal fierceness or abundant and unblemished health. We realize how every good thing dates, and grasp better the complexities of life's compensations. That does not mean that we are satisfied with today's conditions any more than we covet the Hereros or Hawaian natives to a morbid degree. Generally speaking, an intelligent and well-adjusted modern man does not place his paradise in the Prairie or in the heart of some bronzed Highland clan, although envying the great and simple assets that such plain conditions imply. He has caught a glimpse of something more subtle and more satisfying. He really at last has a vision of his own; it plunges him back to more refreshing energies and oblivions than the noisy and snarling claptrap of the tribe and clan. "The artist" was formally identified with the savage or the schoolboy to a disobliging extent, largely by thinkers impatient with the retrograde gushings and heroics of a type of rhyming or picture-painting certain, as conservative as a woman, that the thinker was perpetually meeting, full of noisy Kiplingesque protest, at the opening of every street marked out by his sage mind for draining and sanification (to be "saved" because of its "picturesque bits"); and through constantly detecting this absurd bechevelured figure daubing pretty colors, like a malicious and stupid urchin, on every idea that had been pronounced moribund, and that was destined for the dustbin. But clearly this individual, this masquerader, this bag of schoolboy conceits, this old-clo merchant, loaded with rusty broadswords, Spanish knives, sombreros, oaths, the arch-priest of the romantic Bottle, was not an artist type. Gauguin was not an artist type. He was a savage type addicted to painting. . . .

The Physiognomy of Our Time

LIFE, simply, however vivid and tangible, is too material to be anything but a mechanism, and the seagull is not far removed from the hydroplane. Whether a stone flies and copulates, or remains respectably in its place, half hiding the violet from the eye, is little matter. It is just as remarkable to be so hard and big as to be so busy and passionate; though owing to our busyness and passion we have a shoppy interest in the hurrying insect that we do not display for the stone. Life has begun, as language, for instance, begins, with a crowding and redundance that must be ordered and curtailed if the powerfullest instincts of life, even, are to triumph. Where everything is mutually destructive, and where immense multitudes of activities and modes of life have to be scrapped and excised, it is important not to linger in ecstasy over *everything*, simply because it *is;* or to sentimentalize about Life where creation is still possible and urgent; where much life, although pretty, powerful or bewitching, interferes with and opposes the life of something still more bewitching and strong.

The genius of the executant in art, the curiosity of the amateur, imply in their indiscriminate tasting and the promiscuity of their talent, an equal perfection in everything that succeeds in living, happens to move as swiftly, or far more swiftly, for its size, than the swiftest motor car; or to fly as infallibly as the most perfected plane we can imagine. And Marinetti (with his Caruso tenor instincts of inflation, and mellifluous self-aggrandizement and tiptoe tirade), was, in his rant about *speed*, in the same position. He might, ten thousand years before our wonderful time, have ranted about the lizard or the dragonfly, with a deeper wonder at the necessities and triumphs their powers of displacement implied.

An act of creation in art may be as far removed from the life of the fashionable chattering animal as the amoeba from the monkey. Truth is as strange a bird as ever flew in a Chinese forest. What shall we do with it? Does it require a drab and fickle world to shine in? Can it thrive in anything but a rich and abundant setting? Shall it be allowed to become extinct, made war on by some ill-favored reptile? Should it be caught and sent to the Zoo and fed by horrible Cockney brats on bastard buns? It is in any case difficult to admit the claims of the stuffed birds we have occasion to mention to peck at and refill themselves on the carcass of this more splendid creature.

We know that all our efforts indicate a desire to perfect and continue to create; to order, regulate, disinfect and stabilize our life. What I am proposing is activity, more deliberate and more intense, on the material we know and on our present very fallible stock. But that stock must be developed, not in the sense of the prize bullock, not simply fattened, elated, and made sleek with ideas proper to a ruminant species: but made the soul of things in this universe; until as a bird a man would be a first-rate growth, and even as a bullock, be stalled in a Palace. Let us substitute ourselves everywhere for the animal world; replace the tiger and the cormorant with some invention of our mind, so that we can intimately control this new Creation. The danger, as it would appear at present, and in our first flight of substitution and remounting, is evidently that we should become overpowered by our creation, and become as mechanical as a tremendous insect world, all our awakened reason entirely disappeared. Immediately we can put a great deal behind us.

When I put forward my opinion that the aspect of life, and the forms that surround us, *might,* perchance—without too great sacrifice on the part of the painter, without too great a disturbance for our dear conservatisms and delicate obstructionisms—be modified, I start from Buddha rather than from Lipton, Maximilian Harden or Madame Tussaud. But I start from Buddha with so much of the Fashion and spirit of our time as he would have developed living in our midst today; familiar with and delighting in the pleasant inventions and local color of our age; drinking Buchanan's Scotch whisky with relish, smoking Three Nuns; familiar with the smell of Harris tweeds, Euthymol, and the hot pestiferous Tube wind. I do not recommend any abstraction of our mental structure, or more definite unclothing than to strip till we come to the energetic lines required. So we have visualized a respectable and legendary figure, appreciating Dunhill or Dubec tobacco, with no aversion to seeing Mae Marsh, or paying homage to that uncanny piece of meat flinging itself indignantly about nightly under the hungry nose of the Monster of Mirth, the sturdy and priceless ape, George Robey.

Supposing that we destroyed every vestige of animal and insect life on this planet, and substituted machines of our invention, under immediate human control, for this mass of mechanisms that we had wiped out, what would be the guiding principle of these new masses? The same as at present, the wild animal and insect forms? Would we domesticate the universe, and make it an immense hive working for our will, scavenging, honey making, fetching and carrying for man; or what? It is not a birdlike act for a man to set himself coldly to solve the riddle of the bird and understand it; as it is human to humanize it. So we do not wish to become a vulture or a swallow. We want to enjoy our consciousness, but to enjoy it in all forms of life, and use all modes and processes for our satisfaction. Having said *all* forms, we get back once more to the indiscriminate, mechanical and unprogressive world that we first considered. Only now we have substituted, in fancy, an approximate human invention for every form of animate life. It is evidently not this hungry, frigid and devouring existence of the scorpion, the wild cat or the eagle that we are disposed to perpetuate. Every living form is a miraculous mechanism, however, and every sanguinary, vicious or twisted need produces in Nature's workshop a series of mechanical arrangements extremely suggestive and interesting for the engineer, and almost invariably beautiful or interesting for the artist. The Marinetti rant around machinery is really, at bottom, adulation for the universe of beings, and especially the world of insects.

So the froth of a Futurist at the mere sight of a Vickers' biplane is the same as a foaming ode to the dragonfly or the seagull; not for any super-mechanical attribute of the fly or the bird, but simply because one is a flying insect and the other a bird. And this all-inclusiveness of the direction of our thought is the result, primarily, of the all-inclusiveness of our knowledge.

The "gothic" stonemason, whose acquaintance with other forms of art than those he practiced was no doubt relatively nil, was better off than we are. Similarly, the Modern Man, the abstraction that we all go to make, in absorbing the universe of beings unto himself and his immediate life as we have seen him, with his mechanical inventions, commencing to do, is equally in the position of the dilettante. What is his synthesis going to be? So far it has been endless imitation; he has done nothing with his machinery but that. Will he arrive where there is no power, enjoyment or organization of which other living beings have been capable of which he will not, in his turn, and by a huge mechanical effort, possess the means? If he is amused enough with his mind to give that carte blanche, his individual existence as an apelike animal will grow less and less important. As already his body in no way indicates the scope of his personal existence (as the bear's or the barnacle's indicates theirs) it cannot any more in pictorial art be used as his effective delimitation or sign. But that is not to say that a piece of cheese or a coal scuttle can. There is in the inorganic world an organism that is his: and which, as much as his partially superseded body, is in a position of mastery and higher significance over the cheese and saucepan.

Our Aesthetes and Plank-Art

THERE are two attitudes toward the material world that, one or other manifesting itself in him, an artist may very roughly be distributed to one side or the other of a creative pale. These attitudes can be approximated to the roles of the sexes, and contain, no doubt, all the paradoxes of the great arbitrary sexual divisions of the race. An artist can Interpret or he can Create. There is for him, according to his temperament and kind, the alternative of the Receptive attitude or the Active and Changing one. One artist you see sitting ecstatic on his chair and gazing at a lily, at a portion of the wallpaper, stained and attractive, on the wall of his delightfully fortuitous room. He is enraptured by all the witty accidents that life, any life, brings to him. He sits before these phenomena enthralled, deliciously moved to an exquisite approval of the very happy juxtaposition of just that section of greenish wallpaper and his beautiful shabby brown trousers hanging from a nail beneath it. He notices in a gush of rapture that the white plate on the table intercepting the lower portion of the trousers cuts them in a white, determined, and well-meaning way. He purrs for some time (he is, Mr. Clive Bell will tell you, in a state of sensitive agitation of an indescribable nature), and then he paints his picture.

He gushes about everything he sees. He is enraptured at the quality of the curious clumsy country print found on the lodging-house wall; at the beauty of cheap china ornaments, a stupid chair, a staring, mean, pretentious little seaside house. When with anybody, he will titter or blink or faintly giggle when his attention is drawn to such a winning and lovely object. I am, you will perceive, drawing a picture of the English variety of art man. The most frequently used epithet will be "jolly" for the beautiful: and its pursuit will invariably be described as "fun." So we have before us, all said and done, a very playful fellow indeed, who quite enters into the spirit of this "amusing" life, and who is as true a "sportsman" as any red-coated squire; only for the pursuit of "jolly" little objects like stuffed birds, apples, or plates, areas of decayed wallpaper, and the form of game that he wishes rather smirkingly and naughtily to devour, he must be as cunning, languid, and untidy as his distinguished brother sportsman is alert, hearty, and colored like a letter box. For stalking a stuffed bird you have, in the first place, to be a little bit dead yourself.

I have been portraying to the best of my ability the heir to the aesthete of the Wilde period: the sort of man who is in the direct *ligne* [1] of Burne Jones, Morris, and Kate Greenaway. And he is a very good example of how to receive rather than to give.

Now all the color matching, matchbox making, dressmaking, chair-painting game, carried on in a spirit of distinguished amateurish gallantry and refinement at the Omega workshops, before that institution became extinct, was really *precisely the same thing,* only conducted with less vigor and

[1] line of descent

intelligence, as the burst of abstract nature-mortism which has marked the last phase of the Cubist, or Braquish, movement in Paris. These assemblings of bits of newspaper, cloth, paint, buttons, tin, and other débris, stuck on to a plank, are more "amusing" than were the rather jaded and amateur tastefulness of the Omega workshops. But as regards the Nature-mortists and Fitzroy tinkerers and tasters, one or other have recognized the affinity. Both equally are the opposite pole to the credence or intensity of creative art.

The Bawdy Critic

UNDER a series of promptings from Picasso, then, painting in Paris has been engineered into a certain position, that appears to me to bear far too striking a family likeness, in its spirit, to the sensibility of the English amateur to give one much hope for it. In the analysis of what I see as a deep weakness, and a scholarly, receptive and tasteful trend, rather than a creative one, I must put forward a little testimony, and devote a little space to what are otherwise thoroughly unimportant people. The important thing is obviously the painting in Paris, and not the type of English dilettante mind to which I compare it. But if I can make you see this real and striking community of temperament and intention, you will know better where you are when you find yourself in front of an arrangement of bits of newspaper, cloth, cheese parings, bird's feathers and tin. You might not otherwise come to the truth of this mystery at once. For the law that assembled these objects together will appear, and indeed is, more daring and abstruse than the more nerveless and more slovenly color matching and cushion making to which I relate it. Again, it is really only what happens in a picture that is not organized to attract the objects that it depicts. Whether you stick a bit of wallpaper and a patch of trouser leg side by side on a piece of wood, or use the objects in a picture painted on a piece of canvas, it is much the same. The only thing that can be said of these particular experiments is that they demonstrate an exasperated interest in media and the shop side of painting, and a certain mental liveliness. But as regards them, there the life stops.

A desire to accept and enjoy: to accept what is already in the world, rather than to put something new there: to be in a state of permanent pâmoison [1] and rant about everything; the older the thing, the *queerer* that you should find yourself fainting and ecstatic about it, the better—the *funnier,* you see? It is in the possession of this spirit, at bottom, that I am associating these two sets of people.

A composer of music does not, in his best or most specialized moments, fling himself into a luxurious ecstasy at a musical performance. The painter, similarly, does not derive from his own paintings, or other people's, "aesthetic ecstasies" or anything nice like that. He derives from the production of his own paintings, or should, a hundred times more pleasure than any bechevelured hysterical amateur is likely to find in front of *any* work of art. As a matter of fact, in most cases it is out of *himself,* not from the picture, or the art object, that the amateur gets his satisfaction. Hence the arcanely masturbatory tone in which some of them chant in the newspapers of their experiences. "Connoisseurs in pleasure—of whom I count myself one—know that nothing is more intensely delightful than the aesthetic thrill," etc., croons one.

Unsatisfied sex accounts for much. You wonder if it is really a picture, after all, and not a woman or something else that is wanted, for the purposes of such a luxurious thrill. Is not most emotional interest in Music or Pictures, unaccompanied by the practice of the art enjoyed, sex? In fact, the painter or the musician are the only people for whom it is *not* sex. These bawdy connoisseurs should really be kept out of the galleries. I can see a fine Renoir, some day, being mutilated: or an Augustus John being raped!

[1] swoon

The Objective of Art in Our Time

From what . . . I have said as to the tremendous ultimate effect that art has on our lives, it might seem that I was claiming for such painting as I advocate merely a usefulness, regarding it as, in the usual sense, a means to an end. When I claimed that a man painting a plate of apples in his studio could influence, by the way he treated those apples— the aesthetic principle involved in his vision—the art of the architect, commercial designer and so forth, that might seem to be evading an affirmation of the absolute value of the painting productive of such far-reaching effects.

To begin with, I hold that there is never an *end*; everything of which our life is composed, pictures and books as much as anything else, is a means only, in the sense that the work of art exists in the body of the movement of life. It may be a strong factor of progress and direction, but we cannot say that it is the end or reason of things, for it is so much implicated with them; and when we are speaking of art we suddenly find that we are talking of life all the time. The end that we set ourselves, again, and that we are able to imagine but not to compass and possess, is so relative, that we are operating in a purely conventional system of our own.

A picture, in the interminable series of pictures, is in the same position, in one way, as is a scientific theory. Let us take a concrete example of that. Professor Sir W. H. Bragg (to name, I think, the best authority) suggests today that we may have to return to the corpuscular theory of light, abandoning the wave theory that has passed as the likeliest for so long, and which superseded Newton's theory of a bombardment of particles. But it would not be the *same* corpuscular theory that would then be arrived at, but one that had passed through the ether waves, so to speak. It is quite possible that the wave theory may come in for another lease on life, with the constant arrival of new factors of knowledge, beyond the revised Newtonian view of the matter, if such once more prevails. And so it will go on, an ascending seesaw of hypothesis.

Is there a culmination to that series, and whither do those speculations tend? Whatever the answer may be to that, art is in the same position as science, in one sense: that is, it has the same experimental character, and exhibits the same spectacle of constant evolution. To see this evolution at work life-size, we will take the painting of our own times. The French impressionist pictures of the last century provided a new experience in the historic chain. This success was taken over by the school that succeeded the impressionist, other elements were introduced, and again a new thing was the result. This "newness" in both cases possesses the merit of being what the painter of the preceding school would have evolved had he been given a double term of life. It did not mean the death of a good thing, but its fecundation. The inexhaustible material of life, as it comes along, suggests constantly a readjustment and revision of what is there when it arrives. The new thing in art, is not *better* than the thing that preceded it, except at the turn of the tide in a period of great impoverishment and decadence, when a dissolution and death is occurring. It *may* be better, though never better than the best already recorded or existing. It may be worse. But it is a growth out of its immediate predecessor, and is marching in time, also, with the life with which it is environed. A form of it becomes extinct, perhaps, in one race, and is taken up in another.

The way in which science differs, at first sight, from art, is that the progress of scientific knowledge seems a positive and illimitable progression; in the sense that we know more today about the phenomenon of electricity, for example, or of disease, or the structure of the world, than men are recorded ever to have known. There is reason to believe that we shall soon be still better informed. In painting, on the other hand, a masterpiece of Sung or of the best sculpture of Dynastic Egypt is, as art, impossible to improve on, and very little has been produced in our time that could bear comparison with it.

But art is a valuation: in its relation to science it is somewhat in the position philosophy has so far occupied. Science presents men with more and more perfected instruments, and the means of material ascendancy: these appliances are used, and the use of them reacts on the user, and on his estimate of the meaning and possibilities of life. These estimates and beliefs are chalked up, and more or less critically signaled, in the works of the artist, and assessed sometimes by the philosopher. So science, in a sense, is criticized by art at the same time as is man.

The popular current belittlement of the function of what, since Socrates, has been called philosophy, tends, as is always the case, to become vindictive; to thrust too harshly some hero of the moment into the empty throne. No doubt philosophy must become something else to survive, though the character of mind that has hithertofore made of a man a philosopher will still be operative. The pseudoscientific element in philosophy, with the growth of exact specialized science, has brought it to its present pass. That unbridled emotional element found in it, which has discredited most speculation in retrospect, is proper to art, where it can be usefully organized and controlled. All that side of the philosopher has its legitimate outlet there. And the man of science, so long as he remains ideally that, is a servant and not a master. He is the perfect self-effacing highly technical valet of our immediate life. The philosopher as such shows every sign of disintegrating into something like (1) the artist, (2) the man of science, and (3) the psychologist. The artist gets a good share, it is certain, of the booty attending this demise.

At the moment of this breakup it is perhaps natural that art and science should both be momentarily swollen with the riches of this neighboring province suffering partition. The disinherited spirit of the philosopher finds asylum in these related activities. The philosopher, that hybrid of the religious teacher, man of science, and artist, was always, certainly a more artificial and vulnerable figure than his neighbors. Yet neither the artist nor the man of science can take his place.

When, however, the definitely intellectual character of art today is complained of, and artists are accused of theorizing too much on the subject of their books and pictures, one cannot do better than quote David Hume where, in the process of relating morals to the aesthetic sense, he writes: "But in many orders of beauty, particularly those of the finer arts, it is requisite to employ much reasoning, in order to feel the proper sentiment; and a false relish may frequently be corrected by argument and reflection. There are just grounds to conclude that moral beauty partakes much of this latter species, and demands the assistance of our intellectual faculties, in order to give it a suitable influence on the human mind."

The finer the art, the more extended the role the intellectual faculties Hume speaks of are called upon to play.

The concatenation and growth of scientific theories (to return to our earlier argument) may be like the growth of a tree, which from the start is destined for a certain height, volume and longevity. The human mind, evolving its theorizing chain, may have such a circumscribed and restricted destiny. It certainly is as irretrievably rooted in its soil, and on any at present ascertainable base it cannot balance itself more than a certain height in its atmosphere. If you take this restricted point of view (and all human life is lived upon some such assumption) art then will always be its ultimate necessity: it is what the philosopher comes to out of the discomfiture of his system; what, for the man in the street, cannot with impunity be divorced from the attitudes and very form of his religious beliefs; and it is the ideal check on the mechanical encroachments of science.

ART AND GAMES

THE game of cricket, or of tennis, is an ingenious test of our relative, but indeed quite clumsy and laughable, physical prowess. These games depend for their motive on the physical difficulties that our circumscribed extension and capacities entail. It is out of the discrepancy between *absolute* equilibrium, power, and so on, of which our mind is conscious, and the pitiable reality, that the stuff of these games is made. Art is cut out of a similar substance.

The charm of a game consists partly in our inordinate satisfaction with ourselves when we succeed in some trivial physical manoeuver. Such satisfaction would be impossible without the existence of the humorous philosopher of sport. This British invention has produced what is called the "sporting" attitude. Fundamentally that is nothing but a humorous (an artistic or a philosophic) acknowledgment of our grotesque and prodigious limitation. Why we are able to embrace this philosophy without abjectness, is evidently on account of the great discrepancy that our consciousness of this situation predicates between what we can perfectly well imagine, and what, in the limited time, conditions, and space at our disposal, we can accomplish. The man, as "sportsman," says, to all intents and purposes, when he is administering the sporting spirit: "Steady, steady! Easy, e-a-s-y! It'll all be the same a hundred years hence. Don't fling yourself on that ball as though it were a chocolate ice in the tropics, or a loaf of bread let loose upon a famine. It's only a little leather balloon. It's only a game you're playing. We all know you're a very wonderful player, my friend, but don't murder that man, or commit suicide: it's only a game after all." Or if he is being "a sport" at the moment, himself, his gesture of restraint or abnegation will declare: "This is not *real* life. We're only exercising our bodies, laughing at ourselves a little, for the funny little machines that we are; being deliberately children. That is all."

The Englishman is justly proud of this invention, the "sporting" spirit. His attitude, and his games, are a great practical contribution to human life: though they are also peculiarly his own, and it is doubtful if his formula can be satisfactorily used by anyone else. The *revers de la médaille*[1] I will not go into here; though it evidently consists in the fact that, in the aggregate, the Englishman has not a "reality" good enough to place against his "game": or rather he has it, but omits to use it. His achievement is an analytic and practical one; a slowing down, a sedative pill for too harsh vitality. In Taine's description of the English, he refers to the abnormal checks required for so much egotism as he found among them. Turn the coin round, and back to back with the philosophic athlete you will find nothing more than—Queen Victoria (whose name I hesitated to mention, on account of the *lèse*[2] Strachey it entails). The national aggregate sports, on its currency, the athlete: but it has not, as it should have, Shakespeare or Newton upon the other side, but some sceptered symbol of the middle class snob.

According to my view, all intellectual endeavor is in the same contingent category as a game of cricket or of tennis. It is remarkable what can be done with the mind, and the doing it is stimulating: just as it is surprising, or so it is felt to be, that we should be able to leap so high and as far as we do, run a hundred yards under ten seconds, defend our wicket for so many overs, and so forth. But, al-

[1] other side of the coin
[2] as in *lèse-majesté,* or high treason to Strachey

though the mind possesses immensely more scope and resource, and its exercise is vastly more complex and exciting, it ultimately is marking time as much as the body, it has the movements of marching forward, but does not march, but is energetically drumming one spot all the while. Its method is built up, like that of a game, on the same reservations; and even like the appetite for the game, is mixed with a sense of the weak and the ridiculous.

The art impulse reposes upon a conviction that the state of limitation of the human being is more desirable than the state of the automaton; or a feeling of the gain and significance residing in this human fallibility for us. It is to feel that our consciousness is bound up with this non-mechanical phenomenon of life; that, although helpless in face of the material world power, we are in some way superior to and independent of it; and that our mechanical imperfection is the symbol of that. In art we are in a sense playing at being what we designate as matter. We are entering the forms of the mighty phenomena around us, and seeing how near we can get to being a river or a star, without *becoming* that. Or we are placing ourselves somewhere behind the contradictions of matter and of mind, where an identity (such as the school of American realists, William James, for example, has fancied) may more primitively exist.

Our modern "impersonality" and "coldness" is in this sense a constant playing with the fire; with solar fire, perhaps, and the chill of interstellar space—where the art impulse of the astronomer comes in, for instance.

But an astronomer, confronted with a whole drove of universes, is by no means abashed. They are his game merely, and he knows it. He regards the stars as the cattle of his mind, and space as his meadow. He must do, even to the simplest observation; or else he would not be so jolly even as he is.

Some adjustment, then, between the approach of a conscious being to that mechanical perfection, and the fact of his mechanical incompetence (since mechanical perfection will not tally with the human thing) is the situation that produces art. The game consists in *seeing how near you can get*, without the sudden extinction and neutralization that awaits you as matter, or as the machine. In our bodies we have got already so near to extinction. And with these portions of mountain and of star, in which we remain with such hardihood and even insolence—playing fast and loose

daily with our bacillus-ridden, terribly exposed *pied-à-terre* [3]
—we are in a daily aesthetic relation. The delight in physical
danger, another ingredient of our games, the major motive
of the switchback, of mountain climbing and other dangerous pastimes, is the more extreme form of our flirtation with
extinction, or matter, if you like. All the thrill that we obtain from an exercise of the sense of humor is based on
this phenomenon.

In a great deal of art you find its motive in the assertion of the beauty and significance of the human as opposed to the mechanical; a virtuoso display of its opposite.
But this virtuosity, in its precision even in being imprecise,
is not so removed from a mechanical perfection as would
at first sight appear.

There is a passage in Dostoevsky's *Letters from the Underworld* quoted by Lavrin, that has a bearing on the point.
I will quote it before leaving this part of my argument. "If
ever a formula is discovered which shall exactly express our
wills and whims, make it clear what they are governed by,
what means of diffusion they possess: a formula mathe-
matical in its precision, then man will have ceased even to
exist. Who would care to exercise his willpower according
to a table of logarithms? A man would become, in such
circumstances, not a human being, but an organ handle or
something of the sort."

STANDARDS IN ART

THE difficulty of standards in art is very great. But it is
not more difficult in art than in anything else; science alone,
with its standards of weight, can, in its dealing with dead
matter, pretend to a certain finality. No one controverts the
velocity of light, established for us by Römer, though its
constancy may be questioned: little facts like the distance
of the Earth from Saturn remain quiet and unchallenged.
Once these things have been *measured,* there is an end to the
matter. The science consists solely in inventing the most
satisfactory means of effecting these measurements.

Metaphysics, on the other hand, is in a chronic state of
flux and chaos; so much that today the metaphysician seems
to have been driven off the field. As I have said already, I

---

[3] Lewis is punning. The French means "temporary lodging" and it
also means literally "a foot on the ground."

think he will reappear in some rather different form; and he will reappear all the better for his holiday among the hospitable arts and sciences. (For he *must* be somewhere: and I do not believe that he has become a stockbroker, in disgust, or a commission agent.) Kent, in his *Prolegomena,* writes of his science of metaphysics: "In this domain there is as yet no standard weight and measure to distinguish sound knowledge from shallow talk." And, again, "It seems almost ridiculous, while every other science is certainly advancing, that in this, which pretends to be wisdom incarnate, we should constantly move round the same spot, without gaining a single step. And so its followers have melted away: we do not find men confident of their ability to shine in other sciences venturing their reputations here." At least a standard in art is not more difficult to fix than it is in this constantly discomfited sister science.

What has happened to philosophy has also, to some degree, happened to the fine arts. The incessant disputes between schools, the impossibility in which the public finds itself of establishing an interest (whether commercial or snobbish) anywhere, has ended by exhausting its patience, and it falls back on Rolls-Royces and whiskies and sodas with a vicious and defiant glance at the artist. "I hate books," "I hate pictures," or "I hate music," is a remark not infrequently heard on the lips of people who formerly would have derived some satisfaction from supporting the arts. They have backed too many "duds": they know that there is nothing they can encourage or identify themselves with that will not involve them almost in abuse, that will not be violently attacked. It will be almost as though they had done the beastly thing themselves! Such pictures, music or books as would *not* involve them in this, are too stupid and clearly insignificant to waste time about. So, desiring a quiet life, they fight shy of the arts altogether.

And yet, because this produces a vacuum, which as true children of nature they abhor, in their existence as social beings, and makes their life shrink to a valueless and less excusable affair, all this leaves them a little ashamed and worried. All science can give them, and to it they repeatedly turn, in the shape of values, is a scepticism of which they have enough and to spare, and accumulations of animal luxury, which they feel, in its naked effrontery, should in some way be clothed with values, and the intellectual disguises in which their selfishness has always formerly been wrapped.

This question of a criterion is forever the ultimate difficulty where art is concerned. When the social life on which art depends becomes especially diseased and directionless, it appears with more insistence than ever, forced out of the contradictions beneath. This is because the picture, statue or book is in effect a living and active thing, evolving with other living things, and suffering their checks and distresses.

You can have a perfect snowball: what you expect of it is that it be made of snow and nothing but snow. That is all you mean by "perfect" in this case. All snow is the same, and so you get easily enough your perfect snowball.

But the book or the picture again not only is living but gives an account of life. The work of art is produced by means of an instrument not originally shaped for performing these literary or other feats, and one that has to be employed concurrently at a variety of blunting tasks—it may be, even, making a living in a bank, or livery stable. The mind, hybrid as it is, with no end and no beginning, with no nice boundary at which it could be said: "Up to this mark you can depend on a perfect result, and all that arises you are competent to deal with": from this mind nothing can be awaited but such productions as may cause us to say: "That is the work of a good specimen of human intelligence"; just as you say "an attractive woman," "a fine cat," or in French, *"un beau nègre."* [4] Calderon de la Barca, Voltaire, or Plotinus are good human specimens. There is nothing "perfect" about their plays, novels, or treatises. They are good in relation to the ineptitude around them. Strengthen this ineptitude, isolate it into a portion of some body, and you get one of these striking men. But you must not mix it *too* strongly, or vitalize it too much: for he who sees God, dies. Gather into one personality all the graces and virtues of the three men I have taken, and you would have no further need of any one of the three, theoretically. But then a synthesis of their prowesses would be less stimulating for us than one really lively specimen of such a distinguished triad. Amalgamated, they would be a pale shadow of their separate selves.

Perfection, therefore, from this standpoint, appears as a platonic ideal, and is a thing with which we have not very

---

[4] a handsome Negro man

much to do on our present road. With perfect snowballs or with perfect lightning conductors, we have some commerce; but not with "perfect" works of art or perfect human beings. The next point is this: could you disintegrate Voltaire or Plotinus still further; and would you get a still further improvement? I should rather say that Voltaire, etc., were the exact degree of disintegration from some all-inclusive intelligence needed to arrive at what we are adapted to comprehend. And that any further disintegration results in the dispersion of mediocrity—of little Voltaires: and anything more universal must progressively cancel itself.

If you conclude from this that I am treading the road to the platonic heaven, my particular road is deliberately chosen for the immanent satisfactions that may be found by the way. You may know Schopenhauer's eloquent and resounding words, where, in his forcible fashion, he is speaking of what art accomplishes: "It therefore pauses at this particular thing: the course of time stops: the relations vanish for it: only the essential, the idea, is its object."

That might be a splendid description of what the great work of plastic or pictorial art achieves. It "pauses at this *particular thing*," whether that thing be an olive tree that Van Gogh saw; a burgher of Rembrandt or the person of Miss Stein.[5] "The course of time stops." A sort of immortality descends upon these objects. It is an immortality, which, in the case of the painting, they have to pay for with death, or at least with its coldness and immobility.

Those words are, however, part of a passage in *The World as Will and Idea* that it may be useful to quote fully:

"While science, following the unresting and inconstant stream of the fourfold forms of reason and consequently, with each end attained sees further, and can never reach a final goal nor attain full satisfaction, any more than by running we can reach the place where the clouds touch the horizon; art, on the contrary, is everywhere at its goal. For it plucks the object of its contemplation out of the stream of the world's course, and has it isolated before it."

We might contrast this with a Bergsonian impressionism, which would urge you to leave the object in its vital *milieu*.[6] Again, the "presence of mind" in the midst of the empirical reality which Schopenhauer cites as the characteristic of

5 in Picasso's famous portrait of her
6 setting, environment

genius, this coldness is a self-isolation, in any case; for he who opens his eyes wide enough will always find himself alone. Where the isolation occurs, of subject or object, outside or inside the vortex, is the same thing. The impressionist doctrine, with its interpenetrations, its tragic literalness, its wavy contours, its fashionable fuss, points always to one end: the state in which life itself supersedes art: which as Schopenhauer points out, would be excellent if people knew how to use their eyes. But if they did it would no longer be "life" as we commonly mean it.

To continue the above passage, omitting several lines: "This last method of considering things (that of experience and science) may be compared to a line infinitely extended in a horizontal direction and the former to a vertical line which cuts it at any point. The method of viewing things which proceeds in accordance with the principle of sufficient reason is the rational method, and it alone is valid and of use in practical life and in science. The method which looks away from the content of this principle is the method of genius, which is only valid and of use in art. The first is the method of Aristotle; the second is, on the whole, that of Plato."

The act of creation, of which a book or picture is one form, is always an act of the human will, like poisoning your business rival, or setting your cap at somebody; the complete existence and exercise of this will entails much human imperfection, which will be incorporated in the book or picture, giving it the nervousness of its contours, and the rich odors, the sanguine or pallid appearance, which recommends it to us.

In art there are no laws, as there are in science. There is the general law to sharpen your taste and your intelligence in every way that you can. John Constable, in writing of an exhibition, said: "Turner's light, whether it emanates from sun or moon, is always exquisite. Collins' skies and shores are true. His horizons are always pretty." That is about as far as any painter gets, except Leonardo or a very few, in analysis of what he understands so well but about which, on the side of direct concrete appraisement, there is so little to be said beyond affixing a rough epithet.

All that we can definitely say—and we know that, surely, as much as we know anything—is that Bach's music is better than that of Irving Berlin, or that the Sistine chapel is better art than the Nurse Cavell monument, with relation to any end that we can conceive. Only a few people are able to discriminate, it is true, between these respective works of art. A freak might be found who would derive identically the same intellectual satisfaction from gazing at the Nurse Cavell monument that Picasso would from gazing at Michelangelo's paintings in Rome. And for this freak there would be no difference between them. But if that were so, it would be Michelangelo that he would be looking at, in reality, or what is Michelangelo for us. And in that case he would be mad.

Every time has its appointed end, and its means are proportioned to it. Beauty occurs in the way that is met in motor-car construction or the human body. No more in pictures than in anything else can it be isolated from some organic principle. It is a portion of the Means, nothing else.

A THIRD METHOD, BETWEEN SUBJECT AND OBJECT

THE function of the artist being to show you the world, only a realer one than you would see, unaided, the delicate point in his task is to keep as near to you as possible, at the same time getting as far away as our faculties will stretch. The motive of this contradictory maneuver is as follows. He is obliged, before he can show you reality, to dissociate himself from the objective world entirely, and to approach it as a stranger or (which is the same thing) a child. He, ideally, must not take any of the acquired practical information of daily life with him, to the point from which his observations are to be made. Any of the fever of combat (where he is at his task) would impair the equilibrium of his instrument.

When anyone says, however, a "realer" world, not only an intenser and more compact statement of it than the usual working of our senses provides, is meant, but also a different world.

For what the artist's public also has to be brought to do is to see its world, and the people in it, as a *stranger* would. There have been so far principally two methods of achieving this. One is to display a *strange* world to the spectator, and yet one that has so many analogies to his that, as he looks, startled into attention by an impressive novelty, he sees his own reality through this veil, as it were, momentarily in truer colors. The other method is the less objective one of luring the spectator to the point from which, inevitably, the world will appear as the artist sees it, and the spectator from that point of vantage paints the picture for himself, but with the artist's colors and his more expert eyes. The first of these methods can be described very roughly as the impersonal and objective method, and the second the personal and subjective one. The latter method (contrary to what is sometimes supposed) seems to be more assured of a positive result: for a lesser effort of intelligence is required on the part of the public. It is the method that usually characterizes the art of an undeveloped society. The former, in which everyone participates more fully, is proper to a "civilized" time. The civilized man again is less willing or less able to abandon his personality sufficiently. He is (each member of the thronging audience) a little artist himself. He will not be meddled with: he must be addressed and moved, if at all, in the capacity of critic. He is not adventurous enough to go far afield. It is a case of the mountain going away from Mahomet where Mahomet will not budge himself, if it is desired that the mountain should not be so near to the spectator.

The artist, unless of a very lucky or privileged description, can only exist, even, by pretending to be one of the audience. Nothing less democratic than that will be tolerated.

By this description of what we call a "civilized" public you may gather that I am not very enthusiastic about it. In that you will be right: but it is not because I contrast it nostalgically with its opposite. A sort of undisciplined raw democracy of the intellect is what "civilized" describes in our time. It is the revolt of the not naturally very wise or sensitive against any intellectual rule or order (parodying or marching in sympathy with political revolution).

What I consider that a certain amount of contemporary art presages, is the development of a new method—a third, if you like—that should not, if it comes, resemble the religious tyranny of the subjective method, and would escape from the half sophistication that the other method begets or for which, partly, it is designed. . . .

THE SENSE OF THE FUTURE

BERGSON'S view that the permanence of the work of art, or its continued interest for us, depends on its uniqueness, on the fact that such and such a thing will *never happen again*, would make of everything in life a work of art. This uniqueness is a portion of everything, and need not be invoked for the definition of art. In fact, the other factors of the work of art of an opposite and general description are those that distinguish it from the rest of life, canceling as far as possible its uniqueness. Indeed, as I have shown, it would seem that successful expression occurs exactly at the point where, should this uniqueness be diminished any further, it would lose in force as human expression. Even one of the only standards of measurement we have is the distance to which a personality can penetrate into the general or the abstract, without losing its force and reality for us.

The object, in Schopenhauer's words, "Plucked out of the stream," also is only plucked so far as will still enable it to breathe and live. Or rather—to dispense with the metaphor —the "plucking" consists just in *abstracting* it. When it has been abstracted it is not quite what it was when in the stream. It is always a *different* thing, as we have said, when conveyed to us as an object of contemplation. And yet, it is that particular thing, still, that it was in the stream. For the distance it has traversed in the process of abstraction is insignificant if compared with the distances involved were it to reach an ultimate abstraction.

The question of uniqueness is bound up with that of the "present time" for the "present" is the essence of the unique, or of *our* unique. I will deal with this later on, only considering for the moment our relation to the *future*, which must be considered at this point.

If it is true that all the past is in us, that it is this past, in terms of the present, that the artist shows you when he excites you most;—where, we must ask, in all this, does the future come in? Tragedy drags to the surface your wild monsters, gives them a few hours' frolic, and they are then driven back quietly to their dens. There is another sort of artist (of which the Italian Futurist, now deceased, is an excellent specimen) who should really be called a Presentist. He is closely related to the pure Impressionist. He pretends to live, and really succeeds sometimes, a sort of spiritual hand-to-mouth existence. He has tried with frenzy to identify himself with matter—with the whizzing, shrieking body, the smooth rolling machine, the leaping gun. And his life is such an eternal present as is matter's: only, being a machine, he wears out: but with his death nothing comes to an end, or is supposed to come to an end, but the matter of which his dynamic present is composed.

There are, however, some men who seem to contain the future as others contain the past. These are, in the profoundest sense, also our men of action, if you admire that term: for, as the hosts of the unlived thing, they are the personification of action. I think that every poet, painter or philosopher worth the name has in his composition a large proportion of *future* as well as of past. The more he has, the more prophetic intuition, and the more his energy appears to arrive from another direction to that of the majority of men (namely, the past), the better poet, painter or philosopher he will be.

A space must be cleared, all said and done, round the hurly-burly of the present. No man can reflect or create, in the intellectual sense, while he is acting—fighting, playing tennis, or making love. *The present man in all of us is the machine.* The farther away from the present, though not too far, the more free. So the choice must be between the past and the future. Every man has to choose, or rather the choice is early made for each of us.

We all know people, and not necessarily old people, who live in the past. The past that they survey is only a prolonged present, stretching back as far as their mind's eye can reach. We know a great many more, the majority, of machine-like, restless and hard individuals, who positively rattle with a small, hollow, shaken ego; or, less objectionably, throb and purr with the present vibration of a plodding and complacent mechanism.

The man of the future, the man who is in league with time, is as engrossed *away* from the actual as the first man is in his dear past. There is not such a sad light over the future: it is not infected with so many old murders, and stale sweetheartings, and therefore the man accustomed to its landscapes is of a more cheerful disposition than his neighbor the other way round.

I must leave this attractive figure, and once more hurry on, hoping to deal with him more fully before this essay is completed.

Upon this theme, however, before departing from it, I must offer an exhortation.

You handle with curiosity and reverence a fragment belonging to some civilization developed three millenia ago. Why cannot you treat the future with as much respect? Even if the Future is such a distant one that the thing you hold in your hand, or the picture you look at, has something of the mutilation and imperfection that the fragment coming to you from the past also has, is not the case a similar one? May it not actually possess as well the "charm" you allow to your antiquarian sense? I think we should begin to regard ourselves all more in this light—as drawing near to a remote future, rather than receding from an historic past. The time has perhaps arrived to do that! Have not a few of us been preparing?

The future possesses its history as well as the past, indeed. All living art is the history of the future. The greatest artists, men of science and political thinkers, come to us from the future—from the opposite direction to the past.

THE FUNCTION OF THE EYE

THE practical and, as we say, "prosaic" character of the function of our visual sense does not enable us to experience through it normally a full emotional impression. We cannot dream with our eyes open. Association is too strong for us. We are all, in a sense even, so thoroughly hidden from each other because we *see* each other.

It is more difficult to exercise our imagination when the eye is functioning. (The ear, being *blind*, is in that respect better off.) The practical and very necessary belittlement accomplished for us by the eye at the same time invalidates its claim to priority as the king organ where imaginative expression is concerned, although in every other sense it is so supreme. Even the eye cannot have the apple and eat it too; or be the apple of the mind's eye, and Nature's as well. The eye has to pay, emotionally, for its practical empire over our lives.

In dreams, however, the eye is in every way supreme. Our dreams are so muffled (or are such dreams only a painter's?) that they are nearly as silent as the silent film. There the mind, by arranging things as it requires them for its own delight or horror, can get the full emotional shock, the purely visionary quality that early in life becomes dissociated from our exercise of the visual sense.

In what does this "emotional" quality, the stripping of things and people by the eye of their more significant and complete emotional vesture, consist? Simply in an incessant analysis of the objects presented to us for the practical purposes of our lives. We are given by the eye *too much*: a surfeit of information and "hard fact," which does not, taken literally, tally with our completer values for the objects in question. To make up, from the picture presented to us by the eye, a synthesis of a person or a thing, we must modify the order for which the eye is responsible, and eliminate much of the physical chaos that only serves to separate us from the imaginative truth we are seeking.

The eye, in itself, is a stupid organ. Or shall we say a *stolid* one? It is robust to a fault, where the ear is, if anything, hypersensitive. Everything received through the eye from the outside world has to be "treated" before it can be presented to the imagination with a chance of moving it. The law of this "treatment" is, first, a process of *generalization*. An intense particularization may, however, on the principle of extremes meeting, have the same effect. But, broadly, it is by a *generalizing* of the subject matter that you arrive at the rendering likely to be accepted by the imagination. I am using the word "imagination" to stand for that function of the mind that assesses and enjoys the purely useful work performed by the other faculties; the artist-principle in the mind, in short.

In traditional psychology the distinction between imagination and memory is said to be, that, with the former, the sensations are arbitrarily reordered; whereas "memory" is the term we apply to a fainter picture of something already experienced, but the sensations occurring in the same order, in the order of nature. Dreams are an example of sensations evolved, with great complexity, in a new order, and with new emotional stresses and juxtapositions. The work of the dramatist or novelist is in this category, and that of most painters whose work is remembered. But the work of art does the reordering in the interests of the intellect as well as of the emotions. . . .

PART IV

writers and politics

By politics Lewis meant something much broader and more inclusive than is generally meant by that term. This can be seen very well in his essay on Ernest Hemingway, which is not only an appraisal of his style and approach to experience—it was soon to become a "locus classicus" [1] of Hemingway criticism—but is also an analysis of large cultural trends, the movements of the Zeitgeist, as Lewis would put it, and hardly fits into any neat socio-political category. The essay appeared in his book, *Men Without Art,* published in 1934 and written chiefly to defend Lewis' special conception of satire, which, he claimed, was a common characteristic of all significant modern writing. "Mr. Hemingway," he says in the preface, "in the role he has chosen for himself, is, as it were, a proletarian clown; he satirizes *himself*—but a self that is not his private self at all, but rather a sort of projection of the spirit of Miss Stein into the slow-moving and slow-thinking bulk of a simple-hearted laborer—say an American lumberjack."

The discussion of Sartre and Malraux in Lewis' book, *The Writer and the Absolute,* sticks more closely to strict politics. Sartre was chosen for detailed dissection because, for Lewis, he seemed to typify an absolutistic political attitude that was inimical to the integrity of the community of writers and artists. Truth, he felt, was in the custody of this community, and it could only be perceived and expressed

[1] a passage commonly cited to illustrate or explain a subject

if the writer kept himself free of all propagandistic systems, whether originating on the Right or the Left. "It is the duty of the creative writer to keep himself different (the classic definition of the 'Individual'), just as a jockey has to keep himself *small and light*."

In all of these essays, Lewis evinces those critical talents which led G.S. Fraser to describe him as follows: "Wyndham Lewis seems to me one of the very greatest critics of this century chiefly because he had this extraordinary gift of, as it were, transferring directly to the page . . . the blurted and indiscreet conversational insights of an artist, to artists, about artists. . . . He is not an academic making things clear to students, or a literary journalist being polite at a party, or a lecturer to a lot of old ladies being purring and condescending, but just a man, at once alert and excited, amusing himself about equals, among equals. . . . His genius as a critic was to state, in an unforgettable fashion, the permanently damaging things that could be said. . . ."

from MEN WITHOUT ART

Ernest Hemingway: The "Dumb Ox"

ERNEST HEMINGWAY is a very considerable artist in prose fiction.

Besides this, or with this, his work possesses a penetrating quality, like an animal speaking. Compared often with Hemingway, William Faulkner is an excellent, big-strong, novelist: but a conscious artist he cannot be said to be. Artists are made, not born: but he is considerably older, I believe, than Hemingway, so it is not that. But my motive for discussing these two novelists has not been to arrive at estimates of that sort.

A quality in the work of the author of *Men Without Women* suggests that we are in the presence of a writer who is not merely a conspicuous chessman in the big-business book game of the moment, but something much finer than that. Let me attempt to isolate that quality for you, in such a way as not to damage it too much: for having set out to demonstrate the political significance of this artist's work, I shall, in the course of that demonstration, resort to a dissection of it—not the best way, I am afraid, to bring out the beauties of the finished product. This dissection is, however, necessary for my purpose here. "I have a weakness for Ernest Hemingway," as the egregious Miss Stein says: * it is not agreeable to me to pry into his craft, but there is no help for it if I am to reach certain important conclusions.

But *political significance!* That is surely the last thing one would expect to find in such books as *In Our Time, The Sun also Rises, Men Without Women,* or *Farewell to Arms.* And indeed it is difficult to imagine a writer whose mind is more entirely closed to politics than is Hemingway's. I do not suppose he has ever heard of the Five-Year Plan, though I dare say he knows that artists pay no income tax in Mexico, and is quite likely to be following closely the agitation of the Mexican matadors to get themselves recognized as "artists" so that they may pay no income tax. I expect he has heard of Hitler, but thinks of him mainly, if he is acquainted with the story, as the Boche who went down into a cellar with another Boche and captured thirty Frogs and came back with an Iron Cross. He probably knows that his friend Pound writes a good many letters every week to American papers on the subject of Social Credit, but I am sure Pound has never succeeded in making him read a line of *Credit-Power and Democracy.* He is interested in the sports of death, in the sad things that happen to those engaged in the sports of love—in sand sharks and in Wilson-spoons—in war, but *not* in the things that cause war, or the people who profit by it, or in the ultimate human destinies involved in it. He lives, or affects to live, *submerged.* He is in the multitudinous ranks of *those to whom things happen*—terrible things of course, and of course stoically borne. He has never heard, or affects never to have heard, that there is another and superior element, inhabited by a type of unnatural men which preys upon that of the submerged type. Or perhaps it is not quite a submerged mankind to which he belongs, or affects to belong, but to something of the sort de-

* *The Autobiography of Alice B. Toklas.*

scribed in one of Faulkner's war stories: "But after twelve years," Faulkner writes, "I think of us as bugs in the surface of the water, isolant and aimless and unflagging. Not on the surface; in it, within that line of demarcation not air and not water, sometimes submerged, sometimes not." * (What a stupid and unpleasant word "isolant" is! Hemingway would be incapable of using such a word.) But—twelve, fifteen years afterwards—to be *submerged*, most of the time, is Hemingway's idea. It is a little bit of an *art pur* [1] notion, but it is, I think, extremely effective, in his case. Faulkner is much less preoccupied with art for its own sake, and although he has obtained his best successes by submerging himself again (in an intoxicating and hysterical fluid) he does not like being submerged quite as well as Hemingway, and dives rather because he is compelled to dive by public opinion, I imagine, than because he feels at home in the stupid medium of the sub-world, the bêtise [2] of the herd. Hemingway has really taken up his quarters there, and has mastered the medium entirely, so that he is of it and yet not of it in a very satisfactory way.

Another manner of looking at it would be to say that Ernest Hemingway is the Noble Savage of Rousseau, but a white version, the simple American man. That is at all events the role that he has chosen, and he plays it with an imperturbable art and grace beyond praise.

It is not perhaps necessary to say that Hemingway's art is an art of the surface—and, as I look at it, none the worse for that. It is almost purely an art of action, and of very violent action, which is another qualification. Faulkner's is that too: but violence with Hemingway is deadly matter-of-fact (as if there were only violent action and nothing else in the world): whereas with Faulkner it is an excited crescendo of psychological working-up of a sluggish and not ungentle universe, where there *might* be something else than high explosive—if it were given a Chinaman's chance, which it is not. The latter is a far less artistic purveyor of violence. He does it well: but as to the manner, he does it in a way that any fool could do it. Hemingway, on the other hand, serves it up like the master of this form of art that he is, immeasurably more effective than Faulkner—good as he is: or

---

* *These Thirteen*. William Faulkner.
[1] pure art, that is, art for art's sake notion
[2] stupidity

than say the Irish novelist O'Flaherty—who is a *raffiné* [3] too, or rather a two-gun man; Hemingway really banishes melodrama (except for his absurd escapes, on a Hollywood pattern, in *Farewell to Arms*).

To find a parallel to *In Our Time* or *Farewell to Arms* you have to go to *Colomba* or to *Chronique du Règne de Charles ix*: and in one sense Prosper Merimée supplies the historical key to these two ex-soldiers—married, in their literary craft, to a theater of action *à l'outrance*. [4] The scenes at the siege of La Rochelle in the *Chronique du Règne de Charles ix* for instance: in the burning of the mill when the ensign is roasted in the window, that is the Hemingway subject matter to perfection—a man melted in his armor like a shellfish in its shell—melted lobster in its red armor.

> S'ils tentaient de sauter par les fenêtres, ils tombaient dans les flammes, ou bien étaient reçus sur la pointe des piques. . . . Un enseigne, revêtu d'une armure complète, essaya de sauter comme les autres par une fenêtre étroite. Sa cuirasse se terminait, suivant une mode alors assez commune, par une espèce de jupon en fer qui couvrait les cuisses et le ventre, et s'élargissait comme le haut d'un entonnoir, de manière à permettre de marcher facilement. La fenêtre n'était pas assez large pour laisser passer cette partie de son armure, et l'enseigne, dans son trouble, s'y était précipité avec tant de violence, qu'il se trouva avoir la plus grande partie du corps en dehors sans pouvoir remuer, et pris comme dans un étau. Cependant les flammes montaient jusqu'à lui, échauffaient son armure, et l'y brûlaient lentement comme dans une fournaise ou dans ce fameux taureau d'airain inventé par Phalaris.* [5]

* *Chronique du règne de Charles ix*. Merimée.

[3] refined

[4] extreme, excessive

[5] "If they tried to jump from the windows, they fell into the flames, or were impaled on the points of the pikes. . . . An ensign, dressed in full armor, tried like the others to jump through a narrow window. His cuirass ended according to a style then very common, in a kind of iron skirt which covered his thighs and stomach, and spread out like the top of a funnel, so that he could walk without difficulty. The

Compare this with the following:

> We were in a garden at Mons. Young Buckley came
> in with his patrol from across the river. The first German
> I saw climbed up over the garden wall. We waited till
> he got one leg over and then potted him. He had so
> much equipment on and looked awfully surprised and
> fell down into the garden. Then three more came over
> further down the wall. We shot them. They all came
> just like that.[*]

> "In no century would Prosper Merimée have been
> a theologian or metaphysician," and if that is true of
> Merimée, it is at least equally true of his American
> prototype. But their "formulas" sound rather the same,
> "indifferent in politics . . . all the while he is feeding
> all his scholarly curiosity, his imagination, the very eye,
> with the, to him ever delightful, relieving, reassuring
> spectacle, of those straightforward forces in human na-
> ture, which are also matters of fact. There is the
> formula of Merimée! the enthusiastic amateur of rude,
> crude, naked force in men and women wherever it
> could be found . . . there are no half lights. . . .
> Sylla, the false Demetrius, Carmen, Colomba, that im-
> passioned self within himself, have no atmosphere. Pain-
> fully distinct in outline, inevitable to sight, unrelieved,
> there they stand, like solitary mountain forms on some
> hard, perfectly transparent day. What Merimée gets
> around his singularly sculpturesque creations is neither
> more or less than empty space.[†]

I have quoted the whole of this passage because it gives
you "the formula," equally for the author of *Carmen* and of
The Sun Also Rises—namely *the enthusiastic amateur of
rude, crude, naked force in men and women* but it also

---

window was not wide enough for this part of his armor to pass
through, and the ensign, in his confusion, had thrown himself against
it with such violence that he had the main portion of his body outside but was unable to move, caught as in a vice. Meanwhile the
flames leaped up towards him, heating his armor, roasting him slowly
as in an oven or the famous brass bull invented by Phalaris."
[*] *In Our Time*. Hemingway.
[†] *Miscellaneous Studies*. Walter Pater.

brings out very well, subsequently, the nature of the radical and extremely significant *difference* existing between these two men, of differing nations and epochs—sharing so singularly a taste for physical violence and for fine writing, but nothing else. Between them there is this deep gulf fixed: that gifted he of today is "the man that things are done to"—even the "I" in *The Sun Also Rises* allows his Jew puppet to knock him about and "put him to sleep" with a crash on the jaw, and this first person singular covers a very aimless, will-less person, to say the least of it: whereas that *he* of the world of *Carmen* (so much admired by Nietzsche for its bright Latin violence and directness—*la gaya scienza*) [6] or of Corsican vendetta, he was in love with *will*, as much as with violence: he did not celebrate in his stories a spirit that suffered bodily injury and mental disaster with the stoicism of an athletic clown in a particularly brutal circus—or of oxen (however robust) beneath a crushing yoke: he, the inventor of Colomba, belonged to a race of men for whom action meant *their* acting, with all the weight and momentum of the whole of their being: he of post-Napoleonic France celebrated intense spiritual energy and purpose, using physical violence as a mere means to that only half-animal ideal. *Sylla, Demetrius, Colomba,* even *de Mergy,* summon to our mind a world bursting with purpose—even if always upon the personal and very animal plane, and with no more universal ends: while Hemingway's books, on the other hand, scarcely contain a figure who is not in some way futile, clownlike, passive, and above all *purposeless*. His world of men and women (*in violent action,* certainly) is completely empty of will. His puppets are leaves, *very violently* blown hither and thither; drugged or at least deeply intoxicated phantoms of a sort of matter-of-fact shell shock.

In *Farewell to Arms* the hero is a young American who has come over to Europe for the fun of the thing, as an alternative to baseball, to take part in the Sport of Kings. It has not occurred to him that it is no longer the sport of kings, but the turning-point in the history of the earth at which he is assisting, when men must either cease thinking like children and abandon such sports, or else lose their freedom forever, much more effectively than any mere *king* could ever cause them to lose it. For him, it remains "war" in the old-fashioned semisporting sense. Throughout this ghastly event, he proves

6 the gay science, title of one of Nietzsche's books

himself a thorough-going sport, makes several hairbreadth, Fenimore Cooper-like, escapes, but never from first to last betrays a spark of intelligence. Indeed, his physical stoicism, admirable as it is, is as nothing to his really heroic imperviousness to thought. This "war"—Gallipoli, Passchendaele, Caporetto—is just another "scrap." The Anglo-Saxon American—the "Doughboy"—and the Anglo-Saxon Tommy—join hands, in fact, outrival each other in a stolid determination absolutely to ignore, come what may, what all this is about. Whoever may be in the secrets of destiny—may indeed be destiny itself—*they* are not nor ever will be. They are an integral part of that world *to whom things happen*: they are not those who cause or connive at the happenings, and that is perfectly clear.

> *Pack up your troubles in your old kit bag,*
> *Smile boys, that's the style*

and *keep smiling*, what's more, from ear to ear, a *should-I-worry?* "good sport" smile, as do the Hollywood Stars when they are being photographed, as did the poor Bairnsfather "Tommy"—the "muddied oaf at the goal"—of all oafishness!

I hope this does not seem irrelevant to you: it is not, let me reassure you, but very much the contrary. The roots of all these books are in the War of 1914–1918, as much those of Faulkner as those of Hemingway: it would be ridiculous of course to say that either of these two highly intelligent ex-soldiers shared the "oafish" mentality altogether: but the war years were a democratic, a *leveling*, school, and both come from a pretty thoroughly "leveled" nation, where personality is the thing least liked. The rigid organization of the communal life as revealed in *Middletown*, for instance (or such a phenomenon as N.R.A.) is akin to the military state. So *will*, as expressed in the expansion of the individual, is not a thing we should expect to find illustrated by a deliberately typical American writer.

Those foci of passionate personal energy which we find in Merimée, we should look for in vain in the pages of Hemingway or Faulkner: in place of Don José or of Colomba we get a pack of drugged or intoxicated marionettes. These differences are exceedingly important. But I shall be dealing with that more carefully in my next chapter.

So any attempt to identify "the formula" for Prosper

Merimée with that of Ernest Hemingway would break down. You are led at once to a realization of the critical difference between these two universes of discourse, both employing nothing but physical terms; of how an appetite for the extremity of violence exists in both, but in the one case it is personal ambition, family pride, romantic love that are at stake, and their satisfaction is violently sought and undertaken, whereas in the other case purposeless violence, for the sake of the "kick," is pursued and recorded, and the "thinking subject" is to regard himself as nothing more significant than a ripple beneath the breeze upon a pond.

If we come down to the manner, specifically to the style, in which these sensational impressions are conveyed, again most interesting discoveries await us: for, especially with Mr. Hemingway, the story is told in the tone, and with the vocabulary, of the persons described. The rhythm is the anonymous folk rhythm of the urban proletariat. Mr. Hemingway is, self-consciously, a folk prose-poet in the way that Robert Burns was a folk poet. But what is curious about this is that the modified *Beach-la-mar* [7] in which he writes, is, more or less, the speech that is proposed for everybody in the future—it is a volapük which probably will be ours tomorrow. For if the chief executive of the United States greets the Roman Catholic democratic leader (Al Smith) with the exclamation "Hallo old potato!" today, the English political leaders will be doing so the day after tomorrow. And the Anglo-Saxon *Beach-la-mar* of the future will not be quite the same thing as Chaucer or Dante, contrasted with the learned tongue. For the latter was the speech of a race rather than of a class, whereas our "vulgar tongue" will really be *vulgar*.

But in the case of Hemingway the folk business is very seriously complicated by a really surprising fact. He has suffered an overmastering influence, which cuts his work off from any other, except that of his mistress (for his master has been a *mistress*!). So much is this the case, that their destinies (his and that of the person who so strangely hypnotized him with her repeating habits and her *faux-naif* [8] prattle)

[7] a pidgin language based on English, spoken in the Southwest Pacific
[8] false-naïve

are for ever interlocked. His receptivity was so abnormally pronounced (even as a craftsman, this capacity for being *the person that things are done to* rather than the person who naturally initiates what is to be done to others, was so marked) and the affinity thus disclosed was found so powerful! I don't like speaking about this, for it is such a first-class complication, and yet it is in a way so irrelevant to the spirit which informs his work and must have informed it had he never made this apparently overwhelming "contact." But there it is: if you ask yourself how you would be able to tell a page of Hemingway, if it were unexpectedly placed before you, you would be compelled to answer, *Because it would be like Miss Stein!* And if you were asked how you would know it was not by Miss Stein, you would say, *Because it would probably be about prizefighting, war, or the bullring, and Miss Stein does not write about war, boxing or bullfighting!*

It is very uncomfortable in real life when people become so captivated with somebody else's tricks that they become a sort of caricature or echo of the other: and it is no less embarrassing in books, at least when one entertains any respect for the victim of the fascination. But let us take a passage or two and get this over—it is very unpleasant. Let us take Krebs—the "he" in this passage is Krebs, a returned soldier in a Hemingway story:

> When he was in town their appeal to him was not very strong. He did not like them when he saw them in the Greek's ice-cream parlor. He did not want them themselves really. They were too complicated. There was something else. Vaguely he wanted a girl but he did not want to have to work to get her. He would have liked to have a girl but he did not want to have to spend a long time getting her. He did not want to get into the intrigue and the politics. He did not want to have to do any courting. He did not want to tell any more lies. It wasn't worth it.
>
> He did not want any consequences. He did not want any consequences ever again. He wanted to live along without consequences. Besides he did not really need a girl. The army had taught him that. It was all right to pose as though you had to have a girl. Nearly everybody did that. But it wasn't true. You did not need a girl.

That was the funny thing. First a fellow boasted how girls mean nothing to him, that he never thought of them, that they could not touch him. Then a fellow boasted that he could not get along without girls, that he had to have them all the time, that he could not go to sleep without them. . . .

He liked the girls that were walking along the other side of the street. He liked the look of them much better than the French girls or the German girls. But the world they were in was not the world he was in. He would like to have one of them. But it was not worth it. They were such a nice pattern. He liked the pattern. It was exciting. But he would not go through all the talking. He did not want one badly enough. He liked to look at them all, though. It was not worth it." *

So much for Krebs: now open Miss Stein and "meet" Melanctha.

Rose was lazy but not dirty, and Sam was careful but not fussy, and then there was Melanctha. . . . When Rose's baby was coming to be born, Rose came to stay in the house where Melanctha Herbert lived just then, . . . Rose went there to stay, so that she might have the doctor from the hospital. . . . Melanctha Herbert had not made her life all simple like Rose Johnson. Melanctha had not found it easy with herself to make her wants and what she had, agree.

Melanctha Herbert was always losing what she had in wanting all the things she saw. Melanctha was always being left when she was not leaving others.

Melanctha Herbert always loved too hard and much too often. She was always full with mystery and subtle movements . . . etc., etc., etc. . . . †

There is no possibility, I am afraid, of slurring over this. It is just a thing that you have to accept as an unfortunate handicap in an artist who is in some respects above praise.

* *In Our Time*, pp. 92, 94. Ernest Hemingway.
† *Three Lives*, p. 89. Gertrude Stein.

Sometimes it is less pronounced, there are occasions when it is *almost* absent—Krebs, for instance, is a full-blooded example of Hemingway steining away for all he is worth. But it is never quite absent.

How much does it matter? If we blot out Gertrude Stein, and suppose she does not exist, does this part of Hemingway's equipment help or not? We must answer *Yes* I think. It does seem to help a good deal: many of his best effects are obtained by means of it. It is so much a part of his craft, indeed, that it is difficult now to imagine Hemingway without this mannerism. He has never taken it over into a gibbering and baboonish stage as has Miss Stein. He has kept it as a valuable oddity, even if a flagrantly borrowed one— ever present it is true, but one to which we can easily get used and come to like even as a delightfully clumsy engine of innocence. I don't mind it very much.

To say that, near to communism as we all are, it cannot matter, and is indeed praiseworthy, for a celebrated artist to take over, lock, stock and barrel from another artist the very thing for which he is mainly known, seems to me to be going too far in the denial of the person, or the individual— especially as in a case of this sort, the trick is after all, in the first instance, a *personal* trick. Such a practice must result, if universally indulged in, in hybrid forms or monstrosities.

And my main criticism, indeed, of the *steining* of Hemingway is that it does impose upon him an ethos—*the Stein ethos,* as it might be called. With Stein's bag of tricks he also takes over a *Weltanschauung,*[9] which may not at all be his, and does in fact seem to contradict his major personal quality. This infantile, dull-witted, dreamy stutter compels whoever uses it to conform to the infantile, dull-witted type. He passes over into the category of *those to whom things are done,* from that of those who execute—if the latter is indeed where he originally belonged. One might even go so far as to say that this brilliant Jewish lady had made a *clown* of him by teaching Ernest Hemingway her baby talk! So it is a pity. And it is very difficult to know where Hemingway proper begins and Stein leaves off as an artist. It is an uncomfortable situation for the critic, especially for one who "has a weakness" for the male member of this strange

[9] world view

spiritual partnership, and very much prefers him to the female.

Hemingway's two principal books, *The Sun Also Rises* and *Farewell to Arms,* are delivered in the first person singular. What that involves may not be at once apparent to those who have not given much attention to literary composition. But it is not at all difficult to explain. Suppose you, Raymond Robinson, sit down to write a romance; subject matter, the War. You get your "I" started off, say just before the outbreak of war, and then there is the outbreak, and then "I flew to the nearest recruiting station and joined the army" you write. Then the "I" goes off to the Western Front (or the Italian Front) and you will find yourself writing "I seized the Boche by the throat with one hand and shot him in the stomach with the other," or whatever it is you imagine your "I" as doing. But this "I," the reader will learn, does not bear the name on the title page, namely Raymond Robinson. He is called Geoffrey Jones. The reader will think, "that is only a thin disguise. It is Robinson's personal experience all right!"

Now this difficulty (if it be a difficulty) is very much enhanced if (for some reason) Geoffrey Jones is *always* doing exactly the things that Raymond Robinson is known to have done. If Raymond Robinson fought gallantly at Caporetto, for instance, then Geoffrey Jones—with the choice of a whole earth at war to choose from—is at Caporetto too. If Raymond Robinson takes to the sport of bullfighting, sure enough Geoffrey Jones—the "I" of the novel—is there in the bullring too, as the night follows day. This, in fine, has been the case with Hemingway and *his* First-person-singular.

Evidently, in this situation—possessing a First-person-singular that invariably copies you in this flattering way—something must be done about it. The *First-person-singular* has to be endowed so palpably with qualities that could by no stretch of the imagination belong to its author that no confusion is possible. Upon this principle the "I" of *The Sun also Rises* is described as sexually impotent, which is a complete alibi, of course, for Hemingway.

But there is more than this. The sort of First-person-singular that Hemingway invariably invokes is a dull-witted, bovine, monosyllabic simpleton. This lethargic and stuttering dummy he conducts, or pushes from behind, through all the scenes that interest him. This burlesque First-person-singular behaves in them like a moronesque version of his brilliant author. He *Steins* up and down the world, with the big lustreless ruminatory orbs of a Picasso doll-woman (of the semiclassic type Picasso patented, with enormous hands and feet). It is, in short, the very dummy that is required for the literary mannerism of Miss Stein! It is the incarnation of the Stein-stutter—the male incarnation, it is understood.

But this constipated, baffled "frustrated"—yes, deeply and Freudianly "frustrated"—this wooden-headed, leaden-witted, heavy-footed, loutish and oafish marionette—peering dully out into the surrounding universe like a great big bloated five-year-old—pointing at this and pointing at that—uttering simply "Cat!"—"Hat!"—"Food!"—"Sweetie!"—is as a companion, infectious. His author has perhaps not been quite immune. Seen forever through his nursery spectacles, the values of life accommodate themselves, even in the mind of his author, to the limitations and peculiar requirements of this highly idiosyncratic puppet.

So the political aspects of Hemingway's work (if, as I started by saying, one can employ such a word as *political* in connection with a thing that is so divorced from reality as a super-innocent, queerly sensitive, village idiot of a few words and fewer ideas) have to be sought, if anywhere, in the personality of this *First-person-singular,* imposed upon him largely by the Stein manner.

We can return to the folk-prose problem now and face all the questions that the "done gones" and "sorta gonnas" present. Mr. H. L. Mencken in his well-known, extremely competent and exhaustive treatise, *The American Language* (a classic in this field of research, first published fifteen years ago) affirmed that the American dialect had not yet come to the stage where it could be said to have acquired charm for "the purists." If used (at that time) in narrative literature it still possessed only the status of a disagreeable and socially inferior jargon, like the cockney occurring in a Dickens novel —or as it is still mostly used in William Faulkner's novels, never outside of inverted commas; the novelist, having invoked it to convey the manner of speech of his rustic or provincial puppets, steps smartly away and resumes the narrative in the language of Macaulay or Horace Walpole, more or less.

"In so far as it is apprehended at all," Mencken wrote in 1920, "it is only in the sense that Irish-English was apprehended a generation ago—that is, as something uncouth and comic. But that is the way that new dialects always come in—through a drumfire of cackles. Given the poet, there may suddenly come a day when our *theirns* and *would 'a hads* will take on the barbaric stateliness of the peasant locution of old Maurya in *Riders to the Sea*." *

The reason that the dialect of the Arran Islands, or that used by Robert Burns, were so different from cockney or from the English educated speech was because it was a mixture of English and another language, Gaelic or lowland Scotch, and with the intermixture of foreign words went a literal translation of foreign idioms and the distortions arrived at by a tongue accustomed to another language. It was "broken English," in other words, not "low English," or slum English, as is cockney.

Americans are today un-English in blood—whatever names they may bear: and in view of this it is surprising how intact the English language remains in the United States. But the *Beach-la-mar,* as he calls it, to which Mencken is referring above, is as it were the cockney of America. It has this great advantage over cockney, that it is fed with a great variety of immigrant words. It is, however, fundamentally *a class jargon*; not a jargon resulting from difference of race, and consequently of speech. It is the *patois* [10] of the "poor white," the negro, or the uneducated immigrant. It is not the language spoken by Mrs. Alice Roosevelt Longworth, for instance, or by Ernest Hemingway for that matter. But it is very *American*. And it is a *patois,* a fairly good rendering of which any American is competent to give. And you have read above the affectionate way Mencken refers to *our* "theirns" and "would 'a hads."

English as spoken in America is more vigorous and expressive than Oxford English, I think. It is easy to mistake a native from the wilds of Dorsetshire for an American, I have found: and were "educated" English used upon a good strong reverberant Dorsetshire basis, for instance, it would be all to the good, it is my opinion. Raleigh, Drake, and the rest of them, must have talked rather like that.

But with cockney it is not at all the same thing. There

* *The American Language*, p. 396.
10 provincial dialect, brogue

you get a degradation of English—it is *proletariat*, city-slum English, like Dublin-slum English. That is in a different category altogether to the weighty, rapid, and expressive torrent of the best Dorsetshire talk; and, as I have said, the *best* American is in the same category as the Dorsetshire—or as nonslum Irish—a good, sound accent, too. But the question to be answered is whether the *Beach-la-mar* Mr. Mencken has in mind is not too much the deteriorated pidgin tongue of the United States; and whether, if that is *affectioné* [11] too much by the *literati*—as being the most *American* thing available, like jazz—it is not going to be a vulgar corruption, which will vulgarize, as well as enrich, the tongue. So far it exists generally in inverted commas, as in Mr. Faulkner's books. Is it to be let out or not? A question for Americans.

For fifty years dialect-American has tended, what with negro and immigrant pressure, to simplify itself grammatically, and I suppose is still doing so at this moment.

His (the immigrant's) linguistic habits and limitations have to be reckoned with in dealing with him and the concessions thus made necessary have a very ponderable influence upon the general speech. Of much importance is the support given to the native tendency by the foreigner's incapacity for employing (or even comprehending) syntax of any complexity, or words not of the simplest. This is the tendency towards succinctness and clarity, at whatever sacrifice of grace. One English observer, Sidney Low, puts the chief blame for the general explosiveness of American upon the immigrant, who must be communicated with in the plainest words available, and is not socially worthy of the suavity of circumlocution anyhow. In his turn the immigrant seizes upon these plainest words as upon a sort of convenient Lingua Franca—his quick adoption of *damn* as a universal adjective is traditional—and throws his influence upon the side of the underlying speech habit when he gets on in the vulgate. Many characteristic Americanisms of the sort to stagger lexicographers—for example, *near-silk*—have come from Jews, whose progress in business is a good deal faster than their progress in English.

While England was a uniquely powerful empire-state, ruled

11 fancied or liked

by an aristocratic caste, its influence upon the speech as upon the psychology of the American ex-colonies was overwhelming. But today that ascendancy has almost entirely vanished. The aristocratic caste is nothing but a shadow of itself, the cinema has brought the American scene and the American dialect nightly into the heart of England, and the "Americanizing" process is far advanced. "Done gones," "good guys" and "buddies" sprout upon the lips of cockney children as readily as upon those to the manner born, of New York or Chicago: and there is no politically powerful literate class any longer now, in our British "Banker's Olympus," to confer prestige upon an exact and intelligent selective speech. Americanization—which is also for England, at least, proletarianization—is too far advanced to require underlining, even for people who fail usually to recognize anything until it has been in existence for a quarter of a century.

But if America has come to England, there has been no reciprocal movement of England into the United States: indeed, with the new American nationalism, England is deliberately kept out: and all the great influence that England exerted formally—merely by being there and speaking the same tongue and sharing the same fundamental political principles—that is today a thing of the past. So the situation is this, as far as our common language is concerned: the destiny of England and the United States of America is more than ever one. But it is now the American influence that is paramount. The tables have effectively been turned in that respect.

But there is a larger issue even than that local to the English-speaking nations. English is of all languages the simplest grammatically and the easiest to make into a *Beachla-mar* or *pidgin* tongue. Whether this fact, combined with its "extraordinary tendency to degenerate into slang of every kind," is against it, is of some importance for the future—for it will have less and less grammar, obviously, and more and more cosmopolitan slang.—Mr. Mencken is of the opinion that a language cannot be too simple—he is all for *Beachla-mar*. The path toward analysis and the elimination of inflection, has been trod by English so thoroughly that, in its American form, it should today win the race for a universal volapük. Indeed, as Mr. Mencken says, "the foreigner essaying it, indeed, finds his chief difficulty, not in mastering its forms, but in grasping its lack of form. He doesn't have to learn a new and complex grammar; what he has to do is to forget grammar. Once he has done so, the rest is a mere matter of acquiring a vocabulary."

There is, it is true, the difficulty of the vowel sounds: but that is easily settled. Standard English possesses nineteen distinct vowel sounds: no other living European tongue except Portuguese, so Mr. Mencken says, possesses so many. Modern Greek, for instance, can only boast of five, we are told. "The (American) immigrant, facing all these vowels, finds some of them quite impossible: the Russian Jew, for example, cannot manage *ur*. As a result, he tends to employ a neutralized vowel in the situations which present difficulties, and this neutralized vowel, supported by the slipshod speech habits of the native proletariat, makes steady progress."

That that "neutralized vowel" has made great progress in America no one would deny who has been there; and, starting in the natural language difficulties of the Central European immigrant, the above-mentioned "neutralized vowel" will make its way over here in due course, who can doubt it? These vowels must be watched. *Watch your vowels* should be our next national slogan! The fatal grammatical easiness of English is responsible, however, for such problems as these, as much as the growing impressionability of the English nation, and the proletarianization, rather than the reverse, of the American.

As long ago as 1910 an English traveler, Mr. Alexander Thompson, in a book called *Japan for a Week,* expressed himself as follows:

It was only on reaching Italy that I began fully to realize this wonderful thing, that for nearly six weeks, on a German ship, in a journey of nearly ten thousand miles, we had heard little of any language but English!

It is an amazing thing when one thinks of it.

In Japan most of the tradespeople spoke English. At Shanghai, at Hong Kong, at Singapore, at Penang, at Colombo, at Suez, at Port Said—all the way home to the Italian ports, the language of all the ship's traffic, the language of such discourse as the passengers held with natives, most of the language on board ship itself, was English.

The German captain of our ship spoke English more often than German. All his officers spoke English.

The Chinese man-o'-war's men who conveyed the Chinese prince on board at Shanghai, received commands and exchanged commands with our German sailors in English. The Chinese mandarins in their conversations with the ships' officers invariably spoke English. They use the same ideographs in writing as the Japanese, but to talk to our Japanese passengers they had to speak English. Nay, coming as they did from various provinces of the Empire, where the language greatly differs, they found it most convenient in conversation among themselves to speak English.

If you place side by side the unfortunate impressionability of Hemingway, which caused him to adopt integrally the half-wit simplicity of repetitive biblical diction patented by Miss Stein, and that other fact that Mr. Hemingway, being an American nationalist by temperament, is inclined to gravitate stylistically towards the national underdog dialect, in the last resort to the kind of *Beach-la-mar* I have been discussing, you have the two principal factors in Hemingway as artist in prose fiction, to make of what you can.

Take up any book of his, again, and open it at random: you will find a page of stuff that is, considered in isolation, valueless as writing. It is not written: it is lifted out of Nature and very artfully and adroitly tumbled out upon the page: it is the brute material of everyday proletarian speech and feeling. The *matière* [12] is cheap and coarse: but not because it is proletarian speech merely, but because it is *the prose of reality*—the prose of the streetcar or the provincial newspaper or the five-and-ten-cent store. I have just opened *Farewell to Arms* entirely at random, for instance, and this is what I find:

> "If you had any foreign bodies in your legs they would set up an inflammation and you'd have fever."
> "All right," I said. "We'll see what comes out."
> She went out of the room and came back with the old nurse of the early morning. Together they made

[12] matter, material

the bed with me in it. That was new to me and an admirable proceeding.

"Who is in charge here?"

"Miss Van Campen."

"How many nurses are there?"

"Just us two."

"Won't there be more?"

"Some more are coming."

"When will they get here?"

"I don't know. You ask a great many questions for a sick boy."

"I'm not sick," I said. "I'm wounded."

They had finished making the bed and I lay with a clean, smooth sheet under me and another sheet over me. Mrs. Walker went out and came back with a pyjama jacket. They put that on me and I felt very clean and dressed.

"You're awfully nice to me," I said. The nurse called Miss Gage giggled. "Could I have a drink of water?" I asked.

"Certainly. Then you can have breakfast."

"I don't want breakfast. Can I have the shutters opened, please?"

The light had been dim in the room and when the shutters were opened it was bright sunlight, and I looked out on a balcony and beyond were the tiled roofs of houses and chimneys and the sky very blue.

"Don't you know when the other nurses are coming?"

"Why? Don't we take good care of you?"

"You're very nice."

"Would you like to use the bedpan?"

"I might try."

They helped me and held me up, but it was not any use. Afterward I lay and looked out the open doors on to the balcony.

"When does the doctor come?"

It is not writing, if you like. When I read *Farewell to Arms* doubtless I read this page as I came to it, just as I should watch scenes unfolding on the screen in the cinema, without pictorial criticism; and it, page eighty-three, contributed its fraction to the general effect: and when I had finished the book I thought it a very good book. By that I meant that the cumulative effect was impressive, as *the*

events themselves would be. Or it is like reading a newspaper, day by day, about some matter of absorbing interest
—say the reports of a divorce, murder, or libel action. If
you say *anyone could write it*, you are mistaken there, because, to obtain that smooth effect, of commonplace reality,
there must be no sentimental or other heightening, the number of words expended must be proportionate to the importance and the length of the respective phases of the action, and any false move or overstatement would at once
stand out and tell against it. If an inferior reporter to Hemingway took up the pen, that fact would at once be detected by a person sensitive to reality.

It is an art, then, from this standpoint, like the cinema,
or like those "modernist" still-life pictures in which, in
place of *painting* a match box upon the canvas, a piece of
actual match box is stuck on. A recent example of this (I
choose it because a good many people will have seen it) is
the cover design of the French periodical *Minotaure*, in
which Picasso has pasted and tacked various things together,
sticking a line drawing of the Minotaur in the middle. Hemingway's is a poster art, in this sense: or a *cinema in words*.
The steining in the text of Hemingway is as it were the hand-
made part—if we are considering it as "super-realist" design: a manipulation of the photograph if we are regarding it as a film.

If you say that this is not the way that Dante wrote, that
these are not artistically permanent creations—or not permanent in the sense of a verse of Bishop King, or a page of
Gulliver, I agree. But it is what we have got: there is
actually *bad* and *good* of this kind; and I for my part enjoy
what I regard as the good, without worrying any more about
it than that.

That a particular phase in the life of humanity is implicit in this art is certain. It is one of the first fruits of the
proletarianization which, as a result of the amazing revolutions in the technique of industry, we are all undergoing,
whether we like it or not. But this purely political, or sociological side to the question can be brought out, I believe,
with great vividness by a quotation. Here, for instance, is a
fragment of a story of a mutiny at sea:

I opened the door a little, about two inches, and saw
there was a rope round the companion, which prevented the doors opening. Big Harry and Lips asked me

what I wanted. I said I wanted to go down to the galley. Big Harry said: "Plenty of time between this and eight o'clock; you stop down below." I then went into the chief mate's room, which was the nearest to me. There was nobody there. I went to the second mate's room, he was not there. I went to the captain's pillow, it was standing up in his bed, and I found two revolvers loaded, one with six shots and one with four. I took possession of them and put them in my pockets. I then stood on the cabin table in the after cabin, and lifted the skylight up and tried to get out there. Renken was standing at the wheel, and he called out, "Come aft, boys, the steward is coming out of the skylight." I then closed the skylight and came down again. The after-skylight was close to the wheel, about 10 feet as near as I could guess. I could see him. The light used for the compass is in the skylight, and the wheel is in the back of it. The light is fastened to the skylight to light the compass, and the compass is just in front of the wheel. Before I could get the skylight closed I heard their steps coming aft, and I went down into the cabin and told the boy to light a fire. Shortly afterwards I heard five shots fired on deck . . . about a second afterwards the same as if somebody was running on deck. I could not judge which way they were running; the noise on the deck, and the vessel being in ballast, you could hear as well aft as forward. That was about twenty minutes after hearing the captain call out. I put the revolvers away in my locker. I then took it into my head to take the revolvers into my possession and chance it; if the men came down to me to do anything wrong, to save myself. I put them in my pockets, one on each side. About 5.30 Green, the boatswain, came down first, and French Peter, Big Harry, and all the other lot followed. The deck was left without anybody, and the wheel too, they came into the cabin; Trousillot was there as well. They did not speak at first. The first thing they did was to rub me over. They could not feel anything. I had the two revolvers with me, but they did not feel them. French Peter and Big Harry felt me over. All the others were present. Green said, "Well, steward, we have finished now." I said, "What the hell did you finish?" He said, "We have finished captain, mate and second." . . . The conversation between me and Green was in English, and everybody standing round. He spoke to the other men in Greek. What he said I don't know. I said, "Where are the bodies? Where is the captain?" Green said, "Oh they are all right, they are overboard," and all the men said the same. . . .*

That is not by Hemingway, though it quite well might be. I should not be able to tell it was not by Hemingway if it were shown me as a fragment. But this is by him:

Across the bay they found the other boat beached. Uncle George was smoking a cigar in the dark. The young Indian pulled the boat way up the beach. Uncle George gave both the Indians cigars. They walked up from the beach through a meadow that was soaking wet with dew, following the young Indian who carried a lantern. Then they went into the woods and followed a trail that led to the logging road that ran back into the hills. It was much lighter on the logging road as the timber was cut away on both sides. The young Indian stopped and blew out his lantern and they all walked on along the road.

They came around a bend and a dog came out barking. Ahead were the lights of the shanties where the Indian bark-peelers lived. More dogs rushed out at them. The two Indians sent them back to the shanties. In the shanty nearest the road there was a light in the window. An old woman stood in the doorway holding a lamp.

Inside on a wooden bunk lay a young Indian woman. She had been trying to have her baby for two days. All the old women in the camp had been helping her. The men had moved off up the road to sit in the dark and smoke out of range of the noise she made. She screamed just as Nick and the two Indians followed his father and Uncle George into the shanty. She lay in the lower bunk, very big under a quilt. Her head was turned to one side. In the upper bunk was her husband. He had cut his foot very badly with an axe three days before. He was smoking a pipe. The room smelled very bad. Nick's father ordered some water to be put on the stove, while it was heating he spoke to

* *Forty Years at the Old Bailey.* F. Lamb.

Nick. "This lady is going to have a baby, Nick," he said. "I know," said Nick. "You don' know," said his father. "Listen to me. What she is going through is called being in labor. The baby wants to be born and she wants it to be born. All her muscles are trying to get the baby born. That is what is happening when she screams." "I see," Nick said. Just then the woman cried out.*

The first of these two passages is from a book entitled *Forty Years in the Old Bailey*. It is the account of a mutiny and murder on the high seas, the trial occurring on May 3 and 4, 1876. It was evidence verbatim of one Constant von Hoydonck, a Belgian, twenty-five years of age, who joined the vessel *Lennie* at Antwerp, as chief steward, on October 22. This is a *Querschnitt*, a slice of "real life": and how close Hemingway is to such material as this can be seen by comparing it with the second passage out of *In Our Time*.

That, I think, should put you in possession of all that is essential for an understanding of the work of this very notable artist: an understanding I mean; I do not mean that, as a work of art, a book of his should be approached in this critical and anatomizing spirit. That is another matter. Where the "politics" come in I suppose by this time you will have gathered. This is the voice of the "folk," of the masses, who are the cannon fodder, the cattle outside the slaughter-house, serenely chewing the cud—*of those to whom things are done,* in contrast to those who have executive will and intelligence. It is itself innocent of politics—one might almost add alas! That does not affect its quality as art. The expression of the soul of the dumb ox would have a penetrating beauty of its own, if it were uttered with genius—with bovine genius (and in the case of Hemingway that is what has happened): just as much as would the folk song of the baboon, or of the "Praying Mantis." But where the politics crop up is that if we take this to be the typical art of a civilization—and there is no serious writer who stands higher in Anglo-Saxony today than does Ernest Hemingway—then we are by the same token saying something very definite about that civilization.

* *In Our Time*. Ernest Hemingway.

Jean-Paul Satre: "Plunged Back Into Time"

FOR some time in these pages the scene will now be France. Further, I shall not depart from the concrete henceforth, until the conclusion of the Sartre evidence. This evidence will be of how *not* to be free, or how impossible it is for a writer under certain conditions to be free, or how paradoxically his freedom can be threatened. Everything which regards the independence of thought of the writer, whether in France, America, or elsewhere, is relevant to what ultimately I hope to settle: but France, where more serious writing still is done than in any other country, has always had, after England, first claim on our attention. The French are our nearest neighbors, France is the cultural leader of Europe, its political destiny is involved with ours. So apart from the fact that in this instance one has no choice, as France alone provides the hard logical contrasts required, I do not have to excuse the foreignness.

When I exchanged the method of attempting to conjure up some neutral realm of the mind—a lettered Switzerland of free writers—for the concrete, for Sartre's reporting, I decided to make use of Sartre because I had just been reading his articles in *Les Temps Modernes*. Such contemporary French books as are obtainable also have been occupying me lately: as is quite the rule, in all things of that sort the French astound one by their vitality—whereas the English tend, if not to sag, to fall silent beneath the crushing burden of debt, their kidneys stunned with watery cataracts of beer. Whatever the cause, the literary scene in London resembles a Butlin Camp in an off month, or a mews in a once prosperous quarter taken over by small-time spivs and hardup swells (both sexes, from *Debrett*). Had it occurred to me to make use of the London literary scene instead of Sartre's Paris, patriotism would immediately have stepped in and dissuaded me.

Now Jean-Paul Sartre is as it were the hero of the present volume—or if hero is not exactly the word, I can think of no other. He is one of the least free men of whom I have any knowledge: which is why I have starred him in this book.

The kind of independence of mind which it is essential for the writer to possess cannot be secured in such a society as is depicted by Sartre—and to which the case of Sartre himself bears vivid and exquisite witness. As one watches him feverishly attempting to arrange himself to the best advantage—in accord with the conditions of the postwar forties in France—upon the political scene, which is identical with the literary scene: as far Left as possible without being *extrémiste*: accepting many Communist attitudes but railing at the Communists: peddling an individualism of sorts in the collectivist camp: in a word, attempting to secure all the advantages of an all-out Left position without sacrificing his independence—watching him, one feels what a pity it is that a writer of great talent should have to deflect so much energy into this stupid game. It is even worse when one comes to his novels, for there his talent is unmistakable, they are of great interest. Luckily the damage is not as pervasive as it might be. Still, this admirable observer often falsifies a situation to satisfy some political requirement.

In Russia, I believe, making allowance for the drawbacks of totalitarian life, a writer of this temperament would be better off. Because of course it is not that he is on the side of a new social order that is the trouble. It is the nice and anxious adjustments, the literary falsifications entailed by life in a society which is intensely disturbed politically, but politically hybrid. As a soviet writer he would find that Daniel, the hero of *L'Age de Raison,* had to go, because of his unorthodox sexual habits (as he would also of course here or in the States). This would be a grievous loss; Daniel is a great figure of comedy. But the swarm of excellently observed, clearly differentiated, creatures, which come to life beneath his pen would recommend him strongly to the countrymen of Gogol and Tolstoy.

Sartre ought to live in a one-party state, or in a *no-party* state. That is my considered opinion. Above all, what is needed for his talents to show to the best advantage is a society where a man who announces himself a "revolutionary" immediately has his head cut off. In other words, in a nation that has already had its revolution, an ambitious writer does not have to be worrying about *that* all the time, but can transfer such energy to his *writing*. That is why I suggest Russia.

There is yet another kind of *"pressure,"* with which my reading of Sartre has made me acquainted. I refer to *la pression de l'histoire* *—the pressure of history. That is the subject of this chapter.

I would like to emphasize that the great prominence Sartre has been given in this study is due to something altogether distinct from his literary achievement, which is another question entirely. It is as a *case* that he enters into the scheme of this book. (I do not use this word offensively. His is a *mal du siècle*: [1] we all are in the same century, and all, in one degree or another, in one way or another, sick.) But since I am obliged frequently to refer to his work, in the course of what I shall have to say, I will briefly outline it.

Sartre has written, as I suppose my readers will be aware, of the French offshoots of German "Existenz Philosophie." [2] Martin Heidegger, the most prominent German exponent of this school of thought, is the thinker closest to Sartre, who is merely a gallic variant of Heidegger. If Sartre has borrowed his metaphysics, existentialism owes to him its main international advertisement. Since 1939 any German thinker needs a chaperone or escort to circulate in the outside world, or even someone who will *impersonate* him. Sartre performed this office for the most recent great German pessimist.

We may wonder how a man of Sartre's temperament found his way into the bleak labyrinth of "Sein und Zeit" [3] —or at least how he came to take up his quarters there permanently. There is no spiritual congruity between the creator of Daniel Sereno (*Monsieur Lalique*) the de facto hero of his novel *L'Age de Raison*—between this master of farce, devotee of the absurd—an amused analyst of life's lazy

* P. 1629, *Les Temps Modernes,* June 1947.
[1] disease of the age
[2] Existential philosophy
[3] "Being and Time"

surface (ignoring its fiery center), picking his way with delight through all its unexciting paradoxes—and a philosopher who is the sub-zero climax of German pessimism, whose theme word is not "existence," but "anguish."

This anomaly may be accounted for in the same way as the others which are discussed in this chapter and those that follow. He seems to possess a talent for getting into compartments where he does not belong and then experiencing much difficulty in getting out again—or in feeling that he ought to be something that he is not. So he neglects the excellent material which is by nature his, because of these romantic aberrations. Among the heretics—that is to say those writers who are neither Catholic nor Communist—he stands, with Albert Camus and André Malraux, for what is most alive in contemporary France. Sartre is much the most genial and human of these three. As a novelist he has none of the dry, concentrated force of the novels of Camus, of *La Peste*, of *L'Etranger*: nor the power of that extraordinary play, *Le Malentendu*. Both Camus and he have compiled metaphysical treatises, the principles of which they have developed in their creative writings. But their metaphysical notions resemble each other much more than do the novels and plays that allegedly issue from them. Then the philosophy of the Absurd, as we find it in Camus, is reminiscent of the theories of the Absurd which haunt the pages of Malraux. Sartre's answer to those who assert that his and Camus' philosophy are one and the same is that this is not at all the case: and Camus says the same thing. Camus is more French, says Sartre, than himself, his is the classical Mediterranean pessimism: whereas—presumably he means—*his* (Sartre's) pessimism is of the modern German nihilistic type.—For the rest, Sartre's activity as editor of a fat existentialist monthly (who says there is no paper in France?) as *chef d'école*, [4] lecturer, playwright, etc. etc., is a wonderful testimonial to the intellectual vitality of a bankrupt society.

Now I can return to this new "pressure" of which I have spoken: "the pressure of history." In reply to an inquiry as to what that might signify, some quite elaborate explanation would be forthcoming. What is in fact involved is something as unmysterious as the following. Had you happened to find yourself in the Black Hole of Calcutta, or in the camp at Auschwitz when the gas ovens were working; were you a

[4] head of the school

member of a Hindu working-class family in Lahore in the summer of 1947, a few hours after the announcement of the decision of the British boundary commission, and discovered yourself unexpectedly in Pakistan—even more so were you a poor Moslem in Amritzar about the same time: or had you been a private in a Russian regiment defending Stalingrad —you would be experiencing a great deal of "historic pressure." I do not believe that Sartre could dispute the validity of my illustrations.—Again, had you been a French writer in Paris at the time of the German occupation—were you an active "resister"—you would undoubtedly have experienced the pressure of History, in the form of the Gestapo. I may have overlooked something, but this I believe conveys the idea. History, pushing up against what History is for—Man.

Sartre in this article asserts that we must not "abdicate before what the unspeakable Zaslavski refers to in *Pravda* as the 'Historical processus'." Yet it seems to me that Sartre *does*, after all, abdicate precisely to the "historical process," in a way that Camus does not. It is far from my wish to find fault with Sartre: but in this particular respect I will again compare his attitude with that of his Algerian contemporary, whose fortitude one cannot but admire. The latter does not, like Sartre, waste time pretending to be something that he is not.

Like those who assert that "war brings out the best in people" (it is a saying of which I am not very fond) Sartre tells us that "L'homme tout entier" (man, *all* of him, or total man—a first cousin of "L'homme tout nu," [5] another objectionable abstraction) is only visible during bombardments or massacres, at the moment of a *coup d'état*, or in the torture chamber. This total man is to him so momentous an entity that one cannot help feeling that he "says Yea"—as Nietzsche would put it—to wars, plagues, revolutions, massacres, etc., since these things produce what nothing else does apparently: "l'homme tout entier," or total man. He agrees * that *he* has never suffered the fearful martyrdoms upon which he dwells. ("Certes nous sommes bien loin d'avoir tous ressenti cette angoisse.") [6] But it has "haunted us all like a menace or a promise." (From this word *promise* we are to conclude that he longed for martyrdom.) So vicar-

---

* P. 1629, *Les Temps Modernes.*
[5] man completely naked
[6] We are all very far from having experienced this anguish.

iously and by virtue of a "haunting," we are men whole and entire—"entier" and "tout nu": such is the idea.

Our forerunners knew no such excitements as have been ours. "Those who immediately preceded us, who bequeathed us their culture, their wisdom, their customs, and their proverbs, who built the houses we live in, who planted the statues of their great men all over our cities, practiced modest virtues, and confined themselves to temperate regions." Whereas we, the people of the world wars, of the massacres, bombardments, *coups d'état*—we are necessarily of a heroic mold. Our virtues are either terrific, or else we are submen of the vilest kind. These immediate ancestors of ours, of comfortable prosperous periods, before "air power" held forth the promise to dash you to pieces or shrivel you up from the sky, or the revolutionary brought back the thrilling atmosphere of the Inquisition or the *auto-da-fé*, are to be pitied (and, however we may protest, looked down upon) for never having had the opportunity to be "metaphysical" or to have felt "the pressure of history."

Was not one of those proverbs bequeathed us by some ignoble ancestor (it is not referred to by Sartre—it has just occurred to me): "Blessed is the nation without a history." That's the sort of men they were! They did not love History. They were men of peace.

Now Camus . . . has quite different reactions from these. Far from welcoming "the tragic" as "heroic" material for the literary artist, he is against those things in men which produce it. Incidentally he produces great tragedy that way, as a literary artist, which Sartre does not. He does not wish to see men living in terror—in the midst of massacres, bombardments, tortures, and *pressure*. We find him reacting as violently against those conditions, as Jean-Paul Sartre with a fatalistic gusto exploits them.—But let us patiently follow Sartre upon this path, and allow him to convince us if he can of the beauties of *cyclone literature*.

"Circumstances," he asserts, "have plunged us back into our time." Whereas the novelist of before-the-wars removed himself outside (or above) the contemporaneous, so that his characters might retain their due proportions, and that—thus advantageously placed for all-over observation, judgments might be arrived at (and Sartre in *L'Age de Raison* was of those who thus abstract themselves) this same helicopterizing author would be kicked back into his time in short order.

What happens to the author "plunged back into his time"

in this unceremonious fashion? How can he focus this period of his if he is *inside* it—swallowed by it as Jonah was by the whale?—Well, the following is Sartre's account of how the author converts this necessity into a glorious virtue.

If we are going to handle such a time as the present, we must, as novelists, abandon the Newtonian system, as it were, and pass over into the General Theory of Relativity. (This is not a very original step, even for a novelist to take.) In this way "we people our books with half-lucid, half-dim intelligences."

In pursuance of this theory of historical immersion Sartre moved into the cinematographic method (known as *simultanéité*) of *Le Sursis*.[7] The obvious inconvenience of writing "au sein de l'histoire," [8] covered with blood and sweat and tears—of treating of an epoch which is "incomprehensible" because you have your face jammed up against it—the difficulty and inconveniences of this theory and of all of its class may be explained as follows.—You are in a fire at a theater, say: caught in a stampede you find yourself at the bottom of a pile of struggling bodies. That is the kind of situation that Sartre postulates in his expression "au sein de l'histoire": were it yours and were you able to express yourself, you could certainly give to this "événement" [9] a "brutale fraîcheur" [10] all right—its "opacité menaçante," [11] as likewise its "imprévisibilité." [12] The hot and passionate immediacy of the crudeness of living would be there: and all its *blindness* too.

Of this blindness Sartre makes a great deal: of the beauty of not understanding what is happening to one. Not only helplessness, but noncomprehension, is somehow an asset. At this point another and quite distinct issue becomes visible. It is that issue which possesses most relevance for my present argument. Before turning to it, however, I will attend to the purely aesthetic objections to Sartre's theory.

His "cyclone aesthetic," as we may call it, offends of course against the classic rules of restraint and intelligibility: but it is not for that reason that it fails to recommend itself

7 *The Reprieve*
8 in the bosom of history
9 event
10 brutal directness
11 menacing opacity
12 unexpectedness

to me. My criticism would be this: what this fragmentary peepshow may gain in sensational intensity, it loses in the more comprehensive satisfactions which intensity rules out (or perhaps intensity is not the word but a technique of the naïve close-up). Though it may feed—perhaps overfeed—the senses, it starves the intellect. Then since there is no person of vigorous mind who does not possess the will to understand, nor does anyone care to be left permanently in the dark, this method must always leave a disagreeable sensation, as also will its kaleidoscopic chaos. Any art which condemns its public to the stunned confusion experienced at the climax of a "great historical event" can hardly satisfy for long.

Even apart from all question of shock, or the character to be expected of "crisis literature," there are the unalterable objections to any impressionist technique, the piece of pioneer impressionism—which is a landmark in literary history —to be found in La Chartreuse de Parme, is the classic illustration.* It showed people that all that need be done is to cut a little bit out of a material: the entire bolt of cloth is not indispensable. So you get a minute fraction of a great total event—namely the Battle of Waterloo.—For myself the massive totality, Napoleon in his hat pointed laterally, Wellington in hat pointed fore and aft, Blucher stuffily Prussian—these with all their respective hordes slowly clashing, weaving and reclashing, alone would satisfy me.—Impressionism is too doctrinally the art of the individual.

Having disposed of the purely aesthetic problem, I will now return to the blindness—the "noncomprehension"—of Sartre's victim of History. This type of writer is supposed, you recall, to be confined to the heart of a cyclone, and to know no more than a newborn earthworm would know in that situation. He does not know what a cyclone is—he does not even know it is a *cyclone*.

He apparently does not *want* to know what causes cyclones, or to consider how best to guard against their accidence. All he wants to do is to experience their awful *pressure*—and to express his profound pessimism at the thought of this meaningless adventure between two Nothings. It is an attitude that might recall the Puritan, for whom life could not be disagreeable and wild enough to suit

* It is the battle scene of course to which reference is made.

his taste. What makes it so exquisite for Sartre is that it is purposeless.

"An author who two centuries hence decided to write a historical novel about the war of 1940"—*he* would know a great deal more about it than we do, Sartre affirms. Therefore he would not have to act as if he were practically flattened out beneath "the pressure of history."—But this is strange. I should have thought myself that I know more about it than will anyone two hundred years hence. And I should have said, too, that we knew a good deal now about the causes of wars in general. Of course we feel their *pressure*. Indeed, they leave us ruined, loaded with debt, on each occasion with far less freedom than before. But there is nothing mysterious or, as Sartre calls it, "enigmatic" about them. It is a pretentious affection, I think, to call them that.

If in a war I had my leg blown off by a bomb I should know perfectly well how that bomb had come to be made. Its historic pedigree I should have no difficulty whatever in drawing up. I cannot believe that Sartre is more innocent than I am.

Sartre is too much a man of policy; an opportunist where Camus is not. It is, however, today in France difficult for a writer not to adopt, for political reasons, all kinds of unnatural attitudes. In Sartre's creative work these pressures are not, as I have said, present to the same degree. But whenever some false position has to be taken up, in a novel, to satisfy opinion, a dead patch is there in his writing—wooden and studied as the photo-group of a newly wedded pair.

When I was analyzing the hero in Hemingway's novels, in an essay which had for title "The Dumb Ox" * I described the characters in his books, I remember, as being invariably the kind of people *to whom things are done,* who are the passive (and rather puzzled) guinea-pig type—as remote as it is possible to be, for instance, from Nietzsche's "super" type. The young soldier, in what has been called, not inappropriately, "the greatest love story in modern literature," would have none of his melting Pagliaccio-like pathos were it not for this. But he is of course—as he *must* be—cattle and not butcher.

This is not a shortcoming in a work of art: it defines it merely. It says that the work in question is classifiable as lyrical. As we know, the *jeune premier* [13] must not be un-

---

* *Men Without Art,* 1934.
[13] actor playing the young lover

usually endowed with anything but looks. *Bel canto* is allergic to superman. Then Hemingway has been a chronicler, of exceptional genius, of folk-emotions. It is quite a different matter when a writer adopts the outlook of a bivalve *for himself*. To draw attention to *that* is not complimentary: he is after all not a pathetic figure in a book. The writer is in life (whether you say he is without intermission making himself out of Nothing, or, contrariwise, that his past and future lie outstretched like a temporal landscape across which he crawls). There—in life—one has to acquire a knowledge of the functioning of the social machine. If, for instance, the writer throws a metaphysical mist over the otherwise easily identifiable operation of power politics, or cultivates the attitudes of primitive man toward the violence of the elements, and applies it to the more violent phenomena of social life,* he is highly artificial.

Social action would be altogether paralyzed, that is what I mean, were everyone to adopt the attitude that they were feeling their way about in their time like lost children, describing all that occurred as "inexplicable," or "enigmatic." To which of course it is necessary to add that there have been many other catastrophes in our world prior to world wars *one* and *two*. It is a result of this reasoning that, although the pacifism of Camus seems to me too narrow a position, I prefer it to Sartre's glorification of the "heroic."

Existentialism is of course involved to some extent in the subject matter of this chapter. Existentialism has been called "the philosophy of crisis." Therefore, whatever was its origin, it is regarded, in its effects, and especially because of its phenomenal success, to be closely related to the tragic situation in which men suddenly find themselves everywhere. This resolves itself into a question of how "crisis" should be met: or, to put it in another way, what is the best philosophy for crisis. I think I ought to add, since I have mentioned Hemingway—who with Faulkner has now for some time exercised a considerable influence upon young Frenchmen—that the hero of *L'Etranger,* Albert Camus' admirably written (though not otherwise I am afraid very admirable) novel, is a moron. A moron is not the same thing as a "dumb ox": but they are of the same family.

---

* It is in M. Meursault, Albert Camus' little clerk, that this "crisis literature" reaches its ultimate expression.

Malraux and Escape Through Action

In André Malraux we have another extraordinary case, even more so than that of Jean-Paul Sartre, of a political flirt. His was a far more *violent* flirtation, as everything about him is more violent. Malraux never became a member of the Communist party—and now he is publicity chief in the entourage of the French Franco, General Charles de Gaulle. He did everything that can be done *short of* becoming a party member. He took part in the Communist revolution at Canton: he was with the Russian air force in the Spanish Civil War; he went to party rallies in Moscow. Why did he not regularize this long-standing relationship? I know the answer in Sartre's case: but as regards Malraux I do not think I know it. I can only suppose he is one of those men of action who is really only an actor.

Although Malraux is not an existentialist, he is more *existent* and *concrète* than most. "Il n'y a de réalité que dans l'action," [1] Sartre insists: Malraux's life has been all action, the penalty of which—from the writer's standpoint —is that the vitality in his books is only borrowed from his life, and less dense than it otherwise would be. Yet Malraux studied and wrote of "the Absurd" before Camus, or Fondane, or Sartre: the influence of his mind has been very considerable. My purpose in writing about him here, however, is mostly to fill out the Sartre picture.

When Sartre aspires to be violent he goes to the brain (as in *La Nausée*): he uses madness as Thomas Mann uses disease. His dramatic power is very small: an example of this is *Huis-Clos*, which has the familiar air, from the first page, of a Palais Royal farce, written with great spirit. The stock figures and stock dialogue of the *Garçon d'Etage* and the *Locataire* reek (delightfully) of the French theaters which cater for those who wish to give themselves up to laughter. Comedy it remains to the end, where another writer would have made it Grand Guignolesque. *Les Mouches* though

---

[1] There is no reality except in action.

philosophically interesting, is as unpurgative as a play by Mr. Shaw. The most dramatic thing in it is where the murderer of Agamemnon, seeing Orestes with drawn sword, receives him kindly, saying among other things "I am glad it is too late (to call for help). I want you to assassinate me": which of course Orestes does. Sartre outdoes the classical fatality in the flatness of his dénouement.

Having read most of Sartre's books, I find him a gentle philosophic spirit (which is what I like most about him—I am paying him a compliment)—with a great salacious appetite for life, like many Frenchmen. He is not a bad man, of that I am sure. In his best-known novel, *L'Age de Raison*, the hero Mathieu steals 3,000 francs from a woman performer in his favorite night spot: Mathieu's favorite pupil is thievish—books is what he mainly steals; this young man's sister, Ivich, is a lesbian, who squeezes her thighs together and has an orgasm while sitting in cafés; the de facto hero of the book, Daniel Sereno, is a very active homosexual indeed, who among other drolleries, has an amusing fight with a scrubby little *tapette* [2] in whose room he is passing the night: and so on. In order to play a major role in a novel of Sartre's you have to be able to do some parlor trick of this sort (though homicide is barred). Sartre must not be blamed for this. He writes faithfully about what he knows. If a hospital nurse wrote a book, there would be something the matter with all her characters: one would have ulcers, another would be incontinent, a third would suffer from epileptic seizures.

When Malraux aspires to be violent it is a different matter. Homicide is *not* barred with him. In fact, homicidal propensities are an indispensable qualification for starring in one of his novels. I have here a paper-covered volume, from the cover of which one is vamped by a very interesting dark brooding young man. Its author is M. Claude Mauriac (son of François Mauriac): but he is *not* the dark-eyed young man. That is André Malraux *jeune*, in the days when he was starting his career of political filibustering and Byronism up-to-date. The title of this study is *Malraux. Le Mal du Héros*. It seethes with romanticism, like so much French writing. Malraux is of course the "Hero." The personalities of M. Mauriac (*fils*) and Malraux, in contact as we find them in this book, provide a demonstration interesting to the critic; for the critic cannot fail to remark that Mauriac's is the sort of mind for whom Malraux's books were destined. We may observe his books in action, as it were, within the mind of an admirer, who may be regarded as a reagent. I look upon this book as a critical "find."

With regard to the Hero's "mal," one of the principal forms it takes is a blood obsession—he is "haunted by blood." But Mauriac has not selected this particular hero to write about without having as we shall presently see a certain taste for it himself. Action appears to him to be the highest good. And M. Mauriac is in no doubt as to the *kind* of action which is the most worthy of our admiration. "Perhaps even," he writes, "the intelligence does not reach its final perfection except in action, and preeminently in what is its ultimate form, namely combat." The fighting man is the flower of mankind: the human intelligence only reaches its perfection when it plunges its sword into a human body, or blows it up with a bomb. If no war is going on at the moment, and an *exceptionally* intelligent man is waiting (rather wearily) for peace to stop, he can always pick a quarrel with a stranger in the street, and try to bash his face in.—M. Mauriac does not like people who do not share these views. He growls: "There is no literature more abject than that which speaks ill of war."

Murder is not quite the same thing as spitting your man in a charge, or blowing him up with a land mine, or dropping a bomb on his head: however, let me quote M. Claude Mauriac, where he is considering his hero's penchant for assassination.

> Malraux's obsession with murder assumes the form alternately of temptation and remorse. Do the heroes of his books wish to liberate themselves by a subterfuge from the memory of one of their murders: or do they in fact see in crime—already committed or in prospect —an indispensable experience?

All these writers suffer from the disadvantage of never having killed anybody, says one of (Malraux's) heroes, in speaking of the Russian novelists. He expounds as follows:

> If the characters in their books suffer after having killed somebody, it is because the world has hardly changed at all for them. I say *hardly*. Had it happened

in life, instead of a book, the world would have been transformed for them completely, all its perspectives altered: it would have become not the world of a man who "had committed a crime," but that of a man who had *killed*.

I shall comment as I go along; in the above passage Dostoevsky is doubtless the Russian author most obviously involved: *Crime and Punishment,* the book that would first come to mind. The first thing to remark is that Dostoevsky was very actively a Christian, and none of Malraux's heroes are that. Secondly, to suppose that Dostoevsky was incapable of imagining the state of mind of a non-Christian murderer is to underestimate the insight and imaginative faculty of a great creative genius. But that is not all. The implication of course is that Malraux himself has murdered one or more people. This seems to thrill M. Mauriac (though it by no means follows that Malraux *is* a murderer): he even believes, if I have not misunderstood him, that the murder done by Tchen (in *La Condition Humaine*) is in fact one done by Malraux—his favorite one. Probably his *first* (when he lost his virginity as a man-who-had-not-killed)! This is our point of departure—for M. Mauriac's book begins with the passages I am quoting: that André Malraux was a murderer. A real man—an *homme tout entier*,[3] as Sartre would put it.

I may be mistaken, but I should say that very few of the writers I know have cut a man's throat or plunged a dagger into his heart. Even Hemingway has probably murdered no one. Except for the murdering that a great many of us have to our credit as soldiers, I very much doubt if Hemingway can claim to have taken life—a humiliating thought, which puts him in the same category as Dostoevsky, Tolstoy, Gogol and Tchekov.

I continue my quotation—M. Mauriac is still speaking of *La Condition Humaine*, which he describes, correctly, as one of Malraux's best books. His best, I should say.

Tchen, asking Gisors if he had already killed, and receiving a negative reply, suddenly had the feeling "that there was something lacking in Gisors."
Gisors asked:

[3] a whole man

"The first woman you slept with—what did you feel afterward?"

"Pride."

"At being a man?"

"At not being a woman," Tchen replied. . . .

"And you were right to have mentioned women. Perhaps one has a great contempt for the person one kills. But one despises him less than one does the others."

"You mean than those who do not kill?"

"Than those who do not kill—than virgins (*les puceaux*)."

(Practically all the readers of this book of Malraux's must have been in this sense virgins, or *des puceaux*. What would their sensations be, I wonder? From the great success accorded to it, shame must have been experienced, I suppose. Its readers were intended to feel small, and they did feel small—if writers they must have experienced something of the feeling of the sexually impotent. Being French [with vanity as a national vice—*vide* Stendhal] they must have promised themselves at the first opportunity, with a reasonable assurance of impunity that is, to correct this oversight, due to a sissy upbringing).

M. Mauriac tends to suggest, however, though he does not say so outright, that Malraux only committed *one* murder.

It is always the same murder that these executioners of Malraux's commit, as if a precise recollection, a constant and immutable reference, forbade the novelist to change in the smallest particular narratives of which the intangible contents were once and for all fixed.

"Hong asked me once," said Klein, "what my feelings had been in executing Kominsky. I replied that all the time I was thinking I ought to have used a revolver. . . . With a revolver I should have finished him off without touching him. . . ." *

(The idea in this last passage is that when he was committing his one and only murder he used a knife and that he found contact with his victim's body disagreeable.)

* *The Conquerors.*

Leaving murder, we arrive, under the guidance of M. Mauriac, at sadism.

> To humiliate is one of the principal pleasures of the erotic heroes of Malraux. . . . This madness—dry, meticulous, reasonable even in its ever more imperious unreason—this gloomy fury has a name, which is *sadism*.

M. Mauriac quotes all through the book from Col. Lawrence who greatly influenced Malraux it would seem, and with whom he had, according to this writer, many points of resemblance: except of course that Malraux was not his own hero. He had Garine, Perken and so forth to stand for him. Chapter II of *Le Mal du Héros* opens with a discussion of these parallel destinies; and then an incident in *The Seven Pillars of Wisdom* is placed in evidence. It is Lawrence's account of the execution which he carried out, the victim being an Arab called Ahmed, a member of his escort who in a dispute with another Arab had killed him.*

> Lawrence pushed Ahmed into a damp and somber gully: standing at the entrance he gave him a few moments of respite, which the condemned man spent upon the ground weeping. Then, having made him stand up, he fired into his chest:
> He fell bellowing into the grass: the blood spurted out in bursts, running over his clothes: the convulsions of his body flung him almost up to my feet. I fired again, but trembling so much that he was only hit in the hand. He continued to cry out, but with less and less force, now lying upon his back, his feet toward me. I leaned forward to give him the coup de grâce, beneath the jaw, in the fat of the neck. The body gave a shudder and I called the Ageyls. . . .

Two subtitles accompany this page (in the *Seven Pillars*): A MURDER (this refers to the Arab's act): ANOTHER MURDER (namely the execution).

A lot of dialectic accompanies this ecstatic taking of life in Malraux's stories, however. The second line of the first page of *La Condition Humaine* contains the word "angoisse"—anguish ("L'angoisse lui tordait l'estomac" 4). This is one of

---

* I translate from the French, since a copy of the *Seven Pillars* is not immediately available.
4 Anguish wrenched his stomach.

the words some people get tired of reading in his books:
it occurs very often. Tchen is discovered about to murder a
man lying inside a mosquito net. I speak of this event most
humbly as a mere *puceau*: [5] but would a tough Chinese
have *quite* so many sensations (of a European kind) while
going about this little bit of revolutionary business? Would
he experience "une atmosphère de folie," [6] etc?

In the twenties, in describing not only himself but those
who shared his temperament and outlook, Malraux wrote:
"pensée nihiliste, destructrice, foncièrement négative." [7] According to a critic, M. Gaetan Picon, he built for himself
in contemporary literature a place beside Chateaubriand,
Byron, d'Annunzio, Barrès, Montherlant. This unsympa-
thetic critic speaks of the romanticism which entered into
his revolutionary *parti pris* [8] (and this is what the Communists found embarrassing too): of the "goût du spectacle,
de l'apothéose, de l'apocalypse." [9] Then "le néant" [10] was
haunting the pages of Malraux long before it took up its
quarters as the major concept of Sartre's system. And did he
not write: "In imposing his personality upon the external
world man finds the only outlet which remains to him, his
one and only chance of escaping—imperfectly—from Nothingness (*au néant*)?"

Here you see in this *escape through action* theory none
other than J. P. Sartre's conception of Freedom. How this
action theory of "imposing your personality upon the world"
may very easily develop into a quite substantial *power complex* may be judged by pondering these further words of
Malraux's. "To lead, to be he who decides, to coerce. That is
to live!" Those ways of feeling are contagious, who can
doubt? How many people were there in Western Europe between the wars nursing feverish power complexes, besides the
Duces and the Führers? Malraux's account of his own
power impulses represented them as *an escape from Nothingness*—on the part of a "nihilistic" and "negative" thinker
—would not some such formula have accommodated Hitler
very well? The filling of a void with shouting crowds, and
tramping feet, by a man who was convulsively wrenching
himself out of Nothingness?

5 virgin   6 a feeling of madness in the air
7 nihilistic, destructive, thoroughly negative thought
8 preconception, prejudice
9 fondness for the spectacular, for apotheosis, for the apocalyptic
10 the Nothingness

What was—and is—this Nothingness, which began filling Europe at the beginning of the twenties like an evil fog? Which plunged all kinds of people into acts of violence—which were in a sense acts of *escape*? Which caused men frantically to snatch at power? All men are able to examine this intangible, dark and chilling emanation, and answer that question for themselves.

At the time of the publication of Malraux's *La Lutte avec L'Ange,* a certain M. Mounin, what Sartre would call a Communist watchdog, described it I gather as a "backsliding." But here are his words.

"All that Malraux, we had thought, had got out of his system—'anguish' regarding man's destiny, the 'absurd' obsession of death—erupts into his work once more, without other opposition than that of fragile emotions, of brief evidences *fulgurants* [11] such as we get with Sartre." Another Communist, Pierre Hervé, speaks of his "degradation of man": which is the same criticism that Henri Lefebvre, you will recall, brought against Sartre. In all cases these Communist critics approach the writings in question from a basis of hard debunking good sense. It is a pity these people seem to have almost a monopoly in France of that firmness—where so much is jelly. Why Sartre wrote his *Existentialism is a Humanism* was to counter such criticism as this. So I think I have been able to establish how close is the relationship between Malraux and Sartre, but that both come out of the same Night and Void as the Western European politics of the past quarter of a century.

Postscript. Again I should point out that these writers—Sartre, Malraux, Camus and others of this group—are unusually gifted, remarkable both for their creative ability and philosophical ability. I should be very sorry if it were thought that I was treating them with insufficient respect, or throwing doubt upon their genius. It is their *Weltanschauung* which I deplore. More particularly let me repeat, it is as cases that I have been studying them; namely, as Twentieth Century writers, with what is obviously a complaint, a *mal,* environmental in origin. The freedom problem is implicit in this. In such a study the more we know of the sort of writer involved, and of his milieu, the easier it will be to arrive at a valid judgment.

[11] flashing

A Derelict Author in Search of a Public

I NOW begin a somewhat extended analysis of the contents of what were, in the first instance, two chapters in *Temps Modernes*. These articles, with unexpected promptitude, were republished in book form (in England, *What is Literature?*—Methuen). Here I retain the translation I made from the articles: also I retain the full complement of quotations to facilitate analysis. The significance of this material is my justification for including so much of Sartre's text. In these spontaneous journalistic outpourings he is quite at his best. For the rest, he never deviates from his curious tightrope performance: *ad nauseam* denunciations of "la bourgeoisie," and those writers like Flaubert, who were, he insists, saturated with the bourgeois ethos: unceasing claims to "proletarian" status, reparading of the main Marxist dogma in Marxist jargon—*but* simultaneous repudiation of Marx, denunciation of the Communists, and so forth (with infinite verbosity) without end. One of the things he never tires of attacking is "style"—fetish of the writers who achieved "fame" in bourgeois days (i.e. before 1939). There is a reason for Sartre's dislike of style. It is a very obvious reason, which it is entirely unnecessary to specify more fully.

The pressure—and the submission to pressure, accompanied by a rationalization of same—which I was studying in the last chapter, was pressure truly of the most comprehensive kind: the pressure exercised by "great historical events." It was my contention that the writer should refuse to allow his freedom of thought or of vision—whatever might happen to his other freedoms—to be affected by the most oppressive conditions of which history is capable. Mine was I believe—regarded from that angle—a more *heroic* counsel than the somewhat theatrical cult of the hero outlined by Sartre: though, as I said, this should not be held too much against him since everybody, whether Communist,

Catholic, or heretic, has the word "hero" on his lips with a frequency that I have never encountered before.

As to the employment of existentialism as a mental specific for a period of great crisis: a pessimistic metaphysic actually invented for History's helots would be, as it were, *lyrical thinking*. The Volga Boat Song, or the Welsh "Bottle Song," would answer the purpose better than a metaphysic: and of course any thinking must be discredited which dresses Truth up to accord with the bleak inclemency of History at a given moment.

In the present very long chapter Sartre will be seen in what is at least a more active role: that of the soberly defiant heretic. Without necessarily sympathizing with his heresies, one could approve of the independence he displays, provided that independence were logically grounded, which I am afraid in one respect it is not. But I shall come to that later on.—In the course of his analysis of the brilliant but desperate position in which he finds himself, he does succeed in teaching us a great deal about the fundamentals of the writer's destiny in the contemporary world. It is with a shock of surprise that one listens to a writer who, within two or three years, has become one of the most discussed personalities in the world, explaining how unfortunate his lot is—deriding his international fame, which he looks upon as a particularly scurvy trick played him by fate.

In the first place Sartre is quite clear about his irretrievably *heretical* position.

> In the XIXth Century the writer had to lead an exemplary life and give many pledges of his good conduct to the bourgeoisie, in order to wash himself clean of what in their eyes was the sin of writing. For literature is in its essence heresy. The position has not changed, except in this respect that now it is the Communists who, on principle, regard the writer as a suspect.

He is a heretic for the Communists, as also for the Catholics, though it is the Communists who present by far the graver problems for him: and as you see here, it is only the Communists he mentions. And that is the situation with which we are concerned in this chapter, in all its aspects.

I do not believe that at any time Sartre was very near to joining the Communist party, but he was often no doubt as near to it as he could get without becoming a member.

In his novel *L'Age de Raison* (the first of a trilogy, en-
titled *Les Chemins de la Liberté*), in the attitudes of his hero
Mathieu Delarue we obtain I believe a close approximation
to what must have been his own experience in the thirties.
There is a scene for instance where the hero's brother
Jacques is giving him a piece of his mind. He says:

> "You condemn capitalist society, yet you are a civil
> servant in the employ of that society: you advertise your
> sympathy for the principles of communism, but you take
> good care not to join the Communist party. You despise
> the middle class, yet you belong to the middle class . . .
> live like a *bourgeois*."

There is another episode in the same book where Brunet,
one of his two or three closest friends, for whom he not only
feels great affection but for whom he has an almost superstitious respect—has come to see Mathieu at his flat: come
with the avowed purpose of leading him off to the Communist party headquarters to be signed on as a party member.
Brunet is an official of the party: he uses all his great influence with Mathieu to persuade him to take this one more
little step—instead of fellow-traveling (and getting a great
deal of cheap and easy fun out of it) . . . instead of using
all the Communist jargon, experiencing rages and Communist exultations, to quite simply (and why not?) *become
a Communist*. Anything rather than the perpetual flirtation
—or so the exasperated reader is bound to feel. But I will
quote a page or so—it is Mathieu replying to his friend.

> "I should like nothing better than to work with you,"
> Mathieu agreed; "I need to forget about myself for a
> while—I am sick of myself. And then I think like you
> that one is not a man so long as one has not found
> something one would die for."
> Brunet had lifted his head.
> "Well—so what?" he asked almost gaily.
> "Well! there it is: I cannot engage myself, I have not
> sufficient reason to do that. I rail like you against the
> same people, against the same things—but not *enough*.
> I can't help it. If I joined a procession raising my fist
> in the air and singing the Red Flag, and if I declared
> myself satisfied with that, I should be lying to myself."

Brunet had assumed his most massive air: most peasant-like—he resembled a tower. Mathieu gazed at him with despair.

[Brunet hopes that a more propitious occasion will present itself and that that, as he remarks, will be as soon as possible.]

"I hope so too," Mathieu replied.

Brunet looked at him with curiosity.

"Are you sure that you hope that?" he asked.

"Why yes. . . ."

"Yes? Well, so much the better. Only I fear that that moment will not arrive so quickly as all that."

"I was thinking the same thing," Mathieu said, "I was thinking to myself that it perhaps would never arrive: or too late, or that perhaps there is no such thing as a *propitious occasion.*"

So Brunet departs. Mathieu is left alone to brood over this situation—of being the "fellow traveler" who never gets anywhere since he only travels to give himself an air and to amuse himself.

He comes however to the following conclusions, as he leans out of the window—disgusted with his apartment, the comfortable furnishings of which (especially the armchairs) Brunet has said *corrupts.*

"I refused," he tells himself, "because I wish to remain free: that's what I can say. I can say . . . I love my green curtains, I like taking the air, of an evening, upon my balcony and I do not want to make a change in all that: it pleases me to swell with indignation against capitalism and I should not like to see capitalism abolished, because I should no longer have any excuse for getting indignant: it pleases me to feel myself disdainful and solitary: it pleases me to say *no*—always no: and I should be afraid that they would try and construct for good and all a livable world, because all I could do then would be to say *yes* and to do like other people."

This self-analysis—if that is what it is—will at a later stage, only, acquire for the reader its full significance. I have quoted at such length because Sartre's hero—a professor of philosophy like himself at a Lycée, as he too was at the time, and extremely tall, as an author so lacking in inches as Sartre would be certain to make his mouthpiece—exhibits what must have been almost exactly his creator's state of mind in the thirties, before a definite position had been taken up, while he was still a young unknown professor.

With photographic distinctness we see the stages through which he passed (if I am right) to reach his present position —one of acute discomfort. For there is no ease to be had for a French writer today or reasonable degree of security— no status at all in fact—outside of the Catholic fold or the Communist party, unless his personality is a very strong one. This he makes dazzlingly clear in these articles.

The chain of quotations which will follow will show him desirous of being as far to the left—for tactical career reasons—as it is possible to be, while criticizing Marx and denouncing the Communists. Superficially it is reminiscent of the Anglo-Catholic, employing a liturgy as far as may be identical with the Catholic, but obstinately shy of taking the obvious step and entering the Roman communion. The resemblance would break down at once if examined attentively: for whereas the Anglo-Catholic is sentimentally attached to and full of admiration for the great professionals of religion he imitates, Jean-Paul Sartre most heartily detests the Communists: about that there is no question. He angrily complains that they are keeping him away from the People.

This complaint of his has a distinctly comic sound. Whether he is conscious of this or not it is difficult to say: I suppose he must be. He explains how the proletariat are the writer's natural and necessary public. But he is *without a public,* he protests, since between himself and the People stands the Communist party. "Malheureusement, de ces hommes, à qui nous *devons* parler, un rideau de fer nous sépare dans notre propre pays: ils n'entendront pas un mot de ce que nous leur dirons." [1] An "iron curtain—in our own country, separates us from our own people." But let me quote the rest of this paragraph, translating as I go.

The majority of the proletariat, corseted by a unique party, encircled by a propaganda which isolates it, forms a closed society, without doors or windows. There is only one road, exceedingly narrow, by which one may

[1] Unfortunately, an iron curtain separates us in our own country from these men to whom we *must* speak: they will not hear a word of what we say to them.

gain access to it: namely that provided by the Communist party.—Is it desirable that the writer should take this road? If he does so as a citizen from conviction and out of disgust with literature, that is all right: he has made his choice. But can he become a Communist and remain a writer?

This rhetorical question he answers in the negative. "Since we are still free," he declares, "we will not go and join the watchdogs of the Communist party."

Or again: "If one asks whether the writer, in order to reach the masses, should offer his services to the Communist party, my answer is *no*. The policy of stalinist communism in France is incompatible with the honest exercise of the profession of man-of-letters."

Before proceeding I should perhaps offer an apology.— Quotations are more attractive for the student than for the general reader, it is obvious. But if one gives only a digest of what the writer under discussion has said, uninterrupted by quotations, in order to effect its introduction into the system of the reader with the minimum demands upon his attention, much is lost in the process. There is a tone of voice, a manner of delivery, which only direct quotation can communicate, the importance of which cannot be exaggerated in such a case as the present. So I shall pursue the method of verbatim quotation throughout. If he check the impatient reaction provoked by a bumpy road—since one is all the time bouncing one's way over bits of text enclosed in quotes—I am sure the general reader would at the end be in possession of a much sharper and more accurate picture of the French literary scene he is invited to examine than would otherwise be the case.

The reason, then, given by Sartre for desiring with an almost pathological intensity the proletariat as a public is because "a revolutionary public" is essential (he does not explain very clearly why—though we should of course be great fools if we could not guess, in the year 1952). "To-day," he writes, "we turn toward the working class, which constitutes for us a revolutionary public, such as was the bourgeoisie in 1780." A public like that enjoyed by the XVIIIth Century *philosophes* is indispensable. No explanation. Some might have thought after all that one might prefer to be a XVIIth Century writer *without* a revolutionary

public. But Sartre takes it for granted you understand why it must be an XVIIIth Century writer and public.
Or is this an explanation?

In 1780 the oppressor class was the only one that had an ideology and political organization: the bourgeoisie possessed neither party, nor political self-consciousness, the writer worked directly for it by his criticism of the ancient myths of monarchy and of religion; by presenting it with some elementary notions, mainly of negative content, such as those of liberty and political equality and of *habeas corpus*. In 1850 (on the other hand) in face of a fully conscious bourgeoisie furnished with a systematic ideology of its own, the proletariat remained without form and without a clear notion of itself, shaken with vain and desperate angers. The First International had only touched its surface: everything remained to be done. The writer could have addressed himself directly to the workers. He missed the opportunity, as we know, . . . the circumstances permitted him to bear witness for the oppressed before the oppressor, and to help the oppressed to become conscious of themselves: the essence of literature found itself in agreement with the requirements of the historic situation.—But today, everything is transformed: the oppressor class has lost its ideology, its consciousness of itself vacillates. . . . The oppressed class, squeezed tightly into a party machine, strapped into a rigorous ideology, becomes a closed society: one can no longer communicate with this class without an intermediary.

Here, as you see, is a Marxist interpretation of history, apart from the last few sentences, where he becomes a raving heretic. The world for him begins in 1780 or thereabouts; so far so good. But it ends for some mysterious reason at the October Revolution (even though elsewhere Sartre explains that this oppressor is, in France, dying a natural death, is *in extremis,* and has to be propped up for tactical reasons, by the oppressed)! "The workman seeks to liberate himself," he cries, "and in so doing to liberate men everywhere, for all time, from oppression."

No one at this date could be found who would question the dark facts of industrial slavery, no "intellectual" that is.

All the more is this the case in an era of inflation and Black Markets. The gulf between the haves and have-nots is shamefully visible to everybody. Yet the last-quoted sentences of our author, "to liberate men everywhere, for all time": what is it makes him use such empty words? One knows why Mr. Lloyd George in World War I made use of a phony lyricism, to enjoin men to persist in so exceptional and wearisome a massacre (and why Hitler admired those speeches so greatly): called them "heroes," gilded their horizons with the promise of perpetual peace. But philosophy has a different language from politics. As a rule it is less flowery.

I should think that living in Algeria is a good thing for a Frenchman—seeing that Camus has not these troubles of Sartre's—if it were not that plenty of French writers who have never been to Algeria do not suffer from them either to the same extent. It would probably help Sartre if he knew it was quite unnecessary to go on as he does. The great majority of educated men understand that if you place within easy reach of a large and greedy and stupid baby, entirely uncontrolled, masses of sweetmeats, it will quickly die. This is what Sartre's enemies the Communists, and most other people call capitalism. All men—I do not speak of the Communists, who are professional troublemakers—who would be respected by Sartre know that the world is run as a casino and is not a very stable proposition: further, social change has been greatly speeded up by technology. Sartre incurs the risk, he ought to know that, by his vulgar displays, of discouraging those minds he should most wish to attract.

Because of a law as constant and invariable as the upward movement of the hot and dirty air in a crowded room, leaving the purest air right on the floor, in human affairs what is least desirable rises to the top. This is a scientific fact, the result of the elaborate checking and rechecking of phenomena.—Constant measures have to be taken against bad air, which gets *very bad* at times: this is hygiene. But we have reached a point where heroic programs of purification have been begun. Without being promoters, there are few who are great objectors. There are few who can find Sartre's self-righteous diatribes about the dirty air, the purgative intensity of *his* enthusiasms, etc., etc., other than tiresome.

I always feel with a man like this who, for reasons of policy, adopts an extreme position—in his case borrowing all of Marx except Marxism—that it would be more interesting to him if he devoted some thought to the subject, making it correspond more to the present situation. There is, for instance, a very obvious way in which the analogy breaks down, which would represent the working masses in the XXth Century as playing the part of the *bourgeoisie* in the XVIIIth. The XVIIIth Century French *bourgeoisie* was very rich and influential as was the London *bourgeoisie* in the XVIIth Century which virtually decreed the execution of Charles I. The working class by itself is powerless. Nor is it actually the next class in succession, nor the next but one, beneath the capitalist class.

Sartre's "working class," in the last analysis, is very like Georges Sorel's. There is the same hollow, spurious "heroism" in both cases: although there may be no need to go so far afield.—The great ascendency exercised by André Malraux upon him should always be present to our mind. Claude Mauriac, for instance, where he is refuting an unfavorable criticism of Malraux, cites the first number of Sartre's magazine, *Les Temps Modernes*. There "a fecund although partial humanism" was proposed by Sartre. "The greater part of this," observes Mauriac, "comes from André Malraux: its paternity is so obvious that it was not considered necessary to mention it." * But I shall take up this aspect of Sartre's work later. Meanwhile there remains a simple question to be asked. Why—one is obliged to inquire—since this writer has borrowed the Marxist language and outlook, does he not belong to the Communist party? What does he want to say to the working class that he could not say as a Communist?

Next let us hear Sartre upon the state of the continent. It is difficult to go far astray upon the subject. He begins with the *bourgeoisie*.—The *bourgeoisie*, Sartre tells us, is the "sick man of Europe": analogous to what was once the decrepit régime lingering on at the Sublime Porte. Its fate was bound up with European supremacy, and white empire in Asia and Africa. The *bourgeoisie*, however, "loses its colonies at the moment that Europe loses control of its destiny . . . Two world-states, neither of them bourgeois, neither of them European, dispute possession of the universe." These states are of course Russia and the United States. "Ruined,

* *La Trahison d'un Clerc*, 1945, Claude Mauriac.

but still oppressive, the European bourgeoisie govern in a hand-to-mouth manner." But the "era of national revolutions is past." The revolutionary parties far from wishing to finish off this "sick man," do all they can to prop up the decomposed specter of what, so short a time ago, was the greatest aggregation of power on earth. The reason for this paradoxical support of a power so obsolescent that it could be blown over by the puniest *coup d'état,* is because its overthrow would spell *world war.* Neither Russia nor America is ready as yet for that trial of strength.

All this is probably more or less accurate. On the occasion of the expulsion of the Communists from the French Government in the spring of '47, Thorez, asked by reporters if the General Strike would be declared, answered, "Do you take us for fools!" Togliatti, the Italian Communist leader, when his party was cheated of power, used almost the same words. He said, "Do you suppose we wish to commit suicide!" and Malraux, in his capacity of public relations officer to General de Gaulle, about the same time expressed himself in the same vein: there would be no civil war in France—that Stalin would not allow the French Communists to take extreme action, knowing that the U.S.A. would not tolerate it, and that the Gaullist faction would not proceed to extreme measures either. All of which tallies with Sartre's account, which may therefore be accepted.

Consequently there we have poor M. Sartre, the inmate of a transition which may endure for a decade, with what is practically an ideologic corpse upon one side of him (the *bourgeoisie*) and a working class on the other confined in an ideological strait-jacket, and mounted guard over by a group of fierce Communist "watchdogs": as a third party to this distressing scene there is the Vatican imparting a little spurious life to the *bourgeoisie,* in the form of a powerful center party, the M.R.P., resembling the German Catholic Center in its last and least solid phase.

Under attack by the Communist watchdogs, Sartre reluctantly admits that Existentialism *is* a part of the bourgeois decomposition.

"I make no difficulty about agreeing with the Marxist description of Existentialist 'anguish' as a *phénomène d'époque*—as a phenomenon of period, and of class. Existentialism, in its contemporary form, makes its appearance upon the decomposing carcass of the bourgeoisie, and it is of bourgeois origin."

Then there are members of this putrefying class who escape from it to a sufficient degree to live decent, intelligent lives. This intelligent fraction of the *bourgeoisie,* Sartre says with disgust, is his public. "Ceux-là forment notre public. Notre *seul* public." [2] This is an admission fraught with great bitterness for our author although he hastens to add: "We have nothing to say to these people. They belong, in spite of themselves, to an oppressor class. Victims no doubt, and innocents, but nevertheless still tyrants, and guilty."

Were the author an Englishman, we should here know that our leg was being pulled. (Such piously pink rodomontades have not been heard here since the thirties, the Pink decade. This is a most unusual case, of a French silliness outliving an English.) But Sartre does not smile, I think, even to himself. For he is really at his wit's end what to do: it is for him a matter of capital importance. While in London in 1950 he was interviewed: his followers, he told the reporter, were "the eighteen-year-olds in the Paris bars." A bar-public —in its nonage—is not a very solid background for an author: but to these we have to add the *avant-garde* of the *bourgeoisie* (see above) who might at any moment go Communist. Then the bourgeois is very apt to be a Catholic. Two of them wrote a very ugly little brochure about him the other day! [*] The authors were devout and they greatly objected to him. They wrote for instance:

> Never has a *mal du siècle* presented itself in a less attractive, nor in a less interesting form. Montparnasse cafés, girls pigheaded or mad, tough little libertines . . . knives stuck into open palms, token mutilations— but nothing of all that sings like the last page of Faulkner's *Light in August*.[†] It seems that the Devil has taken the shape of a notary . . . He holds up for our inspection an empty will and testament. He disinherits nobody, but the empty testament is in itself a declaration

* "Sartre, est-il un Possedé?", Pierre Boutang et Bernard Pingaud, *La Table Ronde.*

† Sartre's novels, *Les Chemins de la Liberté,* have to withstand, from the opposite camp, the Communist, namely, blasts of equal severity. His *infantilism,* we read there, "se traduit alors par un goût vraiment excessif pour l'ordure. C'est la magie et la métaphysique de la merde," [3] (*L'Existentialisme,* p. 82, H. Lefebvre).

2 They are our audience. Our only audience.

3 must be seen as an excessive fondness for filth. It is the magic and metaphysic of excrement.

that there are *no heirs,* and that it is drawn up for *no one.* This life is the only life, that is *all there is.* . . . He storms "objectively," the little notary, beneath a transcendental wind, he denies us "essences". . . . He brandishes his act of Nothingness. The act that he has drawn up is "for nothing": he is not even any longer a notary: he will vanish with the dawn, he has summoned no one, he will act for nobody.

His Catholic adversaries show him, even, denuding, as a philosopher, his master's *Existenz* doctrine of its emotional coloring, and transforming it into a dry university thesis.

The [Existentialist] theme of anguish, and that of abandonment (or of dereliction) such as one can trace them from Kierkegaard to Jaspers, and to Heidegger, retained an affective sonority; they constituted one of the elements of what may be called the existential pathetic. These philosophers remained attached to a tradition of poetic humanism. . . . But when we come to Sartre, it is not at all the same thing. With him existentialism repudiates all that is lyrical. A very gifted product of the Ecole Normale takes in hand all the existentialist concepts, accentuating the abrupt technique, but at the same time he undertakes to present them in a purely "objective" tone. The human situation becomes merely "a little factual item": the suppression of the divine is effected in an assured and efficient tone of "c'est comme ça"—that's how it is—which annihilates the tears of tragedy as also those of pity. Heidegger's word *dereliction*—abandonment—no longer (in Sartre's hands) suggests that woman who in a Florentine painting despairs in front of a closed door. No, it signifies now merely that man is dispossessed by God —that henceforth he only has *himself* to rely upon, and that is that.

From the Sartre standpoint the trouble about the more educated and liberal fraction of the *bourgeoisie* as public is here made glassily plain. The bourgeois, however liberal, belongs politically to the party of the Vatican. Too aggressive an atheism—or rather too offhand an attitude about the nonexistence of God—is apt, in the long run, to upset him. He may even be a religious man.

It is upon the contemporary Youth that ultimately Sartre depends: "The Young": the student youth of Paris not necessarily "fellow-traveling" as it was here until recently and as it is apt still to be in the States. Probably even more are Catholic-Fascist. If it is true that considerably more than 50 per cent. is either Communist in sympathy, or of Catholic-Fascist complexion, that is a disastrous situation for an aggressive *front-populaire* [4] atheist who has a bitter quarrel on his hands with the Communist party: in other words for Jean-Paul Sartre.

But let us return to the text of this "derelict" author in search of a public—or with a large nondescript public which causes him great anxiety, because he feels it is too unsolid and uncertain a support.—That Sartre has devoted much careful thought to the burning question of the thirties *to be or not to be a Communist*, the Brunet—Mathieu interview, a fragment of which I have quoted, will have sufficiently suggested. But readers of *L'Age de Raison* will remember how the stern image of Brunet haunts Mathieu like an incarnated conscience. What Brunet is as a man, the Civil War in Spain is as a war. One is Communist integrity incarnated in a man, the other Communist integrity incarnated in a war. The Spanish battlefields, beside his Communist friend Gomez, is where he *ought* to be: the nightspot named "le Sumatra," beside the ravishing little Russian lesbian Ivich is where he *is*.

For instance there is that time Mathieu picks up an evening paper: Valencia has been bombed by Franco airmen. News of this kind invariably produces the same conflict, if he happens to be unoccupied at the moment. It is as if Brunet had entered the room and had said, sternly pointing an accusing finger at the newspaper: "You see Valencia has been bombed!" Mathieu's is the story of a very boring would-be Malraux.—So in this case what is a routine situation—ridiculous as he seems to recognize it as being—develops.

Mathieu is angry: he crushes the newspaper. Angry people crush newspapers. But he is by no means angry *enough*. He falls far short—as always—of getting up sufficient steam to move very far from the Quartier Montparnasse. It is really getting to be a perfectly blood-curdling situation! In Spain he had been presented with a clear case of Privilege outrageously suppressing the long-suffering Many. Every day almost the

[4] Popular Front, political alliance during the thirties between Communist, Socialists and Liberals

newspapers drew his attention to it anew in huge leaded
type: and every day he put the paper down and went away
and forgot about it. He gets up, roused at last: he is very
angry. But it is *with himself*. Not quite realizing this and
feeling that at last something is happening, he rushes out into
the street. It is a lovely evening: men and women are moving
up and down peaceably (petty bourgeois that they are!). They
have had a tiring day working for the capitalists and they
are bathing themselves in the fresh sweet air—but he glares
at them. Why are they not shouting with rage, instead of
peaceably taking themselves out for a walk as if nothing
were happening? He nearly knocks them over, he is so indignant with them. He dashes along apparently for miles and
miles, pushing people that he meets out of the way, his mind
concentrated in a constipated impotence upon events in Spain.
By means of this dramatic locomotion he is attempting to
reach the boiling point. Alas it is no use! He is a kettle that
gets a little hot and bothered, but *will not boil*. He cannot
reach that mad point at which he throws up his appointment,
goes to Spain and joins the International Brigade.

On these occasions he could part company with himself
for being so uninflammable. He calls himself a *salaud, un
type foutu*,[5] and goes and gets drunk. As a Popular-Front
conscience his was a washout.—In these parts of *L'Age de
Raison* Sartre seems to be ridiculing people who in the
European civil war, which had begun in Spain, felt themselves obliged to demonstrate their zeal even when by themselves, and to go through the gestures of flying towards the
fray. I say it *seems*: for sometimes it does and sometimes
not: but is a muddled and intellectually rather squalid self-
reproachful comedy. Before leaving this phase of my subject I will exhibit Mathieu on a bench in the Luxembourg
Gardens, where he has been dejectedly considering the problem of how to find the money to pay for an abortion. When
that problem becomes too oppressive, he always thinks of
his Communist conscience, Brunet.

> Mathieu stopped brusquely (considering this prob-
> lem): he *saw himself* thinking. He experienced a horror
> of this self. At this moment Brunet marches along the
> streets, at his ease in the light: he is at ease because he
> waits. He traverses a city of spun glass that he is
> going to break. He feels strong: he walks gingerly

[5] bastard, a vicious character

swaying a little, with caution, because the hour has not yet struck to smash everything up—he waits . . . And I! And I . . Here I am slumped on a chair. . . . Nevertheless, I also, even I wished to go to Spain.

So he begins as usual to think about Spain: but he becomes very bitter. "Spain, castles in Spain: that is—what? A tepid little lay religion for my use? The discreet and seraphic accompaniment of my real life?" *

I will now give part of Sartre's polemic, upon the undesirability of joining the Communist party to which I have already alluded, and his account of how inexpressibly disagreeable it is, if you in a misguided moment do. You will observe how far he has traveled *away from Brunet* since the period in which *L'Age de Raison* was written (whenever that was, for I do not know, but it was long enough to make him change his views quite a lot).

For Communists a writer is suspect on principle. Even if his conduct is irreproachable a Communist intellectual suffers from this inalterable defect: namely that he entered the party *of his own free will*. What has led him to take this decision is a careful reading of *Das Kapital*, a critical examination of the historic situation, an acute sense of social justice, generosity, a taste for solidarity. All this reveals an independence of mind which has not a very good smell [for the Communist nose]. This man has entered the party as the result of a free choice: therefore he may leave it in the same way. He joined the party because he disagreed with the politics of the class to which he belonged; consequently he might criticize the politics of his adopted class. Thus in the very act by which he voluntarily elects to start a new life, a curse is put upon him which will weigh him down during the whole of this new life. From the very moment of his ordination, as Communist, a long trial will begin for him similar to that described by Kafka (in *Das Prozess*), in which the judges are unknown and the

* *L'Age de Raison*, p. 54.

nature of the charge never revealed, where the only part of the proceedings which is clear is the sentence. It is not a question of his invisible accusers offering, as is customary, proofs of his crime: it is for him to prove his innocence [without knowing what is the nature of his crime]. Since everything that he writes can be held against him as evidence—and of this he is perfectly aware—each of his works will necessarily display an ambiguous character, as being at the same time a public brief for the Communist party, and a secret brief for himself. What appears to the public to be a chain of peremptory affirmations, appears inside the party—in the eyes of his judges—to be a humble and clumsy attempt at self-justification. When he seems *for us* the most brilliant and convincing, it is perhaps then that he is in reality the most culpable. It seems to us at times—and perhaps it also seems to him, that he is rising in the party hierarchy and that he has become its mouthpiece. But this is a test merely, or a trick. The steps of the ladder are so constructed, that when he believes himself approaching the top he is in fact still down at the bottom. Read what he writes a hundred times, never will you be able to decide what is its exact value. . . . The Communist writer is expected to display wit, lucidity, invention, to be mordant. But at the same time that one requires of him these gifts, one blames him for their possession, because in themselves they imply criminal leanings.— How is he to play his part as a critic? His guilt is in him like the worm in the fruit. He can neither please his readers, his judges, nor himself. . . . This unfortunate man is not only one *présumé coupable*;[6] he takes on his shoulders all the past errors of the party too, since his signature is attached to those errors: and he is the scapegoat of all the political purges.

It is not impossible all the same for him to survive a long time, if he learns to hold his good qualities in leash, and to pull on the leash when they threaten to lead him too far. Further, he must never make use of cynicism: that is almost as grave a vice as good will. . . . Let him always keep before him the fact that the

---

[6] allegedly guilty

mind is everywhere shut in by magic frontiers, by fogs —as is the case with those primitive races who can count up to twenty, and are mysteriously deprived of the power to count beyond that: this artificial mist that he must always hold himself in readiness to deploy between himself and undesirable evidence—this we will call without searching for another word *dishonesty*. But all this is not yet enough: let him avoid referring too often to dogmas. It is not a good thing that they should be seen in too strong a light—the works of Marx (like the Bible with the Catholics) are dangerous for anyone approaching them except through an intermediary: in every cell such an official exponent is to be found, and should doubts or scruples supervene, it is to him that you must address yourself. Then if you are a novelist or playwright, guard against putting too many communists into your novels or plays. Should they have defects, they will quite likely give offence. On the other hand if they are without faults, they will be boring. Stalinist policy has no desire whatever to discover its image reflected in literature because it recognizes that a portrait is a challenge. The writer escapes from the difficulty by depicting the "permanent hero" *en profil perdu*,[7] "arranging for him to appear at the end of the story, to bring it to a close." Or else he suggests the presence of the "permanent hero" everywhere, without actually showing him. . . . Avoid, as far as possible, evoking the Revolution: that *dates*. . . . One must slowly wean the people of Europe from their old dreams (of revolution), disaccustom them, and very gently replace the perspective of *insurrection* by that of *war*. If the writer conform to all these prescriptions, he is not loved for it. He is a useless mouth to be fed: he does not work with his hands. He is aware of this, he suffers from an inferiority complex, he is almost ashamed of his occupation, and puts as much zeal into abasing himself before the working class as Jules Lemaître did in 1900 in bowing down before the generals.

If Jean-Paul Sartre proceeds with these polemics—and what he calls the "Communist watchdogs" have bitten him

---

7 three-quarter view, turned away from audience

so severely he is in a highly irritable condition just now—he should in the end have something on the lines of the *Lettres Provinciales,* the Communists replacing the Jesuits for this XXth Century moralist. It will however be confined to crimes against culture. He displays no interest whatever in what has furnished the sensational material of the anti-stalinist campaigns of Max Eastman and Arthur Koestler. What is good about Sartre is that first and last he is the writer. The Paris cafés we learn have been his workshops, his public, we have seen him say, are in the bars. He comes down to the brass tacks of the man living by his pen. He speaks of sales— of the price of a cup of coffee—of the scarcity of paper. He is a man of the métier. [8] To listen to him is like hearing a guildsman endlessly expatiate upon the affairs of the Guild. If people would not interfere with his writing— take away, or lock up, his public, as he sees it, rightly or wrongly—he would never bother himself, I think, with politics. He really is of a philosophic temper, too. He is not at all a naturally angry man: there is very little *Angst* [9] in him, which as his Catholic adversaries indicate, may disqualify him as a theorist of existentialist despair—he is denied the slightest possibility of "dereliction" by an enthusiastic entourage in which the other sex is not conspicuous by its absence. While exercising himself at his punch ball he sportively lashes out at Mlle de Beauvoir, so American reporters tell us, fetching her a friendly wallop so that she falls into the bulbous red eiderdown of his modest hotel bedroom (an example of his *infantilism* M. Lefebvre would say). One cannot visualize Heidegger engaged in lighthearted play with his favorite lady disciple!

It is because Jean-Paul Sartre impresses one as a man not easily disturbed, that it is with a shock of surprise one finds how dissatisfied he is with his position as a writer. He appears even as remarkable an example of literary success as could easily be found. As to his *international* fame, that he dismisses as rather a bad sign than otherwise.

At first sight, certainly [he agrees,] it would seem that the writers of the past would find our condition most enviable. "We profit," Malraux once observed,

8 profession
9 anguish

"from the sufferings of Baudelaire." I do not believe
that that is altogether true. . . . Plays by Cocteau,
Salacrou, Anouilh are performed everywhere: I could
cite numbers of works which have been translated into
six or seven languages in less than three months after
their publication. Nevertheless, that is only brilliantly
successful on the surface. One reads us perhaps in New
York and Tel Aviv, yes: but the scarcity of paper has
limited our printing here in Paris. Thus the public has
been spread out rather than increased. Perhaps ten thousand people read us in four or five foreign countries
and ten thousand more in our own. Twenty thousand
readers—a minor success *d'avant-guerre*. [10] These world
reputations are much less solid than the national reputations of our forerunners. . . .

If we are famous outside France there is no cause
for rejoicing: . . . The nations today, more surely
than by oceans and by mountains, are separated by disparities of economic and military potential . . . in
the end Americans get to know of literary or social
theories professed in Europe. . . . But as one knows,
American intellectuals collect European ideas together
into bouquets, sniff at them for a moment, and then
throw them away. Bouquets fade more rapidly over
there than in other climates.—As to Russia, she gleans,
she takes what she can easily convert into her own
substance. As to Europe, it is defeated, ruined, its destiny has slipped out of its hands, and consequently its
ideas are confined within it. The only concrete circuit
for ideas today is through England, France, Scandina-
via and Italy.

It is, as you will agree, a bleak picture. And it astonishes.
There can scarcely be a high school boy or girl in the United
States who does not know something of Existentialism, in the
same way that twenty years ago Relativity penetrated everywhere. The person mainly responsible for this ought surely to
be elated. But nothing of the sort: he is disappointed, and
deeply depressed. Clearly Sartre is not a vain man: he has,
I conclude, in the back of his mind something quite concrete—what the Americans call "dough" or "jack." Which is
as it should be—he is after all a writer. Then he appears to

[10] before the war

dread the consequences of being "the fashion"—and being so spectacularly fashionable. He feels rather like a very eccentric Paris hat—which has swept the world and been a "wow," but can *never* be repeated.

"In the degree in which an author reaches an ever-wider public he touches it less profoundly, he recognizes himself less in the influence he exerts. . . . And since our reputations extend much farther than our books—that is to say our merits, great or small—we must not see in the passing favors accorded us, more than a 'literary inflation.'"—Then he adds: "It depends upon us to see that literature does not become industrialized." Finally, having enumerated other disadvantages of distension, he says: "But there is worse yet: we have readers but we have no public."

The vanity of international celebrity is the subject with which he opens. All the problems confronting this man "with readers, but no public" follow on from that: eventually reaching his outbursts against the Communists, for locking away from him the public of his choice: for not handing over the proletariat to *him* and themselves going out of business.—It is the overall picture that is so striking: of a man who in a period of "literary inflation," has his ideas (or is it Heidegger's?) exported to America, where *all* ideas fade in a few weeks—are taken a good sniff at by perhaps a million people, then thrown away. As to the home scene in this extended panorama, we have had potential publics reviewed for us by this professional taking a world-wide stock of his position. We see the *bourgeoisie*, which he disdains and would not touch with a barge pole. (Also its background is apt to be Catholic.) There is the proletariat—only available if he becomes a Communist. (But the Communists would hardly encourage him to go on depicting man as a pathetic "derelict," shivering between two *néants*,[11] one before and one behind, inconsolable because of the death of God!)—In this bird's-eye view of Sartre we see, at the center of a vast panorama, extending from Tel Aviv to San Francisco, an indomitable but anxious speck. Granted a close-up of this speck, we find a man shut out, for one reason or another—either voluntarily or involuntarily—from all regular publics: but writing at top speed book after book. Should you, having completed this chapter, fail to understand how infinitely complicated is the life of a writer in the modern age—however

11 voids

famous, for that only makes things worse—in the midst as he is of several ideologies fighting to the death, you are un-enlightenable.

But let me turn again to this small energetic figure. "If," we hear him saying, "the two terms of the possible decision are in fact (1) the bourgeoisie, and (2) the Communist party, then *the choice is impossible!*—we are at once against the Communist party and against the bourgeoisie. That means clearly enough that we write *against everybody*."

There is another choice that is likewise impossible. "The present historical perspective being *war,* we are summoned to choose between (1) the Anglo-Saxon bloc, and (2) the Soviet bloc. We refuse to help either the one or the other in their preparations for this war: so we have fallen out of history—we speak as in a desert."

I do not know if I have succeeded in evoking the image of a man so consumed with this agonizing problem of where to take up his stand (and how to shuffle a little away from the Left without losing the benefits of his leftishness), that he exhibits, makes a parade of, his anxiety in the paper he edits. Since he is symbolic, and something of these difficulties beset all of us, in one degree or another—though few can have succeeded in getting themselves in so involved a situation—we must not too self-obliviously smile.

"Sometimes the view is advanced that our books reflect the hesitations of the *petty bourgeoisie,* which cannot make up its mind whether to come down on the side of the proletariat or of capitalism. It is false—c'est faux!" he cries. "Our choice is made!"

Sartre is beside himself as to whether he is a patch of putrefaction upon the ignoble cadaver of the *bourgeoisie,* or (as he claims) purveyor of "liberté" to the working class. The poor fellow cries: *"It is false! I have made my choice."* But he knows that the implacable "watchdogs" of the materialist dialectic will not take for an answer however passionate an affirmation. They stand upon their terms. "To this they reply," he wearily continues, "that the choice thus made is abstract and inefficacious, that it is merely an intellectual game unless one at the same time lends one's adherence to a revolutionary party." So we come back, as always, to the same infinitely vexatious predicament. "I agree—I know it is only an intellectual game," is his angry retort. "But is it my fault that the Communist party is no longer revolutionary?" *He* is the great "revolutionary," you see, and the Communists are a lot of bourgeois!

Here as his words prove he even is prepared to admit that to claim to be a revolutionary assisting the proletariat to liquidate the "oppressor" is nonsense, so long as he remains politically in splendid isolation. He could not for long maintain the contrary: for confronting as he does the "bourgeoisie" with Marx's "proletariat" is an essentially Marxian proceeding—the extermination of the former, in a dialectical paroxysm by the latter, being de rigueur. But the Communist organization is alone capable of effecting this: so why not join the Communist party? There is no escaping from this logic: and the "Communist watchdogs" as he knows, will never allow him to escape.

All readers of this *writer's complaint* cannot but join in our refrain: why not join the Communist party?—Otherwise for heaven's sake stop continually talking about the "proletariat," the "bourgeoisie," the "petit bourgeoisie," and the other Marxist concepts—concepts to which you have no right. The farther one goes in this reading, the more one feels that Sartre must loathe these monotonous vocables, which are responsible for so much idiotic anguish.

"The drama of our epoch" is his way of describing this conflict.

But we, although we have for the moment nothing to mediate, are nevertheless in the position of mediators: torn between one class and the other, we are condemned to suffer, as it were a Passion, this dual exigence. It is our personal problem, but it is also the drama of our epoch.—One will say of course that this antinomy which lacerates us . . . is the effect of revolutionary snobbism (*le snobisme révolutionnaire*).

Sartre has said it for me. He is even as fine a specimen of this *snobisme* as can be found anywhere: and, as is sufficiently plain, it is a serious ailment—the analysis of which, let me add, would tell us more about these times than anything else I can think of.—A last quotation, where he answers the question which must present itself to any reader:—why should this novelist, playwright, and philosopher have engaged with so much personal feeling in these controversies?

We live in the era of the Hoax. Some of these mystifications are fundamental and belong to the structure of our society, others are secondary. In any case, the social order today rests upon hoax, as also does disorder. National Socialism was a hoax, Gaullism is another hoax, Catholicism is a third: it is beyond question, at present, that French Communism is a fourth. We are not obliged, needless to say, to take any notice of it: we could get on with our work honestly, without aggressiveness. But as the writer is concerned with the liberty of his reader, and since every hoaxed and deluded consciousness—in so far as it is complaisant with regard to the delusion which holds it captive—tends to persist in its delusion, we can only safeguard literature by undertaking the task of disillusioning or enlightening our public.

As to this passage, I should be the last person to assent that the public has not been deceived, corrupted, and poisoned, in one way or another, and in every country. It is not, as Sartre says, very good for literature. I have myself (most "aggressively") purged, or attempted to, the section of the public with which I was most concerned: I even think it is a very difficult age indeed to write in because of this septic condition of every public—either harmed and degraded with the tainted offal fed to it by monopolies, or the equally poisonous pabulum of politics. In that particular I should not feel disputatious. All politics are more like a conjuring trick than anything else—innumerable silk stockings coming out of a top hat, that kind of thing. Then as I said just now, there are none of us who have not had most disagreeable experiences, consequent upon these violent times. If writers, we do not require Sartre to tell us that a writer's politics are of far more consequence than his literary ability: if the author's politics are unpopular, no book is safe, even one on bird life in East Anglia, or the history of Rugby football. All recognize that propaganda is deadly to a literary talent: but none realize that intolerance unless discouraged amounts to the same thing.—If there are many statements of Sartre's that would be recognized as true by any truthful man, the fact remains that he takes up a false position all along.

For him Gaullism, catholicism, and communism in France are rackets—are hoaxes, mystifications. Very well. Suppose he had adopted the jargon and the myths of Gaullism, but, for some inscrutable reason, conducted a violent offensive against General Charles de Gaulle. That would, I think, have seemed very illogical. Or had he installed a prie-dieu and called his room his *cell*: peppered his writings with quotations from Aquinas, at High Mass in the view of everybody had excesses of ecstatic weeping—but violently attacked the priesthood, charging that they were keeping him from God, objected to confession and denounced the liturgy as a hoax (also jeered at the Vatican and sneered at the Pope) people would undoubtedly have regarded him as inconsistent.

I do not see that his public hostility to the Communist party differs in any respect from the above hypothetical cases. He believes all that the Communists believe: but he did not wish to convert this *collage* into a marriage. With him and communism it is an affair of Mathieu and Marcelle. He makes excuses: it would feel quite uncomfortable to be associated with such a *bourgeois* as M. Thorex!—But to look at it for the occasion from the standpoint of the Communists —would he have the Communists erect barricades in the streets of Paris, bring on a showdown, and thereby precipitate a third world war—at a moment when Russia is in no position, as yet, to wage it?

In the thirties Sartre drifted fashionably into the *front populaire* watershed, was the French equivalent of a fellow traveler. Was that pink aftermath of the revolution in Russia a "hoax"—a mystification? He engaged in a path in those days which leads either to communism, or to nothing. It was "le Néant" that he chose.

Twentieth-Century Nihilism

THERE is one thing I feel quite certain I have succeeded in doing in the last chapter: I have shown how the contemporary writer can call his soul his own *but* that at least two remarkably powerful institutions lay claim to it, and that at least one of them will not leave him in peace until he has given it up to them. And I have been demonstrating this by quoting from the works of a man who peddles a doctrine of liberty as absolute existence: who asserts that (quoting Dostoevsky) since there is no God everything is permitted and that we are, owing to this timely elimination of the Deity, paragons of freedom.

To say that freedom of thought is obstructed in the contemporary world, however, would be putting it very mildly. Freedom of thought is, in fact, a crime, according to at least two absolutist codes. And the wretched man who calls his soul his own wastes many weary hours in contriving defences for it.

In some places in Europe the writer's is an anxious and shackled freedom. In order to remain "free"—in order to be something he wishes to be—a man will say a thousand things he does not wish to say, multilate his thought, adulterate his doctrine, compel his will to wear a uniform imposed upon him *against* his will, cause the characters in his books (if a novelist) to behave in a manner that turns them into other characters—to associate with people they would never speak to if allowed to follow their own sweet will.—It has been my argument that to surrender his will to that one of the contemporary machines for compressing souls into given shapes which would leave him most of his original self would be a man's best policy; the machine whose standard shapes were the nearest to the native shape of his own soul.

To secure the evidence necessary to prove that these are queer times for the writer, it may be said that I might have picked a more attractive witness. That there is much silly aggressiveness in Sartre goes without saying. "I have suppressed God the Father" (an often-quoted saying of his) is not the sort of levity that attracts one to him, or would incline anyone to take him seriously. He is much more polite to Marx than he is to God, because he regards the Marxists as much more formidable enemies than the believers in God. He has picked Marx's doctrine to pieces: yet he has not so far asserted that Marx has been "suppressed" by him. The value of Sartre as a philosopher, as literary artist, or as controversialist, is not however the issue. He has a momentary importance, he is quite a substantial enough person to qualify as a witness. As a pluralist—the opposite of an absolutist—I should prefer a various world. Therefore I am for liberty: I should defend the right of far more disagreeable people than Sartre to write what they liked and to be heard, so long as our society continues in theory to secure to the individual freedom of speech, freedom of worship (or of no worship) and so on.

Of Sartre's critics the most effective are the Communists. Of these Henri Lefebvre is the best example, and a highly intelligent man. Lefebvre sees very clearly what a flirt Sartre is, but his reason for being that he does not seem to see.

> This dialectic brings M. Sartre [he writes] singularly close to the *materialist dialectic*: brings him near to it only. Upon the theoretic plane, as upon the political, he flirts with the (Marxist) solution of problems: he brushes it as closely as his anxiety not to compromise himself will allow—not, in fact, ever to bind himself. He gets as close (to Marxism) as possible with the idea of supplanting it.

As you will observe, M. Lefebvre has a different explanation from my own: he believes that Sartre's pushing himself as far to the left as possible—short of communism—was done with the ambition of *supplanting* the Communists. I am sure this is a mistake. Sartre's affectation of more radical principles than he in fact holds is amply accounted for by the prestige and the popularity of the Left—as a protective and precautionary step, and because of great pressure leftwards when he was younger, and of his infatuation for Malraux. The only way he could have escaped these pressures

and infatuations was to move into the ranks of Rome. But
there was no question of so tough a little rationalist doing
that. Today Trotsky and anarcho-syndicalism offer him a
respectable radical alternative to communism, or "Stalinism."
Perhaps at last a solution has been found.

Now I will pass on, however, to my next subject. Its connection with the problems of freedom will be less obvious at
first sight. M. Lefebvre will effect the transition for me, in a
passage where all of Western thought is assailed.

> For a whole series of philosophers, for more than a
> century [he writes] in fact, since Kierkegaard and
> Schopenhauer—there has been a secret, a revelation, a
> mystery, which would unveil itself in a magical illumi-
> nation. The secret of the universe is going to be de-
> livered up to us in an instant—in a flash. This saving
> instant is going to install us in the absolute. Only the
> secret is not going to reveal itself by means of a
> *thought*—the object of which would be beyond, and
> outside, what we *immediately* experience. No, it is here
> and now, hic et nunc. It awaits us, it lays siege to
> us, it haunts us. Present, and enveloped in the pres-
> ent, we are however obliged to tear it out, and to
> bring it out into the light of day—rending and shat-
> tering ourselves in the process.

This is excellently expressed. Formerly ultimate reality
was "beyond and outside what we immediately experience." The origin of the term "existential" is to be
looked for in this *immediacy*—and also *concreteness*. The
hypothesis of an absolute somewhere else than in existence
(as posited in classical metaphysics) is rejected by the Existentialist. For the *reason* is substituted *intuition*. The absolute, implicated with our temporal existence, is to be con-
tacted by ultrarational, intuitive agencies. All ultimate
cognitive possibilities are removed from their traditional seat
in the human reason—that characteristic endowment of man
—and transferred to those means of apprehension we share
with the lizard and the bee. As a knower, even the big toe or
the penis has priority over the mind. The eggs and bacon
we have for breakfast—that rush to cut our nails on
Saturday because if we do it on Sunday the devil will be

after us all the week—becomes the stuff of the *Ding-an-Sich*.[1]

As in so much modern thinking, then, so in existentialism, the human reason is discredited, and takes its place beside the liver and the glands of internal secretion (among which the so-called "fighting glands" are by no means the least important). Man is no longer an essentially thinking animal. Rather he is a willing and wishing animal: so—and above all—an *acting* animal: one step ahead of himself always, existing in the fruit of his acts. The activism of Sartre assumes the strangest forms in his novels. The hero of *L'Age de Raison*, for instance, looks upon his friend Daniel with new respect and reflects how *satisfied* he must feel, because Daniel has asked Marcelle to marry him. To buy a newspaper, or to cross the street, is after all *something:* but to ask your friend's discarded mistress to marry you! *That* unquestionably is *action. That* must make you feel good!—To murder somebody gives you somewhat the same satisfactory feeling, in the novels of Malraux. The heroes of Sartre are nothing like so tough as those of Malraux: indeed, almost any simple little action, like asking a man for a light in the street, impresses them. If a hero of Sartre met one of Malraux's tough homicidal heroes he would almost pass out with admiration.

Then, for the Existentialist, man is solely a creature of flesh and blood (an "existence")! And only if all the flesh and blood goes with him can he go in search of the Absolute. Even Kirkegaard's "leap" never took him outside the walls of his body. At most it was the leap of a flea, never beyond the electric field of the palpitating integument.—Man is a reasoning animal *on the side:* to think is, as it were, his hobby. His feeling is the big thing about him—it takes him farther than his thought. Such intuitional thinking (to which grouping existentialism belongs, merging the absolute in Time) affects a break with all traditional metaphysics, and of course with Christian traditional thinking. Remote as Marxist materialism is from the latter, nevertheless the Catholic and the Marxist unite to denounce the nihilism of the Existentialist. (The nihilistic conclusions of this teaching I will speak of shortly.)

Here Marxist humanism protests [asserts M. Lefe-

---

[1] thing-in-itself

bvre] against the *dehumanization* of the Existentialist. For, as anyone can see, the human reason is a capital ingredient in our concept "Man." And that concept withers beneath our eyes if its rational advertisment and prestige are removed from it and the intellect becomes a little clockwork plaything—highly unreliable —in place of the living breath of what otherwise would be a mere machine.

Thus we find ourselves, not entirely unexpectedly, upon the side of the Marxists, in this particular issue.

Let us now contrast the humanist objections to existentialism of M. Lefebvre, with the words of an American follower of existentialism, Mr. William Barrett. Having pointed out that existentialism is not an isolated system of thought, but merely a new expression of a widespread movement, eminent exponents of which have been Bergson, Whitehead, James, and Dewey: having remarked that "Dewey had insisted on an existential context of thought," this American adherent announces:

What we are present at is no longer a matter of schools, or isolated figures extracting explicit nuggets of influence from one another, but the whole Western mind—Europe and America—bending before a new climate of opinion; as the biologist portrays a whole species, scattered in space and without contact, moving along the same paths of adaption before a new geological upheaval.

Mr. Barrett must I feel have formerly learned to philosophize at Harvard with Professor Whitehead. The latter sage is very prominent in this pamphlet. I am taken back, as a result of the *Existenz* philosophy, to *Time and Western Man*. The cast of "time-philosophers"—as they were there described —is almost *au grand complet* [2] in the pages of Mr. Barrett. The key word of this new school was published about the same date as my *Time* book: its title is *Sein und Zeit*—Being and Time. *Zeit* is of its essence as it is of one and all of these thinkers.

2 all on stage

I recall that eighteen years ago, when I grouped all these thinkers together, in a solid company, with the concept "time" as a quite unifying principle, * and stated what you have just seen Mr. Barrett stating, that "the whole Western mind" was "moving along the same paths," it was objected that I had arbitrarily associated them. When I described them all as suffering from the effects of the same poison, I found few to agree with me except the Catholics. The intellectuals of the thirties were without exception hostile to such a judgment. They felt themselves quite rightly, solidaire [3] with this philosophy: they were an integral part of that "Western mind" which was "moving along the same paths." This involved an unusual degree of isolation for me. Yet today I am very far from being the only person who rejects existentialism as nihilistic and a symptom not of our health and sanity, but of the reverse. I even, at last, am almost upon the side of the majority.

I have spoken of the nihilism of the existential thinkers. Very briefly let me explain my use of that expression. As one or two of the critics of this system have shown, it is the bracketing that has in fact led to the situation we find. A man, having delivered up his soul, not to the Devil but to the tree outside his window—to his coal scuttle and "bedroom suite" and to all the objects he can lay his eyes on, then suddenly cuts himself off from all this, from the external world. This comes about as a result of the Husserlian device called "bracketing." But he finds himself (suddenly, also) in an empty house—a void, a nothing. For this man—this philosopher—had beforehand scrupulously emptied, purified, the consciousness or ego (which is the house of which I speak, of which this wretched man is the inmate) of everything. When he inherited it he found that ancestors during thousands of years had accumulated in it all that a man needs for life. All kinds of quite invaluable gadgets. His vanity is such that he had cleared this out entirely— disinfected it of all telltale odor of "essence," reduced the Reason to the status of a despised drudge. So—having cut himself off from the phenomenal world outside—in this

* Heidegger was not amongst them: though had I known of him then, he would have been one of my most valuable exhibits.
[3] in agreement with

empty shell our Existentialist flings himself on the floor and contemplates this echoless vacuity. Hence all the accompaniments of existential thought—"Angst" or "Anguish," "Dereliction," "Loneliness," and "Despair." This is the despondent vocabulary of the most recent of these cults, with which everyone who has read a little about it will be familiar.

Or again: man has uncovered his nothingness, naturally enough, in identifying himself *absolutely* with his chairs and tables, his Ford car and his tabby cat, producing an "essence" in this act of union—or semi-union, for what I have spoken of figuratively as the "empty house" still remains, and is still called a "consciousness." "Existence precedes essence!" So says Sartre, after Heidegger. And when the Existentialist boils down (figuratively) his chairs and tables, his Ford car, etc., and values them, the result is not far from Zero for the philosophic mind.—It does not help matters at all to assert that man *creates* himself as he goes along (though there are some people stupid enough I suppose to feel rather puffed up at the thought of self-creation): nor is it really an advantage that man is always a few jumps ahead of himself —and in fact is not only largely *nothing* ("permeated with nothingness") but *nowhere*, too.

Upon reflection, and after the momentary elation of feeling that he is battling *his* way into *his* future—like an American marine in a tropical jungle infested with Japs; or "creating" himself, as an artist "creates"—the more modest and sensible man recognizes that he is not after all a work of art—that the *initial* creation was far beyond his powers or that of any man: that as to his *future* (for all his self-creation and following the precepts of action at any price) all that can happen is that the Ford car may increase in size and (with luck) he may do rather more than keep up with the Joneses.

No help comes either, in the Existentialist picture, from the starring of the magical word, *liberty*. Of course I suppose people will get the usual kick at the mere sight of it. Then we are assured by Sartre that owing to the final disappearance of God our liberty is *absolute*! At this the entire audience waves its hat or claps its hands. But this natural enthusiasm is turned abruptly into something much less buoyant when it is learned that this liberty weighs us down immediately with tremendous *responsibilities*. We now have to take all God's worries on our shoulders—now that we are become "men like gods." It is at this point that the Anxiety and Despondency begin, ending in utter despair.

But let us hear Sartre.

> Man is free [he says],* man is Freedom. If, on the other hand, God does not exist we do not find prescribed for us values or directions legitimizing our conduct. Thus we have neither . . . justifications nor excuses. We are alone—without excuses. This I shall express by saying that man is condemned to be free. Condemned, because he has not created himself: free, because once he is thrown into the world, he is responsible for everything he does.

This is a typical Sartre argument. For why should a creature who not only has had no hand in his own creation, but has not been consulted as to whether he wished to exist or not, be "responsible for everything he does?" This does not follow at all. On the contrary, if his life were a difficult and unpleasant one and his behavior became very violent and disorderly, although he might be shot like a mad dog it would not be *just* to do so. The fault would not be his, since he had not asked to live, or had any choice in the matter.

Then "man is condemned to be free." By whom or what is man condemned? And why call it freedom? It is a most misleading word for such a condition as is subsequently described (which description I shall shortly be outlining).—As to God not existing: since many people believe that He does exist, in announcing his nonexistence Sartre might have offered a few reasons for his own disbelief.

Why trouble for that matter to mention God at all? Why not ignore what he regards as this Christian superstition altogether? There is no novelty in a declaration of God's nonexistence—it is a disbelief that is as old as the hills.—The answer to this very natural question is that God plays a major part in existentialist philosophy. (It is a part of it that bores Sartre considerably, but there it is.) There are excellent reasons why he has to mention God.

Existentialism could not exist without the Christian background: to put it in another way, it could not exist without Soren Kierkegaard, who is responsbile for its atmosphere

* *L'Existentialisme est un humanisme*, p. 37, J. P. Sartre.

of crisis and despair—whereas Husserl supplied it with its
vitalist framework. It is surely one of the oddest mass
borrowings in the history of ideas—this removal intact of a
group of expressions belonging to a mystic experience that
had no relation to the system into which they were introduced.*

That the possession of this element in his existential
vocabulary is an embarrassment to Sartre is most evident.
With characteristic hard-boiled bustle he tackles the problem in the book from which I quote above. He has been
talking about his responsibilities.

"Ceci nous permet de comprendre ce que recouvrent des
mots un peu grandiloquent comme angoisse, délaissement,
désespoir. Comme vous allez voir, c'est extrêmement
simple." [4]

I have left this in French that you may catch better the
tone of this voice—exact, official, aggressively matter-of-fact.
For these "somewhat grandiloquent" words are *not* extremely simple to explain away, in an offhand manner. M.
Pierre Boutang, for instance, shows this very well as that
concerns the Existentialist word "anguish."

> On this point [he writes], [†] Sartre is much less
> coherent than Marx, who rejects once and for all in
> his "German Ideology" the conception of creation along
> with *all* problems of origin. If there is no creation
> there is no noncreation either and the idea of an an-
> guish founded upon the noncreation of man by him-
> self is another example of theological nostalgia. The
> idea of *dereliction* again can in no fashion be dissoci-
> ated from its religious significance. Who then can feel
> himself *abandoned* without having been abandoned by
> somebody? Who laments his solitude, without having
> harbored an invincible idea of communion?

But let me return to the text of Sartre, where we shall
be able to observe him at work gelding, explaining away the
mystical jargon of Kierkegaard. I translate:

---

* I refer throughout to the systems of Heidegger and Sartre, though
there are of course Christian Existentialists, such as Jaspers.
† *Sartre, est-il un possedé?*
[4] This permits us to understand what lies underneath rather grandiloquent words such as anguish, dereliction, despair. As you will see,
it is extremely simple.

First of all, what is to be understood by the word *angoisse*? The Existentialist declares without beating about the bush that man is anguish. Here is what that signifies: the man who engages himself and who is quite clear that he is not only that which he chooses to be, but also a legislator choosing at the same time as himself the whole of humanity, can scarcely escape a sense of his total and profound responsibility.

[The reader who was expecting to see a little of the "grandiloquence" removed from this doctrine will be distinctly surprised at this. So Man (every one of us) is a *legislator* (grander and grander!) for the whole of humanity!]

Certainly [Sartre goes on] many people feel no anxiety. But what we say is that they hide from themselves (*se masquent*) their anguish—that they fly from it. Certainly there are many people who believe that in their actions they engage themselves, and when one says to them: "But supposing *everybody* acted like that?" they shrug their shoulders.

You perceive however that we are now in the midst of a homily. A great moralist we have here: then is not "existentialism a humanism?" This factitious curtain lecture continues for some time: the "anguish," however, is accounted for by the staggering responsibility: "The Existentialist believes that man, without any support, without any help, is condemned, at every instant, to invent man." Only a coward or a "quietist" would sigh and murmur, "What a pity it is you have suppressed God the Father, M. Sartre! He would have done all this 'creating' and 'inventing' for me. You are causing me a great deal of quite gratuitous 'anguish'!"—"The doctrine which I offer you is the exact opposite of quietism. There is no reality except in *action!*" When Sartre speaks of "action" it might be Teddy Roosevelt, or Mussolini, speaking.

"Despair" he polishes off much more smartly than "Anguish." "As to 'despair,' that expression has an extremely simple meaning." It turns upon the relation of the two French words *espoir* and *désespoir*—hope and despair. "Désespoir" in the language of existentialism is simply "agir sans espoir." [5] When the grandiloquent word "despair" is used all

[5] to act without hope

that is meant is *act*—create yourself! —but don't hope too much. Sit down and *despair* is the last thing it means: with Sartre you would be doing that just as little as you would be doing it with the "Bull Moose!"—*Délaissement* (abandonment) he says rather crossly, "implies that we ourselves choose our being. It goes with the Anguish."

To express our boredom at having to do for ourselves something that formerly was done for us, is it necessary to employ a word so charged with emotion?—we certainly should ask if we did not know how it got into Sartre's books. Is it necessary to make use of a word so weighted with misery as "despair" to describe the man of action's justifiable skepticism regarding his actions redounding very much to his credit or furthering the interests of humanity? And it would indeed be childish hypocrisy were we intended to take him quite seriously, and believe that Sartre was weighed down with anguish at every moment of his life at the thought of the fearful responsibility of being Sartre, of how the "inventing" by him (in the absence of God) of a *bad* Sartre would darken the outlook for the whole of mankind!

La rigueur philosophique [6] is not to be expected of Sartre. The elaborate requirements of his publicity, his sense of semiofficial responsibility preclude that. I entirely agree with M. Henri Lefebvre that what is honest and rigorous in French atheistic existentialism is to be found in the pages of Albert Camus and Benjamin Fondane. In both cases the irrational—the Absurd—is an openly venerated principle. The unrelenting pursuit of this principle leads Fondane back to Primitive Man, and even farther. "Biological being," I quote from Lefebvre, " 'is' metaphysic and absolute. In an hallucination à la Rimbaud the slug 'is' an angel, and the mole, blind and virginal, represents existence before original sin."

Lefebvre quotes: " 'There is only one means of getting rid of abstraction—it is the qualitative leap into the absurd.' " Fondane and Camus speak exactly the same language: their view of life is almost identical; a very much sterner one than that of Sartre. But "what absurd?" asks Lefebvre: "That of the negro (covered with his painted mask, abandoning him-

[6] Philosophical rigor

self to the fury of his ritualistic dance): that of the Christian, or that of Caligula?" That is a question to which many people would like an answer today beside M. Lefebvre. I gave the answer, over and over again, in a group of books dealing with precisely these questions. For of course a state of mind does not have to be called "existential" (though eventually it has acquired this name) to reveal all these characteristics, more or less developed according to circumstances. Lefebvre for instance quotes van der Zeew as saying that "primitive mentality is distinguished from the mentality of modern man by the fact that with primitive man the subject and the object are separated by a very much smaller interval—primitive life is much more direct (*moins réfléchie* [7]) it is existential." That the young child or primitive man effects with difficulty the separation of subject and object is a commonplace, but the above quotation is a better key perhaps to existentialism than a score of treatises.

Those a little familiar with movements in the various arts during the past forty years will have no difficulty in relating to the existentialist philosophers the infantilism of Klee, for instance, or the superbly effective adaptation to the European scene of the primitive vision (African, Mexican, Pacific Islands) of l'école de Paris, or the more literary primitivism of Gauguin, or the sculpture of Brancusi, Archipenko, etc. All this is of a piece: as Mr. Barrett truly remarks, "the whole Western mind—European and American—bending before a new climate of opinion." It is a more violent and sultry climate than Europeans have known at any time in their history. It is an historic climate, it could be said—historic and political. As the European consciousness has expanded to take in the entire earth, with all its historic cultures, the climate of opinion has naturally become very different. A wind from Asia has blown down into Europe, and one up from Africa. The cool good sense and politeness surviving from the XVIIIth Century until quite recently has got to look like Dresden figures in a Saharan sandstorm. But the European thinks like a European: therein resides the tragedy. Culturally the expansion into universalism has been too rapid. The logical vessel has split wide open.—Let us agree that many undesirable things have rushed in, through the breach in the rationalist defenses.

No work I know of is more beautifully suited to make dazzlingly clear the inner meaning of existentialism than

[7] less reflective

L'Etranger, by Albert Camus. To the "Dumb Ox" of whom I wrote must now be added the "Surd." In little Monsieur Mersault you not only get the irrationality of the "Surd," and the dull speechlessness of the "Dumb," but the "Blindness" which I discussed you will recall *à propos* of Sartre's "cyclone literature" (the deliberate myopia of the man who would not care to show History undressed). But I am beginning to encroach upon my next chapter. Let me in ending this one ask how it comes about that M. Lefebvre, the French Communist, and myself, reveal such strange identity of outlook: why our responses to these phenomena appear so nearly to agree. The reason has nothing whatever to do with the doctrine of communism—we certainly should not see eye to eye if it were a question of that. It has been helpful, of course, M. Lefebvre being so much more intelligent than one has any right to expect of one engaged in Marxist polemic; but it is not that either.

The explanation is to be found in the fact that the Stalinist thinks in terms now of the metropolitan mother-state. But were I legislating culturally for a new and powerful society, like the Russian, I should not recommend a diet of Gide's thievish schoolboys, of Malraux's homosexual homicidal romantics, of Heidegger's "despair" and "anguish," of Camus's moronic little sleepwalking killers, of Klee's infantile pastiches, of Picasso's more obscene masks. Obviously I should regard them as hysterical, artificial, socially destructive. But that is political. I have always myself, since I am an artist, been of two minds. When in the late twenties and thirties I attacked the type of thinking of which Heidegger is, as I have observed, so fine a specimen, it was because I was momentarily dismayed at the prospect of the imminent collapse of the culture of the West, and with it the reduction (as a result of repeated major wars) to political helplessness and helotry of all the Western nations, to which collapse this type of thinking was a contributory cause. The arts that derived from or reflected that philosophy were included in my attack.

For precisely the same reason M. Henri Lefebvre denounces those philosophies and those arts—except that in his case it is, as a good Party man, the Soviet Socialist Republics that he is concerned to protect from contamination (or that branch of them established on French soil); whereas in my case it is Western society I had uniquely in mind. I still automatically engage in the defense of a phantom. Then it happens—and needless to say this has its weight—I am not attracted to those types of thought—I refer to the chronologic school—and they run contrary to certain of my beliefs. But politics alone, at this moment, as we stand at the deathbed of a civilization that is after all ours, is more than a sufficient explanation.

There are other things that belong here—complications I fear. The agencies of decomposition (the philosophies and the arts) served the interests of communism of course: *originally,* in view of this, the "fellow traveler" defended them, violently denouncing anyone who criticized them. Another thing to be considered is that since today we are all precariously existing in the ruins of the Western nations, there would be no sense (if there ever was any) in defending this extinct life, this shell. Consequently what I have said in this chapter about the latest of the temporal absolutisms is an expression of what I believe, and in order to keep the intellectual record straight.

The parallel between the Europe of the twenties and thirties, and the Athens of antiquity after the Spartan Wars, is in some ways so remarkable and instructive that I will, I hope, be forgiven for providing this chapter with a sort of historic footnote.

Let me first quote an eminent authority in which the bare facts of Plato's position are made plain. (The Communists do not require to prove that they are not their militant opposites.) What was a Fascist regime—in XXth Century language—followed years of democratic excesses in Athens; and Plato, invited to participate, refused.

Socrates had made the close acquaintance of Plato's uncle Charmides in the year 431 B.C. and was even then familiar with Critias. . . . Plato tells us that at the time of the oligarchical usurpation of 404–3 . . . he was urged by relatives who were among the (oligarchical) revolutionaries—no doubt Critias and Charmides—to enter public life under their auspices. But Plato first wanted to see what their policy would be.

He was horrified to find that they soon showed signs of lawless violence, and finally disgusted when they attempted to make his "elderly friend Socrates," the best man of his time, an accomplice in the illegal arrest and execution of a fellow citizen whose property they intended to confiscate.—The leaders of the restored democracy did worse, for they actually put Socrates to death on an absurd charge of impiety. This Plato says put an end to his own political aspirations.*

As you see, the "lawless violence" of these militant reactionaries repelled Plato once and for all: and had he been born in the XXth Century there is no reason to believe that Fascist violence would have pleased him any better than Communist violence. It is the dilemma of the "intellectual," in whatever age he finds himself: for power is won by violence, and theories of the State have to cut their way over the bodies of men to power.—Unless we are to say that every person who is not a Communist (or its equivalent) is a Fascist, Plato was not the latter, but he was by birth an aristocrat, and he felt and professed the greatest dislike for Democracy. He admitted that Democracy is exceedingly agreeable. "Is not this a way of life which for the moment is supremely delightful?" But according to him it was altogether too delightful for human beings, and with Aristotle he insisted it could not continue for long, despotism invariably supervening.

So he was a Conservative, and had seen the ancient institutions of Athens overthrown and replaced by a "popular government." The Court of the Areopagus had been the great Conservative stronghold; the all-powerful institution (comparable to the Temple of Ephors in Sparta) into which the Archons, or supreme magistrates of the State, passed as they surrendered their kingly office. This institution Pericles attacked, and in the end succeeded in divesting of practically all its prescriptive authority, reducing it in fact to the status of a criminal tribunal.

That Conservative stiffening of the Athenian State removed, along with all the other popular measures introduced by Pericles, the whole mass crumbled down into the demoralized mob-city—which then proceeded to fight and lose the great and terrible war with Sparta.

The period of Plato and Aristotle was an embittered "post-war"; the period immediately posterior to the breakdown of the Hellenic Civilization in the Great War of 431–404 B.C. Professor Toynbee indicates the comparison between those events and the Great War of 1914–18 (for, when he was writing, the *second* Great War had not occurred)

* A. E. Taylor.

which has perhaps been "a mortal blow" to *our* civilization. Had Professor Toynbee been writing today there would be no need for the word "perhaps."—The *Republic* and the *Laws* of Plato were of course his answer to the situation, as it appeared to him. Only the introduction of a discipline comparable to that of Sparta could lift the state to which he belonged out of demoralization.

"The friends of Socrates felt themselves in danger just after his death, and Plato in particular; with others he withdrew for a while to the neighboring city of Megara, under the protection of Euclides." As happens today, so then—to extend the parallel drawn by Professor Toynbee—political opponents were executed: and Plato, had he remained, might have had the same end as Socrates. The recapitulation of such facts as these enables one to approach with a more intelligent interest the drama being played out in France by the rival bands of intellectuals: with less—or more—dramatic intensity all over the world.—Plato as we see him in the *Laws* and the *Republic* is undeniably a totalitarian autocrat —one of those people who wants a beehive and not a human city. The *Republic* is a book I should not personally recommend for school reading. But if I constructed a Utopia myself I should not exclude Plato, though I believe he would try to break it up. This is a statement of heroic tolerance.

PART V

portrait of the artist in his time

IN Lewis' doggerel poem, "One-Way Song," he gave a pretty accurate portrait of himself:

"I go about and use my eyes, my tongue
Is not for sale—a little loosely slung
Perhaps but nothing more. I esteem my role
To be grand enough to excuse me, on my soul,
From telling lies at all hours of the day!
Or saying the thing that is not, Swift would say."

"Loosely slung," of course, is a reference to his book on Hitler, written in a hurry in 1931 before Hitler came to power and supporting both him and his policies. From every possible point of view, this book was a disaster, a complete collapse of Lewis' critical and stylistic powers. In 1939, trying to undo the damage, Lewis wrote *The Hitler Cult,* in which he described Hitler as a "demagogue" and an "incorrigible German romantic." The Nazis, he asserted, were "the most efficient exponents of machine-age barbarism, camouflaged beneath a bosky peasant homeliness . . . a Sunday School of sunburned state paupers, armed to the teeth."

He also tried to scotch the persistent rumors of his anti-Semitism, natural in this connection, by writing a book entitled *The Jews—Are They Human?* In it he said that "the anti-Semite is a gentile of disordered mind who has become what he is by brooding upon a bogey, rather as a child used to develop epilepsy at the time Napoleon Bonaparte threatened an invasion of England. . . . I expose the stupidity, much more the inhumanity, of this demented post-theological animus, directed against a people who have many faults, like the rest of us (among which an exasperating idea that they have been picked out by the All-Father as his favorite race is not the least, and is not rendered any more endearing by reason of the Nazi 'Aryan' imitation), but who nevertheless as a race, have acted as a leaven very often, in the most stodgy and backward of the European societies, adding the luster of their irresponsible wit to what would otherwise have been a grim, dull business."

It might be said that the Jews were a problem for Lewis and throughout his work one can find both highly laudatory and highly critical references to them; but he was not an anti-Semite and his frank repudiation of the charge stands in contrast to the cautious or openly hostile behavior of such eminent contemporaries and colleagues as Ezra Pound and T. S. Eliot.

None of these reversals or elucidations of opinion helped to clear the air, however; and in 1950 Lewis wrote the second installment of his autobiography, *Rude Assignment,* to finally set the record straight. It is one of his wittiest and most revealing books. I have included the sections in which he discusses his beginnings as a writer and painter, and such key books as *Tarr, The Wild Body, The Lion and the Fox,* and *The Art of Being Ruled.* As a whole, they constitute a valuable picture not merely of Lewis but of the entire modern movement.

Freedom of Speech at its Zenith

FROM the start I have behaved *as if I were free.* This is the kind of thing we do not notice about ourselves: it is only by forcibly abstracting myself that I can see it. Automatically I became an artist and an "intellectual": yet that should only be done today if you have private means, or of course after you have taken a job.

Should you, however, take a job, it occupies too much of your time. As an "intellectual" you deteriorate. So it resolves itself, as a rule, into money, or no intellectuality.

This statement must be qualified to except the poet. A poem is usually a small short piece of work. It doesn't take long to write "My love is like a red red rose." For the rest of the day you can be a clerk, or an immigration official like the late Humbert Wolfe, or, for that matter a milk roundsman or window cleaner.

Mr. T. S. Eliot worked originally in a city bank.—He took a job almost at once. A more agreeable and lucrative one was speedily found for him than bank-clearing. He became a working partner in what was at that time a new firm of publishers. That—if the job is not a very exacting one—is about the best thing a poet can do, who has no fortune.

For a novelist, like Henry James or Flaubert, much time is required: it is not like verse. The two best novelists I know —outside the Russians—came first to my mind, and both possessed considerable private means. This is not an accident, as it might seem to the casual observer. No poor man could have written Henry James' books. Among the Russians, the novelist who accomplished most was Count Tolstoy, a rich landowner. Perhaps the best craftsman among them was Turgenev: he was a rich landowner too. Dostoevsky, in some respects the greatest Russian novelist, had no money: in order to get it he wrote with feverish haste. We are told by Russians that the writing at times is almost unbearably bad, and the *longuers* [1] and absurdities almost everywhere in his novels must have had something to do with these conditions.

Had Flaubert, James, and Tolstoy been poor men, taken a job early (as schoolmaster or petty official) or struggled along to keep the wolf from the door, we should certainly have had no *Salammbo, Bouvard et Pécuchet, The Wings of the Dove, The Ambassadors,* or *War and Peace.* It is a great pity people do not understand this.

All kinds of novelists, born poor, will, I am quite aware, be mentioned in refutation of what I have said: and some would have to be allowed. But I am sure that the most searching statistics would confirm my view. There is always *something.*

James Joyce, for instance. To that penniless language teacher a strange accident happened. A Quaker lady, Miss Harriet Weaver, at the psychological moment, made him the present of an adequate income, putting down a capital sum to be used in that way, so that he could live thereafter in peace and do his work. It was therefore as a *rentier* that he wrote *Ulysses* and *Finnegans Wake.* With emotion Joyce told me, while engaged upon *Ulysses,* that he, his wife, and his children would have been on the streets had it not been for this benefactress, unknown personally to him.

Again, there is D. H. Lawrence. But that novelist of genius was born the son of a coal miner, which has tremendous romantic appeal in England—or had. It made all the difference when he was a struggling young writer, as being a Lord helped Byron. In spite of that marked advantage over other "poor boys," his posthumously published correspondence resounds with the howls of the wolf at the door.

Much of Lawrence's work is ill-written—he who could write so beautifully, as *Sea and Sardinia,* or *Mornings in Mexico* testify. Too often he caricatured himself and put his name to much second-rate novelettish padding. The explanation?—in large part, *money!* I am sorry. It is most squalid. But lack of money, for the creative mind, is like a raging disease.—If you have epilepsy like Dostoevsky, or tuberculosis like Lawrence, the toxins of the physical ailment neu-

[1] prolixities

tralize to some small extent the toxins of the economic complaint. But still distortion and deterioration result.

Under present circumstances, therefore—or I should say prior to the socialist era, which is just setting in, and in which there will be no *rentiers*—to be a serious novelist you must have money of your own. This is the rule. If you have not, you compromise, you begin thinking constantly of the larger of the Two Publics—which is far too big. You take to writing "mystery" fiction (all kinds of highbrow lore getting mixed up with the processes of criminal investigation, until you find it puts people off if you quote St. John of the Cross): or you write for the Films, or you do far too much journalism. As much "mystery" and film writing as journalism is just as bad as taking a job. The best part of your time is devoured.

This reasoning is rooted in an understanding of the new Machine-age conditions in the book market, which . . . push the good book into a small, unremunerative, "precious" or "highbrow," backwater: and in an appreciation of the progressive effect of the industrial age in undermining intellectual values. The same industrial age will, *in the end,* I am ready to believe, produce a new and more intellectual civilization than that of the wigged wits who took snuff and pointed their toes, or that of the bewhiskered clubmen, who drawled about Thackeray or Darwin through their "roman noses." It is of the meanwhile that I write. The only Public the writer can live on, just will not "take" anything above the mental standard of the Hollywood soap-opera plot, or lush sex matter.

It is these conditions, furthermore. which are responsible for the large-scale and well-organized coterie, like the "Bloomsburies." Most of the contemporary politico-literary periodicals being to all intents and purposes closed, coterie-manned, enterprises, is traceable to the same pressures. Wherever you look in art-world or literary circles, you see little congeries of people huddled together and scratching each other's backs. It is unfriendly conditions that produce this depressing spectacle.

These preliminary observations upon the economics of art were in preparation for what I shall have to say of my own situation, and to that I now will turn.—It is true that we do not want to learn how much an opera cost to write, or to produce, only to see it performed. But in any account of the work of the composer the circumstances under which the work came to be done play a determining part.

Wagner's correspondence, as an instance, is overfull of money matters: but it cost him among other things an immense practical effort to bring into being those smoky palaces of sound we call *The Ring*. My own reason for making economics more than a discreet incidental in this account of my career, is on account of the function of money as a weapon—often a very disgusting one—in the hands of those with whom the writer or artist is apt to find himself at odds. It does also provide distinct enlightenment regarding the terms on which the arts exist and thrive.

It would be inaccurate to say that I have produced about thirty books and pamphlets because I had money. On the contrary I had none while I was engaged in writing all but two or three of them.—This may suggest that I am presenting myself as an example of the small minority not conforming to my economic law for novelists. But in the first place I have written hasty books (not fiction, but books of a journalistic character). More important, I had what is called an "allowance" as a student: and I was a student for a long time. I should, I feel sure, never have started—or arrived, in my roundabout way, at the point at which I started—had much money not been spent to launch me.

I do not regard this as something to be accompanied by shamefaced apology. It happens—in addition to everything else—that I am one of those vessels that need to be a long time on the stocks. Once I put out into the wintry sea I have generally succeeded under my own steam in reaching port; but like those other vessels I have used as illustrations for my economic exordium, I cannot claim always to have done so without adventitious aid. Then had it not been for the extreme kindness of friends, notably Sir Nicholas and Lady Waterhouse, there is much I could not have done at all.

You only have to consider that a long and difficult book, which will take at least a year to write—doing no other work to speak of, grinding away all day with as few breaks as a popular dentist—is a problem of rent, food, heating, and lighting. With the *rentier*, all that is provided for. All he has to think about is writing the book. But what can the equally gifted man without income do? He can save up, retire to an inexpensive spot, budget for what is usually an inadequate period, with one packet of cigarettes a week and two pints of bitter beer on Saturday evenings.

The results have seldom been satisfactory. How could it be otherwise? Just as you cannot be a weekend Michelangelo, so these little areas of uncomfortable freedom, hijacked from an inexorable commercialism, are too near, at their extremities, to what you have escaped from, and their middles too uneasily conscious of their extremities.

Finally, I will gladly concede that it is *disgusting* and *degrading* that Money should play so important a part in the lives of poets, novelists, musicians, and other artists: but this is only because of the destructive power of this engine of coercion, not because money is inherently in a less poetic category than many other things which pertain to the intimate life of the poet or other artist. In the epoch out of which we are passing into something else it was regarded as vulgar to talk about money. A strange prudery—but no doubt utilitarian. Today I always make a point of asking a man of "private means" how much money he has got. If an Englishman, even now he still flushes angrily, stammers, and decides I am a cad. Put that question to an American, and all that happens is an outburst of boasting ("blowing" as they call it in the States) and an array of highly unreliable figures.

The connection of *economics* and of *freedom* is obvious (Epictetus being a type of man so rarely met with that his contribution may be neglected). Before beginning the autobiographical preliminaries to the story of my career up-to-date—which is an epic of freedom—let me speak for a moment of freedom again.

The history of freedom is well-known, but seldom remembered. The majority take it for granted, as they take the water supply. Such widespread freedom as we have enjoyed spread down from the top, very rapidly, during the "liberal" epoch, until, at the time my student days began, great numbers of people were in possession of freedom only enjoyed formerly by princes of the blood.

Originating in the period of which Disraeli and Arnold are perhaps the most symbolic names, a strange merger of privilege and of democracy occurred. This amounted to a popularization and great expansion of privilege (but an ultimate decline in and cheapening of authority). The Public School system mass-produced the "gentleman": some were gentlemen already, others became so by training and propinquity.

Upon all was conferred without distinction something like Roman citizenship in the shape of the Old School Tie.

There were, too, the greatly increased facilities of travel: "Cook's" and other Tours which would supply a party of twenty or thirty people with the Grand Tour at a ridiculously low rate. Again, there was the rapid growth of great centers of luxury, like Paris, London, or Vienna. These, and many factors of a like nature, produced a capitalist elysium for really substantial numbers of people—not only for the magnate class. It was very widespread: and the great industrial machine poured out inexpensive luxury articles in profusion, so that, in the end, the little doctor's son, who had been a day boy at Dulwich College, in his orthodox tweeds, was almost indistinguishable from the duke (greatly to the duke's disgust) : and the *mademoiselle de magazin* [2] could collect one costume at least in which she bore a striking resemblance to a socialite.

Only the working mass remained much as it was. This, at least in England, was part of the plan: for the new class was a watered-down and swollen aristocracy that had been evolved (for purposes of empire) and only the snobbery was not diluted. It was therefore a freedom based upon selfish, as well as theatrical, principles.

The freedom, however, was wonderful: and the duke joined in—threw away his strawberry leaves, stopped only speaking to other dukes, and married the chorus girl with the fattest legs: the clergyman got broader and broader, revealed himself as a freethinker, teaching his thunderstruck flock that the "pale Galilean" was an awfully brainy and good-hearted fellow but no more, all the rest being Hebrew mythology (but still drawing his stipend): wholesale caterers became masters of impoverished hunts—most of the London clubs left their doors ajar, and the Stock Exchange tumbled in: but snobbery comically kept pace, to gild and polish the select meretricious democracy.

The arts did their gilding too—the Nineties, with its brilliant groups, corruscated in this sunset of English power. For its long-enjoyed advantage as the first and major industrial nation was a diminishing asset, and this overexpanded ruling class would soon be left up in the air. The Nineties was a genuine decadence: that was the first, the second came after world war i. (To compare carefully these two decadences is to understand what had happened to England in the interval.)

Emerging from my schooldays, I found myself in the debilitating post-Nineties world of the first decade of the century. My views regarding politics were those of a young alligator. I had money in my pocket: not a great deal, but enough to live. I was given to understand I should always have money in my pocket—so I thought no more about economics, my own or other people's. I drifted into this relaxed and relaxing atmosphere and there was nothing at first to prick me into wakefulness. I tasted what people call perfect freedom therefore. There were no obstacles. Everything was easy: I was healthy: the mind slept like a healthy infant, in the sunlit smithy in which world war i was being hammered into shape.

How One Begins

My career began at about the age of eight. I stitched together pieces of paper and wrote the first of many books of this order. They were no stupider than the Volsungensaga but in range even narrower, being confined altogether to war, instead of practically altogether to war.

In these booklets my first art work appeared: stiff and hieratic friezes of heavily accoutred mannequins. These long chains of matchstick men—Klee men—each trailing a musket or grasping, in a hand like a bomb, a hatchet, went right across the double page. Half of the personæ obviously are Redskins, with plumed war bonnets, and an assortment of weapons appropriate to the Indian brave: the other half must be Palefaces. These lines of lifeless foemen converge, where they meet gesticulation is sometimes indicated. There is much action in the text, but practically none in its visual accompaniment.

I was a denizen of the "Leatherstocking" world. I started life at eight as a war chronicler therefore. It never ceases for me to be unpleasant that the tiny mind of a little animal like myself at eight and earlier should be filled by its elders with such pasteboard violence, initiating it into this old game of murder. Born into a military aristocracy life begins full of excited little bangs and falsetto war cries.

When I look at a photograph I have here, among many others in a portfolio, I see the same self that was responsible for the booklets: but this time he is not a child, he is in uniform among belted, pouched, tin-hatted, fellow soldiers of world war i. I perceive a sort of repetition—it is the same pattern, only the bangs and cries of battle had become real, for the figure in the photograph, not academic.—And I am ashamed to say that even then I still saw these things as a child does.

The next landmark in my career—and it was an event which had a decisive influence upon the subsequent course of it— was the discovery by my housemaster at Rugby that my study (which I shared with a boy called Middleton) had become an "artist's studio." In it I had set up an easel, procured oil paints, a mahl stick, and a palette. At the time these unorthodox happenings were brought to the attention of the housemaster I was engaged in copying the head of a large dog.

I remember a very big boy opening the door of the study, putting his big red astonished face inside, gazing at me for a while—digesting what he saw, the palette on my thumb, the brush loaded with pigment in the act of dabbing—and then, laconically and contemptuously, remarking, "You frightful artist!" closed the study door: and I could hear his big slouching lazy steps going away down the passage to find some more normal company. The English, I am afraid, are mostly of that stamp.

At length someone apprised the housemaster, at all events, of what was going on in his house. What Public Schools were for was to turn out a stupid but well-behaved execu- tive class to run the Empire Kipling crowed and crooned about. Nothing so anomalous as a fourteen-year-old fag painting in oils at a giant easel had ever been recorded. My presence before this had not gone unremarked: but it was something of a different kind, in that case, that had stimu- lated interest, and concern. For four terms I had not changed my form (I was still in the Lower Middle School) and showed no tendency to do so. The housemaster put two and two together: two such unusual things must be connected.

They in fact hardly had any connection: but it was all for the best that he was a man content with the obvious.

He concluded (quite rightly) that I had got into the wrong school. He thought that an art school was where I really ought to be; and he wrote my mother to this effect. Meanwhile he arranged for me to have special instruction in drawing several times a week. An old Scot, a beautiful silver mustache shading his red lips, gargled away at me in a Glasgow accent, but gave me much practice in the portrayal of plaster casts, and provided me with reports of unrestrained enthusiasm. I was a much needed advertisement for him, of course, and his function in that birthplace of Football.

The effect of the housemaster's letter upon my parent was mixed. She of course deplored my slackness and indifference to algebra and Latin (forgetful of the fact that these schools specialized in instilling a contempt for learning in the "flanneled fool" liable for the rest of his life to live with such metaphors in his mouth as "sticky wicket," and the "muddied oaf," content for the remainder of his days to feel that he is "playing the game," oblivious of what the particular game happens to be).

But she was predisposed to favor the idea of my becoming an artist: and my unexpected prowess as an oil painter enabled her to forget the ignominy of the dunce's cap. She herself had always painted—used to go to an art school in that Bloomsbury Square at the end of Great Ormond Street before her marriage and was not displeased to think that I evinced this unconquerable desire to do what she herself had always done in a desultory way. There was perhaps vanity in this.

When a schoolboy, I passed some weeks every year in Paris with my mother. These visits were not calculated to cure me of my interest in the arts. It was then I first frequented the galleries, the Louvre and the Luxembourg. The innumerable oil paintings of all the schools, in one big lazy blur of cupids, shipwrecks, madonnas, and obese women, exercised a pleasurable mesmerism upon a schoolboy whose responses were far below a phlegmatic surface: whose instincts far outran his consciousness.—However, the outcome of the whole matter was that after a stay of about two years and a half I left Rugby, and became a student at the Slade School, University College, London.

The latter institution was at that period presided over by Professor Brown, with Tonks as the guiding spirit and policy maker. All the emphasis was on drawing. Wilson Steer and Russell made up the full professorial cast. A training was provided of a type so uncraftsmanlike that it surprises me it remained uncriticized. The model of draftsmanship insisted upon by Tonks was cinquecento: but the painting that of an academic, inexact, impressionism, such as is now to be met with at Burlington House. Steer knew more than the others, but was a strangely somnolent bovine individual, of little use as a teacher. He moved around the life class with a heavy, cautious step, as if avoiding puddles, and no one could call him a chatterbox. Sometimes he never spoke at all. But I did not remain very long at the Slade and then went to Paris, renting a studio in the Quartier. At this point my life as an artist in fact began.

It may perhaps have been remarked that in the last chapter I made no mention of anything but the literary side of my history—which was in the main because this book is concerned, more than anything else, with that side, or with matters arising out of the fact that I am a writer, and of a kind (as in the case of satire) exciting people to retributory action. In the present chapter, except for the booklets manufactured as a child, for the unfolding of sagas, I have spoken only of beginnings as a painter. Already I was writing at the Slade (and to that presently I shall return), but it had no bearing as yet upon my movements or mode of life.

Further, there is nothing of economic relevance, those questions do not exact attention until later. As to the Fine Arts, it is not difficult for even mechanics or a laborer's son to get as far as an art school. The trouble is—once there—the urgency of the position, so that he is compelled to go in for training in commercial techniques, and can never keep his head above water long enough to become a straight artist, rather than a man working for his living by doing commercial designs.—If you go to see an exhibition of a young painter's work at a West End Gallery, in nine cases out of ten you may be sure he did not start economically from scratch. But hundreds who have so begun are passing every year through municipal or State Schools. It is they who produce the pictorial advertisements for vacuum cleaners, face creams, bile beans, or cigarettes you see in the papers or on the walls of the Underground.

About Paris I cannot write with a suitable restraint. It

was the great humanist creation of the French, on a par with their cathedrals: indeed there is the same space, and lift, in the one as in the other. But, above all, the human being was never forgotten in its rambling growth: the same thing that made the French so graceful and polite, or the world's best dancing masters and pastry cooks, made this place supremely pleasant. To make a perfect place to live in—no other people has done that with their capital city, which has either been too formal, too tidy, too snobbish, too squalid, too tall, too much a Business Babylon, or too much like a museum.

For centuries Paris had dominated Europe socially and intellectually, no European could say his mind had delivered itself of a thought until Paris had recognized its existence, no woman was dressed until Paris had dressed her; and even up to world war i, it was intact. It was just the hectic ruin that people lived in after that. In its heyday the rest of Europe—from which Vienna must be excepted—crouched in their overcold, or overhot, capitals, culturally provincial. But Paris was expansive and civilized, temperate in climate, beautiful and free.

I went there in its late sunset: its multitude of café terraces swarmed with people from every corner of the earth: it was still *la nouvelle Athènes*,[1] divinely disputatious, with an immense student population for whom the publishers poured out "libraries" of masterpieces, all the sciences and the arts most daring and up-to-date, priced at a few francs. For it was the impecunious in great numbers who bought them: there may have been a luxury business in books but it did not obtrude itself upon the student, and would have been of no interest to him. It was not a city of the rich, like New York—the poorest student could sit all day long (and often did) for the cost of one cup of coffee without being interfered with and observe the crowds, or be entertained by his neighbors, or by the *soulard*[2] who drifted from café to café, extracting a few sous by his imitation of the courtship of two canaries, or the ululations of owls, with his wizened mustachioed lips.

It is dangerous to go to heaven when you are too young. You do not understand it and I did not learn to work in Paris. Many things, however, found their way into my mind

1 the new Athens
2 drunkard

as I moved about.—First of all, I altered my appearance. Driven, by a vocational ferment, out of the British rut of snobbish sloth, I now become transformed, in contact with the Latin life, into something so different that had I a few years later encountered someone I had been to school with he would not have recognized me. I still went to a tailor in Brook Street for my clothes, but persuaded him to cut them into what must have seemed to his insular eye outrageous shapes.

Gradually the bad effects of English education wore off, or were deliberately discarded. Being with "foreigners" all the time who never "played the game," I rapidly came to see that there was, in fact, no game there at all. It was a British delusion that there was always a game—to whose rules, good or bad, you must conform. However, I need not detail the phases of this metamorphosis: I became a European, which years in Paris and elsewhere (Spain, Germany, Holland) entailed; hastening the process however, with a picturesque zeal. There are in England many invisible assets, to do mostly with character; they are not tangible and make no show of a kind to appeal to the barbaric eye of youth. All that was apparent to me, at that time, was the complacent and unimaginative snob of the system I had escaped from, the spoiled countryside, sacrificed in order to manufacture Brummagem, long ago when it was discovered that England was really a coal mine; and I noted with distaste the drab effects of Victorian mediocrity. I may add that the defects of the French were as hidden from me as those invisible assets I have spoken of belonging to the English.

My literary career began in France, in the sense that my first published writings originated in notes made in Brittany. Indeed, this period in retrospect, responsible for much, is a blank with regard to painting. There was for instance the beginning of my interest in philosophy (attendance at Bergson's lectures at the Collège de France one evidence of that). But what I started to do in Brittany I have been developing ever since. Out of Bestre and Brotcotnaz grew, in that sense—if in no other—the aged "Gossip Star" at her toilet, and Percy Hardcaster. Classifiable I suppose as "satire," fruits of much visceral and intellectual travail and indolent brooding, a number of pieces were eventually collected under the title of *The Wild Body*. To those primordial literary backgrounds, among the meadows and rocks and stone hamlets of Finisterre, thundered at by the Atlantic, in a life punctuated with Pardons, I will now make my way back, and try and remember how my first rational writings came to assume the shape they did.

Early Life and Shakespeare

Iᴛ has been my experience of my few very eminent contemporaries that, after their various fashions, they have been the possessors of abnormally aggressive egos (and I daresay they may have discovered the same symptoms in myself). But what are these unhealthily large egos but one of the by-products of the situation which isolates the so-called "intellectual" from the common life, and demands of him much more domestic morale than is good for him?

When I saw Joyce described, as I did not long ago, as suffering from "elephantiasis of the ego," I felt the usual contempt certain critics always succeed in provoking; for even their truths are so crude as to be invalid as they stand, having all the appearance of ill-favored errors. But *of course* Joyce had "elephantiasis of the ego." Had he not suffered from something which lends itself to such an offensive description, you, Mr. Critic, would have no *Ulysses* or *Finnegans Wake* to gabble about: to blow hot and blow cold about—inflate your little reputation by puffing, and then reinflate it by a confession of disillusionment.

The only people of eminence I was in touch with as a beginner were painters, who enjoyed the usual robust self-esteem of their kind—painting being a much healthier occupation than writing. They overlooked in me the budding artist but accorded a generous recognition to something else. The first literary form I had used was verse, which I was writing while at the Slade. And to these elders I was known as a "poet." The Fine Arts they imagined were already in good hands, namely their own. Verse, as a form of literary composition, preceded my *Wild Body* stories. I wrote a great deal, including a five-act play in blank verse. As early as my schooldays I had formed this habit, but what I wrote then was of a pietistic order.

About the time I went to the Slade I began to write Petrarchan sonnets, but soon changed to Shakespearean. They were easier to do. Some were so like Shakespeare's that as I recall lines in them I am never quite certain whether they are Shakespeare's or mine. It remains for me a mystery how so dumb a youth as I was can have produced them. It is nothing short of planchette, or automatic writing. Since the publication of Shakespeare's famous sequence many people have, it is true, written sonnets that could at first glance be mistaken for his. But they were usually experienced craftsmen.

My sonnet sequence contained no dark lady, all that side was appropriately absent, but if anything they exaggerated the Shakespearean pessimism. These pastiches, at all events, attracted attention among a small number of people. Here is a sonnet-like composition of that period, which I remember a luminary of those days singling out for commendation.

> "Doubt is the sole tonic that sustains the mind,
>   The keynote of this universe entire.
>   Self-conscious certainty is Doubt, and blind
>   God-worship but Doubt's sanctified attire.
>   God fashioned us in Doubt: for Eden-trees
>   Were planted there in God's initial Doubt:
>   . . . hope doth but tease
>   Us into . . . where certainty could not."

One of my earliest friends was an architect, the author of a book called *The Canon*, who became my friend because of these sonnets. Sterling was his name. I was so young then that everything is misty: what we can have conversed about heaven knows. Certainly not Shakespeare. I had no idea until William Rothenstein told me, at a later date, that Sterling had written a book of great interest. Nor, being backward and obtuse, had I the least idea that this poor man, when he took me out to tea and fed me on Meringue Chantilly (for I was inordinately greedy and probably did not have to be pressed very much to eat three or four) had in all likelihood to fast himself afterwards to cover this expense. We used to go to Buzzard's in Oxford Street where he spent as much, I expect, for a tea as would buy him a week's breakfasts. He supported out of his slender reserves an aged mother and sister—my informant again Rothenstein—and

ived in a small dark flat in the Adelphi. For two or three
weeks no one saw him around. At last they broke in: he was
ying just inside the front door with his throat cut. The rats,
nfesting the London sewers, had chewed away some of his
flesh. It seems that he had appointed William Rothenstein
his literary executor, who, in due course, discovered a sheaf
of my sonnets. These he at first believed must be Sterling's,
until he identified their only true begetter. Very much later
he told me about this, and what has happened to them I do
not know. They are, I suppose, my property, for they were
only lent to Sterling to read.

It was therefore an innovation for me to take to prose,
when I began preparing material for stories in Brittany—at
the time I felt a little of a comedown, or at least a con-
descension. My first attempts naturally were far less successful than the verse. The coastal villages of Finisterre in which
I spent long summers (one of them with the artist, Henry
Lamb) introduced one to a more primitive society. These
fishermen went up to Iceland in quite small boats, they were
as much at home in the huge and heaving Atlantic as the
torero in the bullring: their speech was still Celtic and they
were highly distrustful of the stranger. They brawled about
money over their fierce apple juice: when somebody was
stabbed, which was a not infrequent occurrence, they would
not call in a doctor, but come to the small inn where I
stayed, for a piece of ice. A great part of their time was
spent, when not at sea, jogging up and down between
"Pardons," all the women provided with large umbrellas. Their
miniature bagpipe is a fine screaming little object, to the
music of which star dancers would leap up into the air,
as if playing in a feudal ballet. On the whole, however, the
dancing was sedate and mournful, compared with Rubens'
peasants.

Long vague periods of an indolence now charged with
some creative purpose were spent in digesting what I saw,
smelled and heard. For indolent I remained. The Atlantic air,
the raw rich visual food of the barbaric environment, the
squealing of the pipes, the crashing of the ocean, induced
a creative torpor. Mine was now a drowsy sun-baked ferment,
watching with delight the great comic effigies which erupted
beneath my rather saturnine but astonished gaze: Brotcotnaz,
Bestre, and the rest.

During those days, I began to get a philosophy: but not a
very good one, I am afraid. Like all philosophies, it was built

up around the will—as primitive houses are built against a hill, or propped up upon a bog. As a timely expression of personal impulses it took the form of a reaction against civilized values. It was militantly vitalist. Only much later was I attracted to J.-J. Rousseau, or it might have had something to do with his anti-social dreaming.

The snobbishness (religion of the domestic) of the English middle class, their cold philistinism, perpetual silly sports, all violently repudiated by me were the constant object of comparison with anything that stimulated and amused, as did these scenes. I overlooked the fact that I was observing them as a privileged spectator, having as it were purchased my front-row stall with money which I derived from that other life I despised. In spite of this flaw the contrast involved was a valid one: of the two types of life I was comparing, the one was essentially contemptible, the other at least rich in surface quality: in the clubhouse on an English golf links I should not have found such exciting animals as I encountered here—undeniably the golfers' values are wanting in a noble animal zest. This is, however, a quandary that cannot be resolved so simply as I proposed—namely, the having-the-cake-and-eating-it way.

The epigraph at the beginning of my first novel, *Tarr*, is an expression of the same mood, which took a long time to evaporate altogether. It is a quotation from Montaigne. "Que c'est un mol chevet que l'ignorance et l'incuriosité?" [1] Even books, theoretically, were a bad thing, one was much better without them. Every time men borrowed something from outside they gave away something of themselves, for these acquisitions were artificial aggrandizement of the self, but soon there would be no core left. And it was the core that mattered. Books only muddied the mind: men's minds were much stronger when they only read the Bible.

The human personality, I thought, should be left alone, just as it is, in its pristine freshness: something like a wild garden —full, naturally, of starlight and nightingales, of sunflowers and the sun. The *Wild Body* I envisaged as a piece of the wilderness. The characters I chose to celebrate—Bestre, the Cornac and his wife, Brotcotnaz, le père François—were all primitive creatures, immersed in life, as much as birds, or big, obsessed, sun-drunk insects.

The body was wild: one was attached to something wild,

[1] Are not ignorance and lack of curiosity—a soft pillow?

ke a big cat that sunned itself and purred. The bums, alcoholic fishermen, penniless students (generally Russians) who might have come out of the pages of *The Possessed*, for long my favorite company, were an anarchist material. And as ringmaster of this circus I appointed my "Soldier of Humor," who stalked imbecility with a militancy and appetite worthy of a much more lighthearted and younger Flaubert, who had somehow got into the universe of Gorky.

There is a psychological factor which may have contributed to what I have been describing.—I remained, beyond the usual period, congealed in a kind of cryptic immaturity. In my social relations the contacts remained, for long, primitive. I recognized dimly this obstruction: was conscious of gaucherie, of wooden responses—all fairly common symptoms of course. It resulted in experience with no natural outlet in conversation collecting in a molten column within. This *trop-plein* [2] would erupt: that was my way of expressing myself—with intensity, and with the density of what had been undiluted by ordinary intercourse: a thinning-out which is, of course, essential for protection.

Observing introspectively this paradoxical flowering, this surface obtuseness, on the one hand, and unexpected fruit which it miraculously bore: observing this masterly inactivity, almost saurianly-basking sloth, and what that condition produced, something within me may quite reasonably have argued that this inspired *Dummheit* [3] was an excellent idea. *Let us leave well enough alone!* may have been the mental verdict. I know everything already: why add irrelevant material to this miraculous source? Why acquire spectacles for an eye that sees so well without them? So there was superstition, and, I suspect, arrogance.

But I am gazing back into what is a very dark cavern indeed. An ungregarious childhood may have counted for something. A feature of perhaps greater importance was that after my schooldays, even with my intimates, I was much younger than those with whom I associated, since I had left school so early. And, finally, at school itself, developing habits as I did which appeared odd to the young empire builders by whom I was surrounded, may have stiffened the defense natural to that age.

The rough set of principles arrived at was not, I have said, a very good philosophy. Deliberately to spend so much time

swollen congestion
stupidity

in contact with the crudest life is, I believe, wasteful of life. It seems to involve the error that raw material is alone authentic life. I mistook for "the civilized" the tweed-draped barbaric clown of the golf links. But, as a philosophy of life, it principally failed in limiting life in a sensational sense. After two or three intermediate stages I reached ultimately an outlook that might be described as almost as formal as this earliest one was the reverse.

"Wildness" of some kind or other—often more personally picturesque and romantic than mine—has been by no means an infrequent thing with the Anglo-saxon. As a reaction no doubt against the respectability of English life, many, like George Borrow, have gone to live in "dingles," wandered about the earth with gypsies, taken service with the wild Corsairs like Trelawney, or become Bedouins, like Doughty. France, too, has produced a not insignificant crop of such men: Paul Gauguin, for instance, who worked in Brittany before going to Tahiti: actually dying at a fishing port in Finisterre after a scuffle with a fisherman in which he hurt his leg. His Breton idylls I think are the best of his work.

Augustus John—whom I knew at a very early age—has been the most notorious nonconformist England has known for a long time. Following in the footsteps of Borrow, he was one of those people who always set out to do the thing that "is not done," according to the British canon. He swept aside the social conventions, which was a great success, and he became a public lion practically on the spot. There was another reason for this lionization (which is why he has remained a lion): he happened to be an unusually fine artist.

Such a combination was rare. The fashionable public found as a rule that it had been leo-hunting some pretentious jackal. Here was one who had gigantic earrings, a ferocious red beard, a large angry eye, and who barked beautifully at you from his proud six foot, and, marvelously, was a great artist too. He was reported to like women and wine and song and to be by birth a gypsy.

When I first saw this extraordinary individual was while I was a student at the Slade School. I learned that Augustus John was an art master in Liverpool. He had had the scholarship at the Slade, and the walls bore witness to the triumphs of this "Michelangelo." He was a legendary "Slade School *ingenious*," to use Campion the doorkeeper's word. A

arge charcoal drawing in the center of the wall of the life
class of a hairy male nude, arms defiantly folded and a
bristling mustache, commemorated his powers with almost
a Gascon assertiveness: and fronting the stairs that lead upwards where the ladies were learning to be Michelangelos,
hung a big painting of Moses and the Brazen Serpent.

Everything in the place was in the "grand manner": for
Professor Tonks, as I have already remarked, had one great
canon of draftsmanship, and that was the giants of the
Renaissance. Everyone was attempting to be a giant and please
Tonks. None pleased Tonks—none, in their work, bore the
least resemblance to Michelangelo. The ladies upstairs wept
when he sneered at their efforts to become Giantesses.

Now undoubtedly John had come nearer to the Michelangelo ideal than anybody else. One day the door of the life
class opened and a tall bearded figure, with an enormous
black Paris hat, large gold earrings decorating his ears, with
a carriage of the utmost arrogance, strode in and the whisper
"John" went round the class. He sat down on a donkey—
the wooden chargers astride which we sat to draw—tore a
page of banknote paper out of a sketch book, pinned it upon a
drawing board, and with a ferocious glare at the model (a
female) began to draw with an indelible pencil. I joined the
group behind this redoubtable personage. To my great surprise, a squat little figure began to emerge upon the paper.
He had forsaken the "grand manner" entirely, it seemed. A
modern Saskia was taking shape upon the banknote paper:
drawings that followed all came out of the workshop of
Rembrandt Van Rijn. Needless to say everyone was tickled
to death. They felt that the squalor of the Dutch, rather than
the noble rhetoric of the cinquecento, was, and always had
been, the thing. John left as abruptly as he had arrived. We
watched in silence this mythological figure depart.

For weeks afterwards Professor Tonks' life was a hell on
earth. I am sure he had no inkling of the cause. However tall
and graceful the model might be, displaying her young
English charms before our hardened eyes, Tonks was presented, as he went his rounds, upon the students' drawing
boards, with nothing but dumpy little images. I tried my
hand at it, but found they did not come out very well, so I
went back to a version of my own of Signorelli.

The exact date of my first visit to John's studio I do not
remember, but it was shortly after I left the Slade, I think.
William Rothenstein (to whom I had been introduced by

his young brother, who was at the Slade) was taking me there. We approached the top-floor flat in Charlotte Street: there was the noise of children, for this patriarch had already started upon his Biblical courses.

I was with John a great deal in those early days, in London, later in Paris, and on one long vacation on the coast of Normandy. At St. Honorine des Perthes (the latter occasion) I wrote verse, when not asleep in the sun. Unlike most painters, John was very intelligent. He read much and was of a remarkable maturity. I cast this all in the past tense, for I am speaking of a time long past: but I may add that I never see Augustus John today but he speaks of some book he has been reading, generally one of the few at the moment worth attention.

Nietzsche was, I believe, the paramount influence, as was the case with so many people prior to world war i. The other day I was interested, in listening to a broadcast by Herbert Read (in a *Crisis of My Life* series) to find he had selected Nietzsche as the decisive influence, overshadowing the rest of his early reading. Germans of whom I saw a good deal in Paris as a student were very contemptuous: they called Nietzsche "a salon-philosopher."

But for me Nietzsche was, with Schopenhauer, a thinker more immediately accessible to a Western mind than the other Germans, whose barbarous jargon was a great barrier —Hegel, for instance, I could never read. A majority of people, I daresay, found in the author of *Zarathustra* a sort of titanic nourishment for the ego: treating in fact this great hysteric as a powerhouse. At present that is what I like the least about Nietzsche: and I was reasonably immune then to Superman. The impulse to titanism and supernatural afflatus pervading German romanticism has never had any interest for me. On the other hand that side of his genius which expressed itself in *La Gaya Scienza*, or those admirable maxims, rather resembling Butler's *Notebooks*, which he wrote after the breakdown in his health, were among my favorite reading in those years. . . .

First Published Work

IT is unlikely that I should ever have uprooted myself from Paris had it not been for warnings that the economic position for me had suffered an alteration: that my father, who had gone to America, showed every sign of stopping there: finally, that the time might not be very distant when I should have to begin to make money. It was understood that it would be by painting that this would be accomplished, and indeed writing was never mentioned in that connection. At that period the image of Grub Street was uppermost in people's minds, whenever the subject of writing as a calling was mooted.

So, although visiting Paris every year, I now returned to London. It was little more than a gesture for some time, as I took no immediate steps towards professionalizing myself. At last, however, I exhibited a largish canvas in the Ryder Street Gallery, St. James, run by Robert Ross. It represented two sprawling figures of Normandy fishermen, in mustard yellows and browns, which was purchased by Augustus John—a circumstance which gave me unusual pleasure.

Except for this painting, and perhaps a drawing or two, I sold nothing to start with: I think my next sale of work occurred during my brief association with "Bloomsbury." I refer to an overlifesize gouache of three smiling women, which reminded Mr. Clive Bell, I recall, of Giotto. It was purchased through Bloomsbury influence, if not by Mr. Clive Bell, for the Contemporary Art Society. It found its way to the Tate Gallery, where it remained secluded in the cellar until one day the Thames overflowed, invaded the cellar, and the last seen of it was that of a reddish expanse floating about on the surface of the muddy water.

Actually quite my first success of a practical nature was literary. The *English Review* had just started publication, founded and edited by Ford Madox Hueffer (later known as Ford Madox Ford). I went to its office in Holland Park and Hueffer has described (and I myself I think elsewhere) "the moujik" who unexpectedly mounted his stairs, silently left a bundle of manuscript—but with no address, only the author's name. "The moujik" referred to my hirsute and unconventional appearance. The outcome was that the *English Review* published successively "The Pole," "Some Innkeepers and Bestre," and "Les Saltimbanques." Some weeks later when I went to inquire about the manuscript they gave me a copy of the proofs of the first story, which they had corrected and returned to the printer, as they did not know where I lived. This was a great and pleasurable surprise.

Through Hueffer I became acquainted with Ezra Pound, through whom in due course I became acquainted with T. S. Eliot, Gaudier Brzeska, Dolmetsch, H. D., Aldington, and many others.

When Hueffer married Violet Hunt, the novelist, that expanded still further the orbit of his somnolent but systematic sociability. It was at dinner at Mrs. Hueffer's for instance that I first met Rebecca West. She was a dark young maenad then, who burst through the dining room door (for she was late) like a thunderbolt.

These intellectual Hosts were of that valuable kind of human, who shuns solitude as the dread symbol of unsuccess, is happiest when his rooms are jammed with people (for preference of note). I was commissioned by Violet Hueffer to do a mural to go over the mantelpiece of her study. This was a concession to "les jeunes," [1] but her spirit dwelt with the pre-Raphaelites, as did half of her husband's.

Hueffer was a flabby lemon and pink giant, who hung his mouth open as though he were an animal at the Zoo inviting buns—especially when ladies were present. Over the gaping mouth damply depended the ragged ends of a pale lemon mustache. This ex-collaborator with Joseph Conrad was himself, it always occurred to me, a typical figure out of a Conrad book—a caterer, or corn factor, coming on board—blowing like a porpoise with the exertion—at some Eastern port.

What he *thought* he was, was one of those military *sahibs* [2] who used to sit on the balcony of a club in Hindustan with two or three other *sahibs*, *stingahs* at their

[1] the young
[2] In India, a term of respect applied by natives to Europeans.

sides, and who, between meditative puffs at a cheroot, begins to tell one of Conrad's tales. He possessed a vivid and theatrical imagination: he jacked himself up, character as he was in a nautical story, from one of the white business gents in the small tropic port into—I am not quite sure it was not into a *Maugham* story—among the more swagger representatives of white empire in Asia.

Those were his failings, irritating to me (though Ezra Pound, who referred to him as "Fatty," appeared to accept him—amused but impressed—as the *sahib* of the officers' quarters). But on the asset side there was a good deal too. Hueffer was probably as good an editor as could be found for an English literary review.—He had by birth artistic associations and could write himself much better than most editors. His literary standards were too exacting for latter-day England. Such productions as he was peculiarly fitted to edit are expensive to run and the circulation insignificant today. He was denied in his milieu the possibility of exerting an influence which would have been productive of more vigorous literary standards. Then his vanity never interfered in the least with his appreciation of books by other writers.

Of Ezra Pound I will say nothing except to remark that, to the best of my belief, he was by way of discovering, or of bringing forward, James Joyce; that he "sold the idea" of Joyce as a writer of great parts to Miss Harriet Weaver (for Joyce the all-important "contact"): that he nursed Eliot's style along until it could stand on its own feet: that by his criticism of the English Nineteenth Century poets (Shelley, Keats and their followers) and substitution of older severer models, he reorientated along with T. S. Eliot the whole of English and American criticism; he imported into England and America the satirico-romantic standards of the French as also their use of conversational, as opposed to "poetic," diction—this in association with Eliot. Thus he and Eliot displaced what up to then had still remained the largely Victorian approach to the appropriate subject matter of poetry.*

It was the result of Pound's busy promotion that *The Portrait of the Artist,* and *Tarr,* were serialized by *The Egoist,* and that T. S. Eliot's verse appeared there. Finally,

---

* In the nineties tentatives in these directions are discernible, but most are imitational. It was not the principle itself that was taken over.

Cathay—described by Hueffer as "the most beautiful book in the world"—was the first, as it remains the most magically beautiful, of versions of the Chinese poets, initiating the technique since used by many other—and inferior—hands.

If I did not exhibit pictures it did not mean that I was unproductive. I was now developing a mode of pictorial expression which was more "advanced" than that of other people at that time. *Avantgardism* in itself, at any time, is not a merit or a demerit. Some people are the changers and some the conservers. What conferred a kind of sanction upon my violent movement away from more orthodox practice was the fact that this was favorable to the development of something that no other method would have brought out so well. As far as England is concerned there is no one else I can think of whose pigeon this was quite so much as it was mine. But of course dear old Great Britain is no place to be an artist in—at least not an artist of that sort. Severity of any kind repels her—as she always smiles good-naturedly about the "logical" French (meaning, it is better to be easy-going, and keep the intellect in its place). You will always find that England will get back to the romantic at the first opportunity. Severity, like Satire, will only in the end be tolerated in the foreigner.

By the time I joined the Omega Workshops—Roger Fry's abortive venture—my position was that of an extremist, I suppose: much further to the left, that is, than any of the others. That was in 1913. About this scheme I first heard some time before that. I have a letter from Roger Fry dated Feb. 21, 1912, in which he says: "Will you come to a meeting to settle the nature of the group of artists which D. Grant, Etchells and I propose to start." There is another of Dec. 7, 1912 from Fry saying: "I'm working very hard trying to raise capital for our decoration scheme. So far the only help promised comes from Bernard Shaw." . . .

The house had been rented or bought: so this scheme materialized, and will serve as a kind of milestone. I worked there with several of my friends and future associates. Frederick Etchells was I think the most technologically minded of us: but with no preliminary workshop training it was idle to suppose that half a dozen artists could cope with all—or indeed any—of the problems of waxing, lacquering, polishing, painting and varnishing of furniture—chairs, tables, cabinets and so forth—or the hand-painting of textiles which the plan involved. Naturally the chairs we sold stuck to the seats of people's trousers; when they took up an Omega candlestick they could not put it down again, they held it in an involuntary viselike grip. It was glued to them and they to it. Later I believe these drolleries ceased to enliven what was otherwise an arty-crafty conception, with a "post-impressionist" veneer. However, certain transactions of a disagreeable nature caused me to sever my connection with the Omega, and as there is no purpose in returning to such matters here I will pass on to my next milestone, namely "The Cave of the Golden Calf." I believe I am going backward, but I have not to hand any record of the actual date.

Strindberg, the Swedish dramatist, had a number of wives, one being a Viennese. This very adventurous woman (whose favorite remark, I recall, was "Je suis au bout de forces!" [3] although, often as I heard her say it, I never saw her in that condition, her "forces" being at all times triumphantly intact) rented an enormous basement. Hence the term "Cave." She had it suitably decorated with murals by myself, and numbers of columns by Jacob Epstein: hired an orchestra—with a frenzied Hungarian gypsy fiddler to lead it—a smart corps of Austrian waiters and an Austrian cook: then with a considerable amount of press promotion she opened it as a nightclub.

With the Epstein figures appearing to hold up the threateningly low ceiling, the somewhat abstract hieroglyphics I had painted round the walls, the impassioned orchestra, it must have provided a kick or two for the young man about town of the moment. It was about my first job: and if I had acquired the taste for alcohol (as I had not) I might have got a kick or two myself. As it was I had to try, and as best I could, to cope with a patroness forever *au bout de forces*.

Already I had begun to make a little money, here and there, as you will have observed. I did not receive a great deal for my nightclub murals (actually $168). I was quite unknown, however, and would have done them for nothing. I only went for one or two days a week to the Omega—where for such a part-time attendance what was paid was a nominal fee only: my fisherman picture was modestly

priced. Until world war i I was in receipt of an allowance
of some sort, though as I made rather more I progressively
dispensed with it. Without this backing I do not see (as
already stated) how I should have negotiated the difficulties
attendant on new courses. For there is no passion here for
artistic expression. It is generally on the basis of parlor
games—or children's games—that experimenting in an art exists. So artificial floating is essential. I could not have lived,
only paid for haircuts and cigarettes, with any money I
made up to autumn 1913: on the other hand, in the tired
intervals of the hack work (had I obtained it) I might have
evolved something superficially resembling the abstract pictures to which I shall be referring next. But they would have
been perfunctory: I should have been obliged to leave them
like indecisive experiments. Such questions resemble problems of cooking it: it is a case where time is all-important.

It was, after all, a new civilization that I—and a few
other people—was making the blueprints for: these things
never being more than that. A rough design for a way of
seeing for men who as yet were not there. At the time I
was unaware of the full implications of my work, but that
was what I was doing. I, like all the other people in Europe
so engaged, felt it to be an important task. It was more than
just picture making: one was manufacturing fresh eyes for
people, and fresh souls to go with the eyes. That was the
feeling. A necessary part of this work was of course propaganda: without that the public would merely conclude that a
few young artists had gone mad, and take no further notice
of what they did.

It was at this point (circa autumn 1913) that I began again
to do a great deal of writing, most of it merely the journalism
entailed by propaganda. (Some had to be rather silly.) My
friends and myself began holding exhibitions of pictures:
with Miss Kate Lechmere I opened "The Rebel Art Center," in
Great Ormonde Street, involving prospectuses—for lectures
that were never delivered, and classes that were never held,
as the war supervened—and a good deal of press controversy. Finally I planned and launched that hugest and
pinkest of all magazines, *Blast*—whose portentous dimensions, and violent tint did more than would a score of exhibitions to make the public feel that something was happening. A great deal of editorial work, and again much
writing, went into that. Then the war came, and that ended
chapter i of my career as a writer and artist with an un-

ceremonious abruptness; if it can be called a chapter, for it had not got very far.

Off and on, however, I was confined to my bed now for a number of months, having contracted a troublesome infection. I began working on a novel, planned earlier, namely *Tarr*. I had decided to join the army and wanted to leave this token book, lest the worst should happen (although as then written in its first uncouth form, it would not have been a very satisfactory testament). Also, not wishing *Blast* to stand as a solitary explosion, I began to collect material for a second number.

The outbreak of war, although naturally quite different to the coming of "total" war, with its blackout, flight to the country and so on, did on the instant reorient people's lives. As I was shut up so much of the time I now had very few contacts, after so oversocial a life a most pleasant change. This period of sickness I spent mostly in the company of Capt. Guy Baker. It was he who made a collection of my drawings and gouaches which later he bequeathed to some museum.

Baker had been a "young captain," in the army in India, but had resigned, I think, because of a breakdown in health. Tears came to his eyes readily, like the Iron Duke whom he resembled. His health got so bad—a little in sympathy with me, I believe—that at last he was obliged to go to his home in Gloucestershire for a while. When he returned, he looked a new man. But soon—at the sight of me, still with my legs upon a chair—he relapsed into invalidism. He would limp round in the morning and we would discuss our respective symptoms. When subsequently, much later, I joined the army, *he* joined it too, though how they ever came to accept him I never understood: about the time I reached the Front, he had hobbled off there too with his regiment.—I felt about him just as if I had picked up a lost dog—a nice friendly but not very healthy looking animal, he even had a wriggle of the haunches which resembled a dog's wriggle of bashful sociability. Evidently when his military life came to an end, everything shut up and went out for this poor chap. The other officers of his regiment he had expected to go through life with—he was lost and missing from that small corps of tanned and snobbish men. He had money: but he had no interests. He found himself among a lot of complex individuals who had read a lot of books, of whom he was mortally afraid. But we got on famously, it was like having

a woman around. The epidemic which immediately succeeded the war, with its millions of victims, found in poor
Baker an easy prey.

Tarr, which had appeared in serial form in *The Egoist*,
was published in 1918 and was entirely rewritten for an edition ten years later, was finished during my convalescence.
In Part III I am writing in some detail about it, so I need
to say no more now: except, a little prematurely perhaps,
I will quote in full a letter written me by W. B. Yeats. I
had sent him a copy of the 1928 edition.

> DEAR WYNDHAM LEWIS. This is a belated letter of
> thanks but I am a slow and capricious reader. I read
> nothing as a rule but poetry and philosophy (and of
> course detective stories) and when *Tarr* came I laid it
> aside, till I had finished a course of those I had set out
> upon. Then about a month ago I took up *Tarr*. It does
> not excite me as *Childermass* did yet it is a sincere and
> wonderful work, and its curious, almost unconscious
> presentation of sex, those mechanical images and images
> of food—there also is mechanicism, unites itself in my
> mind with so much in contemporary painting and
> sculpture. There is the feeling, almost Buddhist, that we
> are caught in a kind of steel trap. My only objection
> to your book is that you have isolated an element for
> study, as if in a laboratory, which cannot be isolated
> unless we take the elements out of the actual world as
> in romantic art (or in *Childermass*). This is not a de-
> fect of treatment, but of the contemporary form you
> have chosen. How interested Balzac would have been in
> Anastasya's business dealings with Soltyk—and in her
> character as a whole. The art politics of all these peo-
> ple! Is it not the prerogative of science to isolate its
> deductions? If sex and their love life is a steel trap
> then I want to set up against it the religion of Buddha
> and so restore the unity of my thoughts—of Buddha or,
> let us say, "Seraphita."
>
> I shall be in London at the Savile from Tuesday next
> for ten days or so and hope to see you.
>
> Yrs
> W. B. YEATS.

As this is a history of a career, not a person, I now
move on to February 1919. At the Goupil Gallery I was hold-

ing my first one-man show. It had the simple but expressive title "GUNS" because throughout it represented pictures of the war, with special reference to the artillery. These were practically all drawings: some compositions, others individual figures drawn from life or studies of guns.

The catalogue contains such titles as "Pill-Box"—"Battery Shelled"—"Walking Wounded"—"Battery Salvo." These were the titles of pictures which in every case, though decidedly angular, were naturalistic. What did this mean? Let me quote from the *Foreword* I had written to my catalogue.

"The public, surprised at finding eyes and noses in this exhibition, will begin by the reflection that the artist has conceded nature, and abandoned those vexing diagrams by which he puzzled and annoyed. The case is really not quite that. All that has happened is that in these things the artist has set himself a different task. . . . I never associated myself with the jejune folly that would assert one week that a Polynesian totem was the only formula by which the mind of man—Modern Man, heaven help him!— might be expressed: the next, that only in some compromise between Ingres and the Chinese the golden rule of self-expression might be found. . . .

"I have attempted here only one thing: namely, in a direct ready formula to offer an interpretation of what I took part in in France. I set out to do a series dealing with the gunner's life from his arrival in the depot to his life in the Line."

I add that "experimentation has been waived": that "I have tried to do with the pencil and brush" what the storyteller does with his pen. And where I am saying that in the midst of war "serious interpretation" is not possible, I have a good saying—expressing something that is echoed everywhere in what I have written, at all periods. It is: "Truth has no place in action."

Later on I assert that the Man of Action has his counterpart in the works of the mind. "Another comes to pictorial expression with one or other of the attendant genii of passion at his elbow." These "genii of passion" may lead him to the truth: that of passion. But in the moment of passion, or the moment of action, there is no truth.—And even the truth of passion, it seems to follow—although I do not say this here—is an inferior truth: just as the man of action is an inferior man to the man of mind.

My main reason, however, for quoting passages from the

Foreword, relates to that part of it which was written to anticipate the bewilderment of the public who would come to the gallery expecting to find abstractions, outrageous conundrums in paint, and instead would discover relatively lifelike war scenes and traditionally drawn figures of soldiers. It will be remarked that I repudiate a fanaticism in the past for the "abstract." It is open to the same artist, I suggest, to undertake, on the one hand, any experiment, however far it may lead him from the accepted canons of visual expression, or, on the other hand, to "tell a story" which the simplest could understand. This he has as much right to do as the literary man, a Dickens, or a Chekov, or a Stendhal —or, for that matter, as earlier artists, who without exception showed no squeamishness about "literary" subject matter.

From this position I never departed. It is as much my position today as it was then. Had it not been for the war I should not have arrived at it so quickly. War, and especially those miles of hideous desert known as "the Line" in Flanders and France, presented me with a subject matter so consonant with the austerity of that "abstract" vision I had developed, that it was an easy transition. Had you at that time asked me to paint a milkmaid in a landscape of buttercups and daisies I should probably have knocked you down. But when Mars with his mailed finger showed me a shell crater and a skeleton, with a couple of shivered tree stumps behind it, I was still in my "abstract" element. And before I knew quite what I was doing I was drawing with loving care a signaler corporal to plant upon the lip of the shell crater.

There was another factor. I had begun writing, on a larger scale than before: with *Tarr*, more seriously. When in the *Foreword* just quoted I claimed never to have been any fanatic, in one sense that was true enough, in another not. An illustration or two will help. Gaudier Brzeska, the sculptor, I regarded as a good man on the soft side, essentially a man of tradition—not "one of Us." To turn to literature (for theoretically my narrow criterion included that) I looked upon the Imagists (Pound, H. D., Aldington, Flint) as *pompier*.[4] About all that my first impulse would have been to shout, "à la gare!" [5]

4 conventional or stereotyped style in art
5 let's get out of this!

At this distance it is difficult to believe, but I thought of the inclusion of poems by Pound etc. in *Blast* as compromising. I wanted a battering ram that was all of one metal. A good deal of what got in seemed to me soft and highly impure. Had it been France, there would have been plenty to choose from. Now this was certainly what might be called a fanatical way of going about the promotion of an idea. To place against this, I never denied myself the pleasure of drawing a human face naturalistically. A great deal of *avant-garde* propaganda appeared to me pretentious and silly; and I heartily detested, and had violently combated, Marinetti's *anti-passéisme*,[6] and dynamism.

So much for my attitude in the *Blast* days. My literary contemporaries I looked upon as too bookish and not keeping pace with the visual revolution. A kind of play, *The Enemy of the Stars* (greatly changed later and published in book form) was my attempt to show them the way. It became evident to me at once, however, when I started to write a novel, that words and syntax were not susceptible of transformation into abstract terms, to which process the visual arts lent themselves quite readily. The coming of war and the writing—at top speed—of a full-length novel (*Tarr*) was the turning point. Writing—literature—dragged me out of the abstractist cul-de-sac.

The writing of *Tarr* was approached with austerity. I clipped the text to the bone of all fleshly verbiage. Rhetoric was under an interdict. Even so, it soon became obvious that in order to show the reader character in action, with its attendant passion, there was no way of reducing your text to anything more skeletal than that produced by an otherwise normal statement, even if abnormally abrupt and harsh.

In the course of the writing, again, I grew more interested with every page in the life of my characters. In the end— apart from the fact that I abstained from the use of any clichés (even the inoffensive mates of more gregarious words), eschewed sentimental archaisms, and all *pretty language* as it might be called—*Tarr* turned out a straightforward novel.

So my great interest in this first novel—essentially so different a type of expression from more or less abstract compositions in pure form and color—so humanist and remote from implications of the machine, turned me into other paths:

6 resolute opposition to the past

one form of expression must affect the other if they co-exist within the confines of one brain. Then so sudden and dramatic a break in one's life as the "great war" played its part.

The war was a sleep, deep and animal, in which I was visited by images of an order very new to me. Upon waking I found an altered world: and I had changed, too, very much. The geometrics which had interested me so exclusively before, I now felt were bleak and empty. They wanted *filling*. They were still as much present to my mind as ever, but submerged in the colored vegetation, the flesh and blood, that is life. I can never feel any respect for a picture that cannot be reduced, at will, to a fine formal abstraction. But I now busied myself for some years acquiring a maximum of skill in work from nature—still of course subject to the disciplines I had acquired and which controlled my approach to everything. The considerable collection of my drawings in the Rutherston Collection in the Manchester Museum, and the painting of Edith Sitwell in the Tate Gallery, London (the latter completed at a later date), represented the work of this period.

Thenceforth in the matter of the visual arts I have done two things concurrently: this has held up to the present moment. I have never departed from a dual visual activity. It can really be reduced to what I did when I had nature in front of me, and what I did when I was not making use of nature. In the first case I have done work in the main strictly representative or naturalist—that is to say a faithful imitation of nature, within the limits prescribed by any art work. Of this type of work the portrait of T. S. Eliot (Durban City Gallery, S. Africa), painted in 1938, is a good example, as is my presentation portrait (School of Medicine, St. Louis, U.S.A.) of Dr. Joseph Erlanger, 1944.* "Froanna" (Glasgow City Gallery) or the meditative bust in the City Gallery, Carlisle: the pastel of Mrs. O'Brien of Montreal, 1945, or the portrait head of Rebecca West, 1932, are other examples.

Side by side with this nature work I have done numbers of things varying in the degree in which they departed from nature. In a large and fairly homogeneous group produced in 1941–42 and in the paintings and drawings done between 1934 and 1938 (the major part seen in a one-man show at the

* Dr. Erlanger was awarded the Nobel Prize in that year.

Leicester Galleries, London) I have varied between realist fantasies and semi-abstraction. The satiric realism of "Beach Babies," and the semi-abstract "Stations of the Dead," * or "Stage Scene," both appeared in the same exhibition.

In the "Surrender of Barcelona" (which was in the English Pavilion at the New York World's Fair) I set out to paint a Fourteenth Century scene as I should do it could I be transported there, without too great a change in the time adjustment involved. So that is a little outside the natural-nonnatural categories dominating controversy today. . . . I have now, I think, given an account of how becoming-an-artist occurred in my case. From 1924 onwards writing became so much a major interest that I have tended to work at my painting or drawing in prolonged bursts, rather than fit them into the intervals of the writing or planning of books. Writing and picture-making are not activities, I have found, which mix very well, unless one becomes the servant of the other, as was the case with Blake, or with Rossetti.

The Puritans of the Steppes

ASKED to describe what influences were decisive in my life as a writer—indeed in the question addressed to me the somewhat alarming word *crisis* was used, what, I was asked, had constituted for me the crisis as a result of which I became what I am—I was at first at a loss to know what to say. It had to be a book, too, which raised a further obstacle: for no book I could think of had mastered my mind in the way required by the question.

There had been nothing violent about the birth of my mind. There was no dramatic and sudden enlightenment, but a long series of enlightening experiences—with the steady accretion of the technical means for the communication of the burden of experience. It seemed at first quite impossible to point to any one influence responsible for my

* Collection Naomi Mitchison.

development; though no doubt I could sort out the sources of enlightenment into weaker and stronger impressions.— However, for the purposes of the talk * I had agreed to give it would be better if I could identify something that could be said, as an impression, to exceed all the others, and to have left a permanent mark.

So I went on a search, backward into my young life, keeping my eyes open for the intellectual *coup de foudre*.[1] For guidance I divided my activity into the creative and the critical: and since—as I believe I have already remarked— the critical with me grew out of the creative, it must be to the source of the latter that I must give special attention.— And at last, stepping warily as I moved about in the misty youthful scene (everything before world war i has become almost an alien land) I came up against a solid mass of books—not *one* book, as I had thought I might—which supplied the answer. This was something that revolutionized my technique of approach to experience—that did not merely give me a great kick at the moment, and then quickly fade, as most things do.—The mass of books to which I have referred is the creative literature of Russia. And when I took down some of these half-forgotten volumes—went again with Pierre in his incongruous white hat and green coat on to the field of Borodino, and with Raskolnikov lifted the ax to strike down the aged usurer—I very nearly had *another* crisis, hardened as I am now to such influences.

For the purposes of my broadcast the search was ended. I had no occasion to go any farther, and I started at once to write out what I proposed to say. But for anyone who has read *The Apes of God* or *Childermass*, it will be obvious that those influences however strong, were not the last: on the surface, at least, all trace of them had vanished in the twenties. But in my earliest essay in the writing of fiction, *Tarr*, it is another matter: and it is to that story this chapter and the next are devoted.

Dostoevsky, on the European continent, continues to exert a magical influence; as an instance of which I may cite the Swiss theologian, Barth, who acknowledges two main sources of inspiration, namely Dostoevsky and Kierkegaard. I have noted several instances, by the way, in which these two

---

* This section was first delivered as a radio lecture, broadcast by the B.B.C. in its "Crisis" series, March, 1947.
[1] thunderclap, lightning bolt

names have been bracketed in this manner. In England there has been a decline in sympathy with the Nineteenth Century Russian novelists, which partly is fashion, and in part to do with the long infatuation of British intellectuals for everything Russian of a much more recent date. This raised an ideologic barrier to enjoyment. But these great novelists of Czarist days should not be looked upon as a sort of rival of the contemporary Russian. A careful reading of their books assists, on the contrary, to an understanding of the Russians of today. Stalin dancing upon the table at a victory banquet is a page from Gogol. The unexpectedly able Russian generals, beating off the Panzers, at Smolensk, or before the capital itself, one recognizes as one reads of Kutuzov at Borodino, more than a match for Bonaparte.

As a student in Paris, in French translations, I first read all these Russian books, and I lived for some time wholly in that Russian world—of *Poor Folk*: in the tragic family circle of the Karamazovs; with Verhovensky, Shigalev, and the nihilists; with Rudin, losing interest and departing when he saw the spell he had cast had collapsed; listening to the Kreutzer Sonata and noting the big hips of the lady's man; or submissively assisting at all the exclamatory archness of those Varvaras and Natalies.

So my "crisis"—if we wish to retain that over-forcible expression—was even more than a collection of books: it was a world. As I have described myself as doing, tracing my steps back, I was not suddenly stopped by a wall of books. Rather I passed imperceptibly into a warmer, richer, atmosphere—as crossing the Atlantic one enters the area of the Gulf Stream; I heard again the raucous voice of La Baboulenka crying: "You do not know *what*? By heavens, are you *never* going to drop that roulette of yours? Are you going to whistle *all* your property away?"

And I saw the ruined General wilt before the glare of his aged mother, borne aloft like a carnival figure in an armchair.

Paris was full of Russian students (this of course was before the Russian Revolution), who walked about in pairs, in tight black semimilitary jackets. They conversed with no one —they were contemptuous of Western levity, stern and self-absorbed. It has been said that when Dostoevsky wrote *The Possessed* there were in Russia no Stavrogins or Verhovenskys, that they came much later and this was a divination of the future. In that case these characters, now become flesh and blood, were met by me every day on the Boulevards, and they decidedly looked the part.

These were the new Puritans, who were to dominate Europe: a generation with many points of resemblance with the black-coated sectaries who began to swarm in England in the first days of the Seventeenth Century, and who subsequently transmitted their passionate disciplines to, and became the genius of, the North American continent, the "New World."

The world of imagination I inhabited at that time, however, was anything but puritan, taken as a whole. For this great volume of creation produced in the Nineteenth Century by a group of men over a space of fifty or sixty years there is no parallel since the Renaissance—to which the Tudor stage, of course, was the greatest English contribution. The impression conveyed is of a release on the grand scale of prodigal energies.

All the writers, it seems to me, responsible for this new world of the spirit are of the same half-Western, half-Eastern, ethos; which, among other things, gives them a peculiar value—like everything about Russia. They must, in consequence, for the Western European, remain a great universalizing influence. And all the Russians, Tolstoy almost as much as Dostoevsky, were conscious of their curious relationship to the West—of it, and yet not of it: conscious also of something like a mission with regard to it, namely as the purveyors of sincerity to the overinstitutionalized European. We find this missionary spirit, itself institutionalized, its ethical passion dimmed in the process, in the contemporary Russian.

A cultural seesaw, of westernizing and anti-westernizing, proceeded among the intellectual leaders: but to hold themselves apart from the West—a little contemptuously apart —was by far the more popular attitude.—From *The Gambler* and elsewhere in the pages of Dostoevsky a very shrewd analysis of the Western European could be compiled. There is for instance the Junker: "he had legs which seemed to begin almost at his chest—or rather, at his chin! Yet, for all his air of peacock-like conceit . . . his face wore a sheepish air." Then there is the Frenchman: "He was a true Frenchman in so far as, though he could be lively and engaging when it suited him, he became insufferably dull and wearisome as soon as ever the need for being lively and engaging had passed. Seldom is a Frenchman naturally civil:

he is civil only as to order and of set purpose. Also, if he thinks it incumbent upon him to be fanciful and original, his fancy always assumes a foolish, unnatural vein, compounded of trite, hackneyed forms. In short, the natural Frenchman is a conglomeration of commonplace, petty, everyday positiveness."—No more today than yesterday, I think, do we appreciate how genuine sincerity can take even a self-righteous form, and how insincere and untrustworthy, in many respects, the West must seem to these Puritans of the Steppes, whose lineaments already are visible in the dramatis personæ of the Nineteenth Century Russian classics. When however, self-righteousness grows so extreme that it violently liquidates all whom it regards as sinful, it is natural it should awaken hatred and alarm.

A great deal of what I read as a student I either did not understand, or took no interest in. I knew, for instance, what I was witnessing everywhere in Dostoevsky; namely the almost muscular struggle of the struggle of the human will to repulse evil and cleave to the good—or to embrace evil with a convulsive violence, and then to repent, with more convulsions. It was the unrelievedly gloomy epic of spiritual freedom—which the further you went, got to look more and more like predestination.—But in the first place I was not myself of a gloomy temperament: also since I was not interested in problems of good and evil, I did not read these books so much as sinister homilies as monstrous character patterns, often of miraculous insight.

I am inclined, I find, to attribute to myself less understanding, when I first read all these books, than I in fact had. But what is quite certain is that the politics in Dostoevsky—almost as distinctive a feature of his work as the mysticism, and, I now am of opinion, far too much influenced by it—these very unusual politics were entirely lost upon me at that time. Three years ago I read again *The Possessed*. There were all the names and scenes, just as in the past, when first I read it. But it was a very different book. Evidently as a student I had read it somewhat as a child reads *Through the Looking Glass*. That is the only possible explanation.

Dostoevsky was an arch counterrevolutionary, and it is not only in *The Possessed* which is the highwater mark, almost a counterrevolutionary tract—that this passionate reaction is to be found. But when in his letters one reads that he thought of postponing a journey owing to the news, which had greatly upset him, of the death of the Czar's aunt, that makes one feel that when he refers to himself in his diary as a "conservative," in this one particular he was right. Yet what an extraordinary work *The Possessed* is! Stavrogin, Tihon, Verhovensky, Shatov—what a prodigious company.

Allowing for a great deal that was unintelligible, the impact of such books was due to much more than their vitality. Perhaps Ivan Karamazov supplies the correct answer, where he is speaking of the young men who sat drinking and talking in the corners of the Russian taverns. "They've never met before, and when they go out of here they won't see each other again for the next forty years. But what do they talk about for the moment that they're here? Nothing but universal problems: Is there a God? Does the immortal soul exist? Those who don't believe in God discuss socialism and anarchism, and the reorganization of mankind on a new pattern; which are the same questions, only tackled from the other way up."

That was what "Russian boys" had their minds filled with apparently, and what these books showed them ardently discussing in taverns as they drank, as if the fate of the universe hung upon their words. Well, what do young Englishmen discuss under similar circumstances? Probably "the Dogs," or football. What do young Frenchmen discuss? Undoubtedly women, and their smartness in handling same.— So it was in everything. Here was a more serious world altogether, thought I. Then what consummate realists these people were!—with their slovenly old gentlemen with a great reputation for sanctity—the "saintly fools" of the monasteries, with their embarrassed "bashful" smiles, smelling slightly of vodka; the police commissioners who behaved like a Marx Brother; Napoleon Bonaparte persuaded that he was directing a battle, while in fact everyone had forgotten his existence and fought it in their own way: the Chagall-like figures skimming along the surface of the water in pursuit of the river steamer; or the celebrated cloak of Gogol, or his walking Nose.

I too "came out of that mantle of Gogol": a lot of things have happened to me since, but there was a time when I did not follow my own nose, but *his*. Paris for me is partly the creation of these books. I now realize that if I had not had Chekov in my pocket I should not have enjoyed my Dubonnet at the "Lilas" so much or the beautiful dusty trees and beyond them the Bal Bullier. It was really as a character in Tolstoy—I remember now—that I visited a *bal musette*.[2] And the hero of the first novel I wrote reminded a very perceptive critic of Stavrogin.

In view of all this I think we may really say that the first time, moving down the rue des Ecoles, I arrived at my particular bookshop, opposite the "Montagne," to find a book by Faguet, and took away *Tales from the Underworld* as well, *crisis* was at hand.

The Schicksal—The German in My Fiction

So I was for some years spiritually a Russian—a character in some Russian novel. As such I made my bow in London— to the deeply astonished Ford Maddox Hueffer—which lemonish pink giant, it is true, in his quilted dressing gown, with his mouth hanging open like a big silly fish, surprised *me*. Though the muscovite spell had lost much of its primitive strength, it was partly, still, as a *Russian* that I wrote my first novel *Tarr*.—But it was not about Russians: it was almost entirely about Germans.

The hero—Otto Kreisler—was a German student. Just now I said how this first of my fictional figures provoked a comparison with Stavrogin. Rebecca West, in the *Nation*, wrote at the time in the most generous way. "A beautiful and serious work of art that reminds one of Dostoevsky only because it too is inquisitive about the soul, and because it contains one figure of vast moral significance which is worthy to stand beside Stavrogin." Rebecca West was by far the best book critic at that time, this was a notice that afforded me great pleasure and encouragement: but I have quoted it for its bearing upon what I have to say here. Among the old press notices where I discovered it I came across these other observations in a paper called *The New Witness* long since extinct. "A book of great importance . . . because here we have the fore-

2 popular dance hall

runner of the prose and probably of the manner that is to come."

In form *Tarr* does resemble somewhat a Dostoevsky novel. Not only is this the case in the nature of the subject, but to some extent in the treatment. Its dynamism is psychological, of the boa-constrictor type—a steady enveloping compression. Although there is much action, it is the mind not the senses that provide it.

The parallel to Dostoevsky must not be exaggerated however, as Miss West pointed out. The writing, with its abruptness and for that time a new directness, its strong visual notation, is as unlike as possible the Dostoevsky diffuseness.

The character of the German protagonist aside, however, *Tarr*—neither in order to repel new attacks nor put old ones in their proper perspective—would call in fact for especial exegesis. It has not to be defended, because it was never assailed. Some pundits in the twenties said it was ill-written: this referred to the first edition, and was perfectly true. It was a very carelessly written book indeed. That criticism does not apply to the revised version (1928).*

At the time of the first publication of *Tarr* it was extremely favorably reviewed—and the era of puff and blurb in place of criticism had not then begun. *That* started with Mr. Arnold Bennett, when he turned reviewer and star salesman for the publishers, and was the godfather of as fine a brood of third-rate "masterpieces" as you could hope to find anywhere.

But there was no reason why *Tarr* should be received otherwise than well in 1918 since at that period I had offended no one by the analysis of the world of bestsellers and of fashionable rackets, nor had I given utterance to any political judgments liable to excite contemporary fanaticism.

A better novel than *Tarr*, namely *The Revenge for Love* (1936), just cannot be mentioned, or considered by the average critic at all, and in my lifetime will never be republished (it is out of print) because its theme is political and its intentions have apparently been misread. It is not a book of political edification but one of political realism. I am quite content that people should read it much later on, when all the dust of these present conflicts has settled. They will, I think, perceive that it is not quite what contemporaneously it

* Phoenix Library. Chatto and Windus. 1928.

has been supposed to be. I say this, not at all to arouse an interest in it: merely to put on record the extent to which the literary world of this time is as intolerant as the worst religionism—it does not burn but it boycotts. How by this malevolent suppression I am injured I need hardly point out, as much in my reputation as in my pocket.

Retrospectively, then, the principal figure in *Tarr*, the German Otto Kreisler, has its importance in such a survey as this. Seeing what was occurring when I actually was writing this book (1914–15), seeing what the history of the last thirty years has been like—and still is—it has great political relevance. It was not written, I need hardly say, for any jingo reason, for the writing of it had been started considerably before the outbreak of war. But the first edition was disfigured, I am sorry to say, by a "patriotic" preface: the main figure was a *German*—he was *a bad man*—the Germans are our *enemies*—all our enemies are bad men naturally—the Germans are all bad men. That sort of thing. I blush.

As some slight excuse I must repeat that at that time a great war was a great novelty for English people and everyone I knew was mentally squaring up to "the Hun." Myself I was annoyed with the Germans for being so militaristic (did not realize how our *own* wealth, power, and dominion also rested upon force and in our slyly camouflaged way what militarists we were too) and disturbing my life as they were doing, with their infernal *Machtpolitik*,[1]—But I will not prolong my apologies: it was a moment of great popular excitement, and I had been infected by it.

Not only is the most substantial male figure in the book a German, the heroine, Bertha, is likewise German—is in fact, of Germanic culture encountered in Hauptmann and Sudermann. Otto Kreisler represents the melodramatic nihilism of the generations succeeding to the great era of philosophical pessimism. Whether national socialism is the ultimate term of that malady it is impossible to say. Nietzsche was another and more immediate source of infection: and to his admonition "When you go to consort with the *Weib*,[2] take your whip with you," Kreisler had been attentive. "He (Kreisler) approached a love affair as the *Korpsstudent* engaged in a students' duel—no vital part exposed, but where something

1 power politics
2 woman

spiritually of about the importance of an ear might be lost—
at least stoically certain that blood would be drawn."

As a student in Munich I became very familiar with the
German student and his habits. Later in Paris I had many
German friends—most of them "bourgeois-bohemians." There
was no original for the figure in the book: but there was a
great abundance of images and other impressions out of
which material my figure could be put together. Paris was
the scene selected: and it was no imaginative feat to see this
rigid, scarred, and frowning figure of a typical ex-student,
brushing upwards his mustaches as he fixed his eye coldly
upon some specimen of the opposite sex.

Kreisler was a man still, after a number of years, in receipt of a modest allowance from his father. For a prolonged
period of training as an artist he has nothing to show. He is
not an artist, is devoid of talent: but it is not that. He likes
sitting at café tables watching impassibly the movements of
the gregarious habitués, his eye resting sometimes in painful
contemplation upon the women haunting this spot. But he
never moves: he enjoys drifting silently with time, until they
should reach the brink of the cataract.—The brink is not far
off: he is expecting his allowance to discontinue at any moment: all the more so as his father is married to his late
fiancée. When that happened he began sitting with greater
immobility than ever in front of his *chopines*.[3]

There is no escape from the machinery of the *Schicksal*[4]:
he stares bleakly at the café clock, as though it were a
timepiece in a Poe story, ticking stolidly along until the pre-
destined moment is reached when it releases the chopper
suspended over him and it thunders down upon his neck.
Too old at thirty-six to make a fresh start, when the allowance stops life for him must stop too. "Doomed Evidently" is
the title of the chapter where he comes upon the scene. And
the subject of this book is in fact the elaborate and violent
form of suicide selected by Herr Kreisler, involving a number of other people. He is revenging himself upon society for
the fate that has overtaken him. Since the jig is up, he decides to have some *macabre* fun: to make a rumbustious exit.
Finally he kills someone in a duel, and arrested as a vagrant,
hangs himself in a rustic jail.

The ponderous Germanic machinery of the mental proc-

[3] pints of wine
[4] Fate

esses of the leading characters thuds forward to its climax.
Kreisler had developed a myth peculiar to himself on the
subject of Woman. Casually observing the progress of this
individual's life from year to year, you would probably decide that its main events were love affairs. This, however, in
the light of a careful analysis, would be an inversion of the
truth.

When the events of his life became too unwieldy "he converted them into love: as he might otherwise, had he possessed
a specialized talent, have transformed them into art. He was
a sculptor—a German sculptor of a mock-realistic and degenerate school—in the strange sweethearting of the 'free
life.'—The two or three women he had left in this way about
the world—although perhaps those symbolic statues had
grown rather . . . lumpish—were monuments of his perplexities."—Or in another place: "Womankind were Kreisler's
Theater. They were for him art and expression: the tragedies
played there purged you periodically of the too violent accumulations of desperate life."

He possessed something like an astrological technique for
interpreting the significance of his encounters with these creatures, who seemingly composed a fateful pattern in his life.
His sexual superstitions supplied the motif in his ritual of
self-destruction. The *Weib* now in his father's bed cuts off
the thin stream of vitalizing gold, like a *couchant* [5] Fate.

These are a few facts or descriptive details about the main
figure, samples of the treatment, specimen parts of the ponderous mechanism set in motion, like a demonstration in
predestination. But from the first this romantic German is a
man as good as dead already. He has accepted violence as
the natural end to a violent berserk nature. The part of the
book in which we first see him has for title "Doomed Evidently"—the fatality, far from being masked, is advertised.
The "Schicksal" or Fate presides throughout, in playful
mood.

This condemned man hero, or rather protagonist, is expected to awaken neither sympathy nor repulsion in the
reader—for it is not a moral tale: he is a *machine* (a "puppet," not a "nature"), aloof and violent. His death is a tragic
game. In these respects the analogy with his countryman of
two decades farther on, in the thirties—still under the same
influences as himself—is obvious. Herr Hitler and Herr

[5] bedded or lying

Goebbels were "Doomed Evidently." That too was an empty mechanical tragedy, their death a foregone conclusion.

The book should have been called *Otto Kreisler*, rather than *Tarr*, who is a secondary figure. Incidentally, Tarr was the name of a well-known cricketer: and the character is, of course, not German, but English. In the first sixty pages Tarr is to be observed disentangling his sex life—a very different one from that of Kreisler, though momentarily he is involved with a German Schatz [6] belonging rather to the universe of Kreisler than his own. The involvement is in the sharpest contrast with the Kreisler type of involvement, which is always melodramatic and rooted in a stormy pessimism and painful wonder. Tarr's is skeptical and humorous, full of the English understatement of passion, and antagonism to animal mysticism.

Tarr at the start is found stolidly rushing from one person to another to discuss his sexual conflict. Finally he gets round to the object of his passion in person. With her he discusses it too, Bertha, emotionally constructed to deal with *Kreislers*, not with *Tarrs*, adapts herself as best she can.

The warming-up process, indulged in by Tarr with the first chance-met acquaintance, proceeds as follows: a typically English scene. "So they sat (in the café) with this absurd travesty of a Quaker's Meeting, shyness appearing to emanate masterfully from Tarr . . . Tarr had a gauche puritanic ritual of self, the result of solitary habits.—Certain observances were demanded of those approaching him, and were quite gratuitously observed in return. The fetish within—souldwellers that is strikingly like a wood-dweller, and who was not often enough disturbed to have had the sylvan shyness mitigated—would still cling to these forms. Sometimes Tarr's crafty demon, aghast at its nakedness, would manage to snatch or purloin some shape of covering from elegantly draped visitor. . . . Tarr possessed no deft hand or economy of force: his muscles rose unnecessarily on his arm to lift a wine glass to his lips. He had no social machinery . . . was compelled to get along as well as he could with the cumbrous one of the intellect."

In the physical description of the young Englishman, Tarr, may be seen a caricatural self-portrait of sorts, though not of course in his character or behavior. The glasses worn by Tarr did not occur in my own case at that age; but I sat for some

[6] sweetheart

of the merely visual attributes— "Tarr had wings to his hips. He wore a dark morning coat whose tails flowed behind him as he walked strongly and quickly along, and curled on either side of his lap as he sat. It was buttoned halfway down the body. He was taller than Butcher, wore glasses, had a dark skin, and a steady, unamiable, impatient expression. He was clean-shaven with a shallow jaw and straight thick mouth. His hands were square and unusually hot— all these characteristics he inherited from his mother, except his height."

The daguerrotype coat with curling tails and heavy side pockets—a garment I had seen Central Europeans wearing —was the type of garment which in an earlier chapter I described the scandalized Brook Street tailor as furnishing me with, after my own design.

These descriptions, supplemented by quotations should answer the same purpose as a "trailer." As it is possible from those brief glimpses of next week's movie to obtain a fairly accurate idea of it, so you should now know enough about this novel to understand me when I say that no Russian actually *could* have written it. This is the conclusion I came to when I began examining it again.

It is probably Dostoevskian only in the intricacy of the analysis of character and motive, and a comprehension of that never failing paradox, *the real*, in contrast with the monotonous self-consistency of what man invents without reference to nature, in pursuit of the ideal.

Though this book would never have been written quite as it is without my having been a hallucinated inmate of that Russian world as a student: though when I read the *Gambler* and cry with laughter as a *new* set of Poles replaces those who have been thrown out of the Casino and solemnly take up the plundering of La Baboulenka where their compatriots had been forced to leave off, I feel I might very well have written that myself, that that is how I see life: nevertheless the fatality—to go no farther—depicted in the case of my German is of an entirely different quality from that in the Dostoevskian universe. The "signifying *nothing!*" of Shakespeare is nearer to it than the nihilism of Shigalev.

A Renaissance Prophet of Action

THE LION AND THE FOX is my first political book. It is something else, too, of course: but here I am going to consider only the political implications of Shakespearean tragedy, which I attempted to lay bare—not any of its other aspects, psychological, literary, or historical. I should add that its publication was unavoidably postponed: its true date is before, not after, *The Art of Being Ruled* (1926).

It would be difficult to have a better press than *The Lion and the Fox*. There was nothing in this book to annoy anybody. The seed of many of my subsequent books, however, was in the political thinking to be found there: and it has been, of course, the political thinking in my writings that has (1) given my routine enemies an opportunity to get at me; and (2) has genuinely enraged or puzzled, or both, a number of people.

There is little or no political theory in *The Lion and the Fox*: it is a study, more than anything else, of the handling of the hero or titan by Shakespeare in his great group of tragedies. As, however, most of these were public figures, some views on the subject of government could not fail to emerge. There is a profusion of evidence in, for instance, *Coriolanus* of Shakespeare's private reactions. To this key political play I will presently return.

Shakespeare was entirely emancipated from the emotional legacies of feudalism. I even refer to him as a "bolshevist," and he possessed, it seems to me, a very radical mind. As much as Machiavelli, he lived in a revolutionary time, shortly to witness the execution of the reigning king; with then an interlude of very modern Cæsarism. The crowned head, for him, was like any other, of course: he knew a great deal about kings.

In Machiavelli's case the "Prince" was, it is important to recall, a *new* self-made ruler, a martial adventurer: one, that is to say, who did not inherit power, but seized it. This Italian was only interested in the founding of States, and he thought uniquely of power.—The attention paid by Shakespeare to his doctrines would certainly not be that of one sharing this nasty obsession. What would attract him in Machiavelli would be the latter's exposure of the manner in which the thirst for power maddens men, and how ruling is in fact a disease.

I will begin what I have to say by turning to the chapter headed "Coriolanus and Aristocratism." Let me quote p. 238 practically intact. "Coriolanus, as a figure, is of course the super-snob. Of all Shakespeare's heroes he is the coldest, and the one that Shakespeare himself seems to have felt most coldly towards. He was the child of Volumnia, not of Shakespeare, and one that never became anything but a schoolboy, crazed with notions of privilege and social distinction, incapable of thinking (not differing in that from the rest of Shakespeare's nursery of colossi), but also congealed into a kind of machine of unintelligent pride. He is like a Nietzschean, artificial, 'aristocrat,' with little nobility in the sense that Don Quixote caricaturally embodies the noble, but possessing only a maniacal intolerance and stiffness. . . ."

The following description, for instance, of the behavior of the little son of Coriolanus by a friend of the family is "true to life," but too true not to have been observed with a mind detached from any infatuation with the speakers. It is impossible that this picture of a little Coriolanus growing up "just like his father" is not meant to illuminate Coriolanus for us:

> *Valeria.* O' my word, the father's son; I'll swear, 'tis a very pretty boy. O' my troth, I looked upon him o' Wednesday half an hour altogether; has such a confirmed countenance. I saw him run after a gilded butterfly; and when he caught it, he let it go again; and after it again; and over and over he comes, and up again; catched it again: or whether his fall enraged him, or how 'twas, he did so set his teeth; and tear it. O, I warrant, how he mammocked it!
>
> *Volumnia.* One on's father's moods.
>
> *Valeria.* Indeed, la, 'tis a noble child.
>
> *Virgilia.* A crack, madam.

"Indeed, la, 'tis a noble child" is a remark that would certainly not pass the censorship in a despotic super-feudal state, or recommend its author to a Nietzschean autocrat. And had Shakespeare wished to engage the sympathy of almost any audience with this fine little fellow he certainly would not have chosen such a pretty and also flimsy thing as a butterfly to show him wreaking one of his "father's moods" on.

A performance of *Coriolanus* at the Comédie Française, in the feverish thirties, at which I assisted, was productive of the next thing to a riot. At that moment in the play when Coriolanus passionately denounces, in the presence of the Tribunes of the People, the populace, the French Theater audience, unable to contain itself any longer, leaped to its feet. Men shouted defiance at one another, fists were brandished: in some instances hot partisans of the aristocratic principle seized vociferous proletarians by the throat, bellowing "communard!" (Where I sat the "aristos" were in far greater force than "le populaire." There were some brisk exchanges.)

Although Shakespeare had no fondness for the Coriolanuses of this world his distaste was not doctrinaire. "It was human nature about which Shakespeare wrote, and he did not write on a tone of morals, nor on one of class prejudice or class illusion." This play is an excellent place in which to study the functioning of an inductive mind, recording all impressions upon equal terms, with the absence of *parti-pris* [1] of a chemist or cartographer. He knew a number of very tiresome aristocrats of course—they sat on his stage and got in his way. But he liked the mob just as little. Whenever Coriolanus, or some other of his characters, is heaping abuse upon the multitude, he only had to think of the Pit at the Bankside and he could load their tongues with vitriol. He was if anything too little a man of doctrine or of principle. He saw that there was some bad in everybody. He made no ideological exception.

Machiavelli was a prophet of action of existentialist type. Action he regarded as the only reality. It would be impossible to find a more single-minded advocate of the agent principle. "Shakespeare," as I wrote, again, "differed profoundly from such a theorist of 'action' as Machiavelli . . . he was without that mechanical appetite for what he would

[1] prejudice

regard as a useless and degrading performance of a series of (however logically perfect) tricks." And this would apply also to the Machiavelli obsession regarding power: for with him power was the highest end of action.

Machiavelli's political philosophy took the form of the glorification of an heroic man—a "Prince"—a model for other "Princes," a paragon.

To that extent there is a certain license for comparison. Both the political philosopher and the philosopher-dramatist were interested in the pathos of the One—solitary, charged with responsibility. Their interests, however, are traceable to quite different stimuli. All Shakespeare's heroes die violent deaths. Machiavelli's, theoretically, never die. They are replete with Roman *virtù*: [2] but this they combine with the most consummate craft (hence the metaphor of *The Lion and the Fox*). They never die if they can possibly help it, and the whole idea is that they should *not*. His whole doctrine is a prescription for the most triumphant success: the avoidance of death by assassination through the violent forestalling of all potential assassins.

Shakespeare associated Machiavelli with Montaigne as one of his two main sources of philosophic inspiration. But the doctrine of personal power so dear to the former played, as I have said, no part in this. It was not necessary that it should. Here, after all, was the first scientific hard-boiled theory of the State. It would be the brutal, matter-of-fact exposure of the criminal callousness underlying all government that would appeal to the Renaissance mind, whether English or continental. Some regarded it as a caricature of statecraft. But all felt they understood the State better after reading Machiavelli.

The literate in Tudor England would know Machiavelli, it is probable, indirectly, through a translation from the French (1577) of the *Contre-Machiavel* of Gentillet, in which Machiavelli was represented as Anti-Christ No. 1. Some were more shocked than others: all were delighted.

Thereafter none failed to interpret the struggle for power —which is what politics are—rather more in its nakedness, than "clothed and in its right mind." In other words, the insanity at the root of that ferocious struggle was made plain to them. As dramatists, they saw that all these "great people" it was their task to write about were, for the most part, mad.

2 virtue

The "sad stories of the death of kings . . . all *murdered*" were told, if anything, with more savagery and fatalism on account of the bleak doctrine of this extraordinary Florentine —three hundred and ninety-five references to whom were once catalogued as occurring in the literature of that period. His influence is comparable to that of Darwin in the present age.

Darwin was more inclusive. He revealed what was then called "Mother nature" as "red in tooth and claw." A dear kindly old motherly body became overnight a homicidal old hag. Life was seen as a mad fight for survival—the "unfit" were trampled under foot by the "fit."—On the other hand Machiavelli was mainly responsible for tearing the mask off those who seek and exercise power over others. As I express it in *The Lion and the Fox,* he "gave away the position of the ruler . . . revealing even the very nature of all authority." "Every organized duplicity felt itself unmasked by one of its own servants and satellites."

Frederick the Great of Prussia, a scarcely less perfect specimen of a power addict than Cesare Borgia, read Machiavelli to good purpose. As a young man he (as a good Machiavellian) wrote a refutation of *The Prince* entitled *Anti-Machiavel.* "The enemy of the human race," he called his master: to which Machiavelli would have smiled his sardonic approval. No Prince could afford to underwrite so indiscreet an advocate.

It was Niccolò Machiavelli's great merit that in the act of worshipping his detestable god he betrayed him. Here is another negative merit: he was not a hypocrite. He will speak complacently of a batch of murders perpetrated by his favorite politician (crimes of State, of course) as we would speak of a "bomber's moon"—promising big lovely piles of dead women and masses of Bosche brats. For we have our innocent moments too. Earlier, the Germans were very proud of the job they did on Warsaw: and the German camp-Ghouls of Auschwitz and Belsen sniffing the gas from their charnel houses would no doubt smile naïvely in one another's eyes, their blue-eyed simple peasant smile. These were their "enmies" they were exterminating, *nicht wahr?* [3] When—returning the ball, so to speak—we hanged our defeated enemies at Nuremberg we were awfully clumsy. They took fifteen minutes to die of slow strangulation, and, because the

[3] isn't that so?

opening was so narrow, when they fell through the trap their noses, in some cases, were torn off. That was extremely clumsy.—But once you start that sort of thing you may end up anywhere. Belsen after all may only be a start. In 1947 a Borgia is a small-time killer. And 1954 may put 1944 in the shade.

Personal rule was of the first importance, Machiavelli thought (on the homely principle of too many cooks spoil the broth). Consequently it was politically sound for Romulus, at the founding of Rome, to dispatch his brother. *Two* brothers would not found as good a State as *one*: no other course was open to him.

Again, when you get that *ruling feeling* and seize a city-state, setting yourself up as its master, to be tolerant is fatal. People would take advantage. They would have bumped you off before you could say knife—for they are incorrigibly violent. So you must wipe out a few dozen straight away. Then there will be no discontent or treachery. You know what people are like—always grumbling and plotting!

Is this extreme frankness of Machiavelli's really a virtue, however? For it is his only one. People in general are almost as unpleasant as he declares them to be. But by what right do you go and plant yourself on them as a ruler? And are you not asking for what you get if you do so? This never seems to occur to our Niccolò. And no one said at that time that they felt impelled to rule over other people *for their own good* and out of a keen sense of duty. People were not so Machiavellian as that in those days. They just said they liked power.

I should be very sorry to be responsible for this little Florentine doctrinaire. Because he was not a hypocrite, that is not everything. Several books have appeared of late in praise of machiavellianism, and friends have said to me more than once that I was responsible. This was, however, an absurd mistake. It signified that the friends in question had not read *The Lion and the Fox* with great understanding, I am afraid.

There is no tendency to make a hero of Machiavelli in *The Lion and the Fox*. When I am showing how close Georges Sorel and Machiavelli are to each other, I write as follows.

"The agent principle for both was the only one. Both have no room in their minds for anything but their arid roman doctrine of 'power' and force. . . . 'Even in his histories,'

Villari writes, 'Machiavelli's men appear incapable of any ambition or passion save the political; there is hardly any mention of letters, art, culture, or religion.' It is where Villari is comparing Machiavelli with the Greeks that he says this, showing how the author of *The Prince* was a true child of Rome, his nature alive only to the suggestions of power and mechanical control . . . political ideas alone seem to have existence."

It would be false to say, as I hope the above extracts will have shown, that Machiavelli was for me a thinker to be admired in his role of enthusiast for power. Those who today are extolling Machiavelli's principles are themselves power addicts. But men for whom "political ideas alone seem to have existence" are today very numerous. They are not the kind of men I am disposed to admire. Those "alive only to the suggestions of power and mechanical control" or an "arid Roman doctrine of power and force," or a doctrine of power and force not Roman, it is not in my nature to applaud.

Machiavelli was a propagandist for Action. For him, as for M. Sartre today, or for Marinetti ("the father of Italian Fascism") yesterday, we only exist when we act. And action in this context means action of a material and mechanistic type. Those "political ideas" which "alone seem to have existence" are adumbrations of action.

But such principles as these I have combated, since the first days of my public life, when I led a band of hecklers into the Doré Gallery in Bond Street where Marinetti was lecturing.

The vitalism with which Futurism was drenched, or with which Surrealism is charged, has no attractions for me. And when those philosophies emerge in politics, they produce in me the same sensations as they do in the arts or in literature.

Machiavelli, however, *did* "give away the position of the ruler." It was he who "revealed even the very nature of all authority," to quote again what originally I said about him. As such the student will always turn to him with such respect as one feels for a clear-minded, as it were austere, impeccably truthful, criminal.

Advice to the Inmates of the
Power House

It is a Power House—we might call it that—in which we live. It is given up to the generating of *power*, the atmosphere is heavy with power. Men stalk or strut about, frowning with importance, because they have access to *power*. Some are heavy with power, as a woman is with child. At the microphone some are almost dripping with power, their words are like bullets or drops of blood, so that the timorous shiver slightly, and the bravest feel none too comfortable.

Socially life in the modern age is like being in an immense building, full of a radioactive something we call "power." It is "malignant," this kind of power, and we are all slightly cancered (just as the inhabitants of Didcot are said to be many of them slightly unwell).*

This disease we name *power* is most unfortunately *power over us*. If we were not there, there would be none of this type of *power* at all: without any Germans there could have been no Hitler. What is really terrifying is that it is all something derived from *us*. A fraction of what makes any prominent statesman so prominent is *us*—you and I. All these Somebodies would be nobodies if it were not for us. The man who walks with the heavy pomp of the *enceinte* [1] is heavy with us, we are responsible. We all are laid under contribution—our toiling hands, our skills, our intelligence.

All are potential blood donors to swell the veins and magnify the bulk of a Moloch called "the State." (For this Power House goes by the name of "the State"). Its Bank is a "Blood Bank." We are forcibly bled to feed it. Its Capital is drawn from our veins.

Not a pleasant situation, of course. Not particularly comfortable. But what is the alternative? Where I spoke of Politics,

---

* Didcot is a center of atomic research in Great Britain.
[1] pregnant woman

in my first part, I made it perfectly clear, you may remember, that there is no escape from this Power House.

Although the power, the presence of unbridled power, causes (in really bad periods) endless suffering, yet *without* Government—that fat spider that feeds on us, upon whose prodigious web we are convulsed like helpless flies—without all that, there would be no libraries, laboratories, universities, theaters, publishers, great buildings: the Power is, in its origins, for those purposes and (oh irony!) to assure us safety and peace.

Like our mortality and the death sentence tactfully deposited upon our cradle, which for the rest of our days we carry about in our pocket—we take it out and look at it sometimes and think for a moment what a funny document it is: like that, just as we are born to die, so are we *born to be governed*. Sometimes we are left alone for a while—nothing reminds us of our situation. As in Kafka's *Der Prozess*, at any moment, however, there may be heard the *knock*. They are there at the door. We, the governee, must always anticipate that domiciliary visit. Moloch wants more blood—his myrmidons are there! For we are born blood donors: and when food has for long been scarce, it is a serious matter being asked for *blood*.

In some periods it is just so bad that life is not worth living, and the libraries, the laboratories, and the theaters lose their meaning for us. But there is no doubt whatever that without a centralized life you get nothing of that kind, which—if the Government at the moment is not *too* impossibly brutal—does give value to life: and (whether in fact one is or not) makes one feel a little better than a cockroach or an ephemeron. Without centralized life you just have innumerable little islands of people—no great society, but infinite itemization and insularity, a prospect which nothing but the insular mind would contemplate with any degree of complacency.

Now in this Powerhouse of ours there is roughly (1) the staff, and (2) the rest of the inmates,—or the governors and administrators and the governees.—You might be inclined to say that with any gumption at all a man must aspire to belong to the staff—to govern rather than be governed. This is not at all the case, however.

Your duties as one of the staff (who handle the Power) take up all your time. It is dull work: only congenial if you are a dull man or a very violent and disagreeable one. No good musician, to take instances, wants to leave his music for politics, nor does a doctor interested in his work, nor a man of science, a poet, or historian, or a novelist. The much-photographed, well-housed, well-fed politician, the object of much deference and flattery, is rather like the much-photographed Hollywood Star—he is only envied by the very simple and untalented people, or by the power addict. On the other hand he has something the glamorous Star has none of —namely *power*. This means licence to interfere with, direct, and control other people. But you may be a very gifted man, like Einstein or Bernard Shaw, and not desire to order people about—arrange what they shall eat for breakfast and where they shall work.

Now I am not one of the staff, I have never had anything to do with Management, have no taste for bossing. I have almost ostentatiously been a *governee*. I have had an active preference for the governed in contrast to the governing.

What I am about to say in this chapter relates exclusively to this subject. Whether I am temperamentally managerial or the reverse: whether my philosophy of life is a boss philosophy—in other words, a power doctrine—or some other kind, I shall make it my first business to show that it decidedly is not a power doctrine.

If we come to see the nature of the problem of civilization with exactness that is a great advance, though we can *do* nothing. Action just implies more power, not more civilization or happiness. A defensive technique can be developed, no more. You will find I have compared it elsewhere with jujitsu.

To conclude, I have an ax to grind, no man alive has not, whatever he may say. But it is as it were an innocent ax. No claim to an impossible benevolence towards the human average disfigures these pages. But I am their great friend compared with the smart alecks who flatter them and use them as pawns in the power game. And now, brother governee, I will proceed with the business of this chapter. I have been accused of being in favor of the Management— also complimented on it. Let us talk about that for a while.

This longish chapter is a thorough rediscussion, as the result of a rethinking, of one or two of the main arguments of a book called *The Art of Being Ruled*. I do not think quite the same now as then. But that will not affect the validity of this rediscussion as a means of answering my critics. Anyone desiring to do so may check up on the text of *The Art of Being Ruled,* which is still in print.

In this reconsideration much new material will find its way into the argument: so that this essay will be a useful adjunct to the original text. I shall endorse all, or almost all, the arguments I am reinterpreting. It is obvious that I could not take up these arguments again, forcibly advancing them in a new form, did I not, in the main, still regard them as valid.— But today I certainly should not write this particular book, or think of treating of these particular subjects.

The Art of Being Ruled is what its title proclaims it to be, namely a treatise expounding the art, or science, *of being governed,* or *ruled.* Yet so sincere a discussion lends itself to misinterpretation: numbers of people have thus believed, or affected to believe, that this is a manual of *how to rule* —not a study of the best method to cope with the ruler.— Had it been written for the benefit of the would-be autocrat or power-thirsty politician, I should be a sort of Machiavelli. This impression I shall do my best to dispel.

In detail what I wrote then referred, in some instances, to transient social symptoms. Homosexuality, for example, on the increase during world war i was a protest against the mass sacrifice of the male youth of the country (women "bravely" consenting), attained epidemic proportions afterward. That passed. In world war ii there was less emphasis upon the male youth—suffering was more equal. Yet since the termination of world war ii homosexuality has again become epidemic in England. Newspapers have raised the question of cleaning up the cities, since this time even in provincial centers it appears there is a swarming of pathics.

My argument, however, did not depend upon such details as these. From the more general features of apathy and decay there was only a partial recovery: and today the natural enthusiasm which would be felt by many people at the advent of a genuinely popular government—at last—cannot but be damped by postwar conditions. The socialists have been handed a bankrupt society to socialize, in a ruined world; the only nation capable of helping them is a capitalist nation. Hence "austerity." And so the symptoms of degeneration remain.

It is not an easy book to write about, because its argument bursts out into manifold byways. There is a further complication. It was my idea at the outset—inspired by the Hegelian dialectic, with its thesis and antithesis—to state, here and there, both sides of the question to be debated, and allow these opposites to struggle in the reader's mind for the ascendancy and there to find their synthesis. I did not take this very far: vestiges of it nevertheless exist, a source of occasional embarrassment.

The Art of Being Ruled might be described from some points of view as an infernal Utopia. For epigraph it has a quotation from Chapman's *Duke of Byron* as follows:

> *and they make*
> *A doctrinal and witty hieroglyphic*
> *Of a blessed kingdom.*

The Utopia, or the "blessed kingdom," emerging from the picturesque analytical labyrinth of this book, is one of quiescence, obedience, receptivity.

An account, comprising many chapters, of the decadence occupying the trough between the two world wars introduces us to a moronic inferno of insipidity and decay (which is likewise the inferno of *The Apes of God*). That was, as it were, Utopia-gone-wrong. For the *abdication* left nothing to be desired.

The loss of appetite for power, and heroism, was for the European—was then and is now—the beginning of bliss: or, to speak more accurately, the beginning of the end of evil. The European has for so long suffered from an excess of Will, that what must ensue from the extinguishing of this would, by contrast, be so wonderfully agreeable as to deserve the name utopian.

This is the reverse of a philosophy of action, as you see. In this tendency, amounting to anti-action, it continues, or makes explicit, what was the indirect teaching of *The Lion and the Fox*. The advantages of the role of the spectator, for instance, rather than that of the performer or man-of-action, I expatiate upon—the "greater mental satisfactions" of the spectator: seeing that the performer is too busy playing his part for indulgence in the delights of the intellect. To avail themselves of the spectator's privileges, "detachment" and "passivity" (wherever the choice is open to them): such is the advice offered to men in general. In a word, something like the *apathy* * of the Stoics is what you will find as the central doctrine of this book. In that consists the

---

* Not to be confused with the current use of the term.

true "art of being ruled." It might be described as a manner of jujitsu for the governed—who are so much the weaker party in their encounters with government.

The art of ruling, on the other hand, consists of course of the extraction of the maximum amount of power from the human material, to be used for the inflation of the ego of the ruler. This is only achieved at great personal risk: it involves continual disappointments and fatigues, hardships of every description. The game is decidedly not worth the candle. A very nasty, dark and unattractive picture I draw, in my book, of the ruler's lot, or of the life of those enjoying great positions.

The method employed by me, in this instance, I am now satisfied was mistaken. That was a Utilitarian mistake. If you prove conclusively to people that a certain course of action will entail infinite hardship and discomfort, and quite likely ruin and death, but that it will show that they are "white men"—or gentlemen, or any pretty verbal bauble of that sort —*that* is the approach which assures success. The more horrid and dismal you propose to make their life the more chance you have of being listened to. I did not know that, however, in 1925.

The date of writing of *The Art of Being Ruled* is in effect, 1925, six years after the termination of world war i. I had recognized that a great revolution was underway; that an entirely new epoch had begun, for England and for the world. It had its roots in those ferments of which Cubism, Futurism, and Vorticism were intellectual expressions.

How many people there are at any time—in years of decay and defeat—who understand what is happening to the society of which they are members is not easy to determine. There must be an appreciable number: but they keep it to themselves, I suppose. In 1925 I was not yet emancipated from tribal, or national, superstition. "Western civilization" had still an exclusive meaning for me: not so much as Prussia meant to Hegel, or France to Barrès (or to Flaubert): but that Western culture which was responsible for my mind's particular configuration, for its rational bent, I could not see disintegrating without emotion.

Such were the backgrounds of my thinking, as I wrote "Man and Shaman," "Sub Persona Infantis," "Natures and Puppets," "Vulgarization and Political Decay." It is out of what I observed happening around me that I built up the "doctrinal hieroglyphic" to be found between pages 47 and 313, which is the kernel of this book, and the part of wide application, outside its temporal context. I was fascinated and amused by the spectacle, as well as extremely depressed. This mingled depression and exhilaration is, I believe, a not unusual state of mind, in times like these.

Some of the implications of what was going on were of a paradoxical nature. That was apparent to me: and it was to that perception that the main value of that essay was due. I saw the advantage to be obtained from this demise of a society, of an ethos, and I traced the road out of the disgusting maze. But for some time I was very sore and that soreness increased, if anything, during the immediately ensuing years. The sentimental side of me suffered (I think now) more deeply than it should.—All that is to be found in those books will never be seen again, naturally, with that sharpness or excitement (it was the "peak in Darien," so to say), or with so much distress. Habit soon anesthetizes; it dulls and blunts.

Everybody had loved the war. London had never been so gay—the news vendors' eternal city—"great British victory!": glamor, death, champagne, syphilis. Financially there was delirium, the bloodbath was a Lucky Dip. The "merchants of death" wallowed in profits: the shoeblack even was in the dough. Harlots lit rose-tipped cigarettes with Bradburys. The war was wonderful. Soldiers enjoyed getting a wound—it meant another wound stripe. It meant being "in blues," back in gay, rich, wicked old Blighty.

But suddenly it *stopped*. It only went on for a paltry four years. Why can't wars go on for ever?

After six years of peace even the biggest fool was dimly aware he had become a debtor—also a citizen of a different kind of State. Here I do not refer to the small wage earner, however. Nothing political registers in the minds of the poor, the majority of workers. They could not eat much less without being dead. All bosses, of whatever political complexion, think they ought to work harder and get less for it. "Western civilization," for instance, means about as much to them as entropy or the second law of thermodynamics. Nothing ever happens to them. They have no history. They have no "stake" in any country. They have no race except the human race. (It is only the sahibs who are "white men.") Talking of sahibs, they say that in India millions of peasants mix up the English with the Moguls. Millions of Englishmen, though they may be more *au courant,* are "political illiterates" just as much as "Untouchables" or Fellahin.

In the educated class it is different. They are stupid, but things *do* happen to them. If somebody is recording what happened in such and such a period—"what men felt or thought"—it is of them the historian is speaking. To that first of the new kind of wars a deep and violent reaction occurred among the moderately privileged, as in what was left of the landed society. (Afterward, of course.) They saw they had burned up their wealth in that big Guy Fawkes bonfire of world war. ("Hang the Kaiser!" howled the Yellow Press. It had made much money. The blood of that old mustachioed mountebank would bring them in another shower of gold.) A society has premonitions of its end. This one began burning up the rest of its money, before "they" took it away from them. Mortification already set in at the edges. They began to stink. I have recorded that stink.

It was not merely a class or a nation that was there inviting observation: the British Isles did not stand alone in obvious climacteric. The very nature of our human stock it was impossible not to regard as calling for an inquiry of some kind. To ask what human beings *are:* of what value is their life, if any. It was necessary to ask whether human life does not have to change radically, or altogether to disappear. "The slowness, sloth, and commonness of the stock of *Homo Stultus*"[2] came under review for more eyes than mine.

Contemplating in retrospect the recent spectacle of senseless violence, brutal whoopee, "blood money," criminal rapacity, blasphemous hypocrisy of propaganda, gullibility, what "man can do to man," contemplating both the intellectual and moral nullity of the immense majority, observers in various countries came to the same conclusions. It was agreed that there were certain ineradicable faults of character in man; perhaps of structure. Often he is skillful and quick. But you cannot leave him alone with a keg of gunpowder: he will immediately set a match to it.—Today after world war ii we feel that the German nation should be kept away from anything sharp or pointed—even penknives and pitchforks are somewhat risky in their hands. After world

[2] man the Fool

war i it was widely felt that the entire human race required supervision. This signalizes a further degeneration.

World war ii, its causes and its aftereffects, differs in every respect from its predecessor. Number Two was not a money war but ideological. Nationally it has been even more disastrous. But nationality in England is largely a Tory cult, and national calamity is not taken *personally* by the population. The war moreover has provided England with the best —or at least to start with the most promising—government it has ever known. No great compliment, but, relatively, a mighty fact.

The old type of national adventurer has been blasted off the scene, in every corner of Europe. So this time there will be no *Im Westen Nichts Neues* [3] or *The Death of a Hero*. These were novels against Junker and against Tory war. Not even the Tory, however, today would encourage such criticism of the violence that has just ended. Though he has been finally ruined by it, has he not destroyed his old antagonist, the Junker?

An obvious danger is to be discerned in this changed mood. In England it is as if no one dared listen to anything against war *itself*. That is out of bounds, as a subject: it is as if the war were still in progress, with its censorships and disciplines. Sentiment of the "We can take it" type has made war taboo. Worst symptom of all is to be found in reactions to the Atomic Bomb. Or, rather, there is no reaction. Its mention is resented, as if it were a rival to the doodlebug and blockbuster, but an unfair and unsportsmanlike one (as might be expected, seeing that it is American, the Briton would growl). It arouses no interest, and is disliked.

If war as a subject is interdicted, those in the last analysis responsible for war, namely the human species, are not fair game either. Of Germans, to whatever party they may belong, you can say what you please: recommend their wholesale extermination, or propose their piecemeal enslavement. But to speak disrespectfully of the human species, drags *us* in. If you assert that such serious defects in our species should be attended to, with a view to neutralizing them, that would be treated as an *attack*. Yet if a doctor informed you that you were ill and would die unless you agreed to a certain treatment, you might reject the diagnosis,

[3] *All Quiet on the Western Front*

but you would not call it an *attack*, or exclaim that it indicated *contempt* for your body.

After world war ii there was no such coyness, or disinclination to think things out to the bitter end; to ask all the tragic questions that a great human blunder provokes. This time there is no admission of tragedy—the habit of covering tragedy up and hiding it away, or "putting a brave face" on it, during the war is still strong. There is nothing but a dreary silence. A much-censored people become self-censored: the English have become a colony of clams. The Press apparently censors itself automatically into what is as good as silence, too.—So now when the need for free debate, and for concerted action, is more urgent than ever, there is only stagnation, and a great aversion to action. In a word, people are less anxious than ever for responsibility. Apathy (the word used colloquially) is unrelieved: the long patient queues are as it were worms. There is none of the baby frolicsomeness of the nurseryland of the twenties. Every decade it is more thoroughly understood by everybody that they have no freedom, and progressively they desire it less.

I have been speaking exclusively of the English scene, where the intellectuals, the writers, and pundits are dismally absorbed in beating the economic Blitz. They appear to be utterly paralyzed: the most they do is to mumble about their childhood on the microphone. What they *think* one does not know, since they write nothing—and indeed say nothing either. They are too afraid that they might say the wrong, or the unpopular, thing.

It must be remembered that the greater number of intellectuals were before the war flirtatiously communist or fellow travelers. It was quasi-obligatory. Almost as much as in the United States, however, the same petty calculation that led the average intellectual to hoist himself on to the marxist bandwagon now prompts him discreetly to drop off it and to walk away. But where to? Generally he just goes on, but unostentatiously, walking in the same direction. Some walk in the *opposite* direction. Some lie down upon the nearest patch of grass and go to sleep and dream of horse buses and hansom cabs.

The years immediately ahead are so overwhelmingly dark and unpromising that only the precarious present has any reality at all for them, and the taverns of course are fuller than ever. Pouring daily through their bladders is a torrent of flat beer (hard liquor cannot be bought by any but the rich). Thus in a bleary dreamland the Britannic intelligentsia old and young kill time and fish for scribbling jobs, or assignments to which no work to speak of is attached.

In France the situation is very different. The ultimate value of existentialism, for instance, is a matter we are not called upon to decide. But such people as Sartre or Camus—with books such as *Etre et Néant, Huis Clos,* or *Miramolin* —at least keep the place alive and keep the "Néant" at bay. They do reply, whether well or ill, to the spectacle of social ruin in which they find themselves, and invent a doctrine of hideous pessimism to match the challenge of the diabolical Zeitgeist.[4]

But now back to the problem of my past sins, allegedly so heinous. Admittedly I approach the human problem with no heroical nor sentimental design. But the cheapjack political journalist, or *salonard,*[5] with his little stock of coarsely-colored political ideals, that come in the mail to him from the "Avantgardiste" mail order house, must not be allowed to get away with the charge that I preach a power doctrine. It is not, has never been, *I* who traffic in power! I must rebut the charge that I offer to the would-be tyrant a tempting prospect of man's helplessness: that I have been responsible for something akin to the introduction of a ravening wolf into a nursery.

One of the first questions dealt with in *The Art of Being Ruled* was that of inherited, or artificially generated, martial ferocity. This is of course the central problem of Europe and its wars. Mr. Bertrand Russell's solution after world war i was "kindliness." Failing that, he considered the solution adopted by the Houyhnhnms towards the Yahoos, "namely extermination," is the only one. He added that "apparently the Yahoos are bent on applying it to each other."

But who are the Yahoos? My grocer and my postman, the teller at my bank, the Smith's bookstall man from whom I buy magazines—they are the kind of men who get "wiped out." But are *they* the Yahoos? I do not think so: for they are quiet, good-natured people. From the "ferocious" solution of the Houyhnhnms I for my part turn away. Nature, I suggest, will step in: has already done so.

[4] spirit of the age
[5] social butterfly

Nature, I mean, will whisper in the ear of the little over-taxed male: "Why be so big and tough and take all the knocks? No one believes in you any more. Stand down, reduce your chest measurement to the C.3 mark. That is the way to survive. The survival of the fittest is out of date. The C.3 man will be there while you are pushing up the daisies!"

The feminization, or neutralization, of the White European, some change affected by the glands of internal secretion perhaps, will produce the desired result. All this, in 1925, seemed indicated by everything with which the social scene was charged. In many directions, even, could be seen what looked like the emergence of a third, or neuter, sex.

That was a uniquely favorable moment to observe the first violent symptoms of disintegration. A little later and they go under the surface and are more difficult to study. The feminist had been followed by the feminizing male—a compensatory movement—and these developments took a spectacular form. New York was far less affected than London; the American he-man is a redoubtable conservative obstacle. But I remember in 1931 in New York a journalist relating some violent incidents in a nightspot, and his subsequent reflections ran like this. "You see how things have changed," he said. "A few years ago if you were rude to a fairy he would go away into a corner and cry. *Now* he gives you a sock on the jaw that knocks you cold and telephones for an ambulance."

The change from the traditional social pattern, dominated by sex, into an asexual pattern, with maleness shorn of all but its merely organic distinctness, will come about in many ways. One of the most obvious, is *via* class war. Man constitutes as it were a *class*. Among the many class wars by which European society is being very effectually disintegrated, the sex war occupied a position of great importance.

Though no longer a "war," the effects of that civil war of the sexes are everywhere evident: in the form of pressures tending to dissolve the Family (which is the stronghold of the "masculine" as much as of the "eternal feminine") is revealed the same great design as was, in the first place, responsible for setting in motion the "sex war," and its Press slogans injurious to the man as husband.

I have spoken of these "wars" in an earlier section, but now I must refer to them again. The "class war" is the prototype—the war of the poor against the rich. Organized upon the same principle are the sex war (man against woman); the age war (old against young); the war of urban man versus agricultural man; of the highbrow against the lowbrow. In all societies there have been these divisions, and many others. These are the seams where the various patches of which our society is composed are sewn together. Unpick these patches—of which *every* society is made up, of necessity—and chaos comes again.

As to urban versus agricultural man, all Marxist parties favor the proletariat as against the peasant: agricultural man is traditionally the great conservative, the factory worker (or formerly the urban populace) the potential revolutionary. By the age war I refer to the tendency to incite the young against their elders. The same motive is again operative here. The revolutionary of course regards the young as his natural allies: the old (with caution and scepticism that years generally bring) his natural enemies.

In most primitive or patriarchal societies the Elders are the leaders: and this tradition is always very strong. Also, the old are the repositories of tribal or national tradition: but it is precisely those traditions that it is the purpose of the revolutionary to undermine. All advertisement of the "young idea," "youth at the helm" slogans, and so on, is encouraged, if not promoted, by Big Business or the revolutionary mind of contemporary politics.

Regarding these "wars" I have always been in two minds. First, as such wars of this sort, as armed conflict, are techniques I cannot applaud, even if I recognize that they are means to ends of which I approve. As I stand for fundamental change, I am for the *end*, at least, in all these instances. Alas that the good so frequently lies at the end of a sewer, or cleverly concealed in a lunatic asylum.

However, the aim throughout is definitely to reduce the "high" to the level of the "low" (as if we were all primitive christians): to dissolve privilege in any shape or form, wherever encountered. And has not the European world been a "man's world?" Its laws the reporter on the sex war front was wont to refer to as "man-made laws." Man, that classic example of privilege, secured his many advantages by *force*. So he stands condemned—in an age committed (theoretically) to the discouragement of physical force—as enjoying power resting ultimately upon physical violence.

As a symbol of the bully and violator of elementary human rights, men often are ironically situated. A weedy and insignificant specimen of the male sex class hardly looks the part. There are a group of functions which involve him in this class struggle. "Apart from *man as father*, or *man as husband*, or *man as leader* (in the tribe of State), there is an even more irreducible way in which man is a symbol of power and domination. Man as man, *tout court*,[6] is an anachronism." Such is the situation I have just indicated.

The discrediting and dethroning of this feeblest and smallest of sovereigns, the little father of the family, in his squalid domestic "castle," is one of the main features of the demasculinizing process.* Many of the specifically masculine attributes would disappear at the same time as the loss of status.

Such is the political aspect of the transaction. But Big Business, as well as the politician, has for many years had the male principle under observation; both have their plans for its elimination. To think of the housewife, for instance, puts the modern economic planner in a rage. The entire horsepower of this good woman, all the year round, consumed in attending to one man and perhaps a couple of children—washing, cooking, scrubbing, sewing, shopping! That must without delay, he insists, be superseded by some kind of barrack life for working people, the male and female segregated, with communal meals, crèches etc. The housewife must go!

There is something besides this: there is the simple question of man's *economic* prerogative. Great numbers of men are engaged in unskilled work which a woman or a child is equally capable of carrying out: on account of the sex prerogative, male privilege, some inefficient little man demands a wage superior to what a woman or child would receive, for doing the same thing.

These operations are obscured just now by the great social changes which have marked the first two years of postwar ii. But those changes will finish what the "suffragette" and the postwar i "sex-war" etc. began. The abolition of the Family as we have known it up to now is more than ever on the agenda of those who have the power to change what they want to change. It is not an idle or ill-founded prophecy to say that a third sex ultimately will emerge. The way in which the more intelligent promoter of these social re-

[6] per se or without qualification

* "We do not want an Englishman's home to be his 'castle,' we want a community to get the best out of every human being." Mr. Silkin, May 17, 1947.

adjustments envisaged the matter was that something like the sterile female workers of the beehive should be, not perhaps *aimed at,* so much as anticipated, in the ordinary course of things.

All this of course is hardly more than a speeding up and deliberate organization of tendencies inherent in the Machine Age. Wasp waists, corsetry and crinolines (aside from the question of their absurdity) could not have survived. The economic injustice imposed on women by barbarous laws must, in a period obsessed by problems of social justice, be ended. It is a something superadded about which I have been speaking.

A few words before leaving the subject of the Family, and of the Third Sex respectively. It would be absurd to suppose that the working man would be the loser as a result of the dismantling and dispersion of the Family. To live cooped up with a snarling woman, or a lazy slatternly one (I am speaking realistically) who adds child after child to the household until there are so many there is scarcely room to move in their little dwelling, is not a thing to look back on with regret for an uprooted overlord. A family group that he is unable to feed and clothe, half of them adopting the habits of scavenger dogs—to have to relinquish *that* male privilege should be easy.

This man would be far happier, who can doubt it, in a monastery: happier still in a men's communal dwelling, collective farm, barracks, bunkhouse, club: anywhere liberated from the crushing responsibilities of sex, of fatherhood and the upkeep of a dirty little "castle." As to the woman, is there any question that *she* would be far better off as a member of a "third sex"—with her pinup boy over her spinster's cot, no children tugging at her like a rag doll, with some such healthy work as a "clippie" * or (a little grander) a confidential secretary? This postscript should suffice to dispose of any feeling that I have been betraying an inhuman streak.

Sex, too, in one of its most obsessive forms, played its part in the early stages of the disintegrating process: the nineties led the way with a great literary martyr.

World war i produced socially more shock symptoms, as I have already observed, than has world war ii. Whether male

* Woman omnibus conductress: post-war ii.

inversion must count as one of them depends upon whether postwar ii can show as severe an epidemic as its predecessor or not. In the Universities of postwar i the Proust-reading, Wilde-worshipping, undergraduate turned daintily to Sodom, while the female student repaired to Lesbos. The building up to the species was suddenly out of favor:* the stocks of the species did not stand very high. Young men wanted to be women. The man's role was patently unprofitable: too much had recently been asked of him. In the decade of *What Price Glory* he reacted violently. If you think this analysis is fanciful, what other cause would you assign to such epidemics? Although only world war can account for the violence of this fashion, however, it may not occur (in the forties as in the twenties) as a result of war alone. War is only part of a larger pattern.

How male inversion correlates with other sex movements is explained by me in chapter iv of Part viii, *A. of B. R.* "It † (male inversion) is as an integral part of feminism proper that it should be considered a phase of the sex war. The 'homo' is the legitimate child of the 'suffragette.' "

What is quite certain is that socially the conjunction of the women and one of these ubiquitous perverts boded no good for the normal male. There was an affinity between the rouged boy and a violent type of young middle-aged woman, of the kind Lawrence wrote about and describes as "sitting on a volcano." Intrigues hatched themselves where Jockey Club mingled with the odor of Ninetyish carnations blooming in buttonholes upon male bosoms.—The male-invert fashion shared many antagonisms with the average woman. An embittered, and no longer young, woman is able to revenge herself upon the he-man, for whom she would no longer be attractive. Often it has been alleged that the "pansy" shelters behind the woman, but, as I pointed out somewhere, it is equally true to say that women act through these militant anti-he-man perverts.

Now to give more careful attention to the purely *class* aspect of these movements. Once "war" between classes began to spread, as a result of Marx's teaching, naturally it did not

* The attitude of the ancient Hebrews to this aberrant sexuality was severely practical. They condemned it as *unpatriotic.* So undoubtedly it is, in so far as it spells sterility.
† Abbreviation to be used for *Art of Being Ruled.*

stop at *economic* class. Wars are fought with armies, and "class wars" similarly are contested by disciplined groups possessed of a high esprit de corps.

What Sorel called an "artificial" bond has to be created, to cement people to each other. And this bond has to be of an *exclusive* nature. They have to cease to be conscious of all the other things they are, outside that particular category. Thus the "proletarian" should forget that he is *also* a Catholic, or vice versa—a Catholic that he is a member of the working class. In the making of a Christian, in patristic times, the same care was taken (cf. St. Augustine) to make the convert banish from his spirit all emotional ties, of family, or of sex, attachment to his home town or nation.

Power here is what is involved. "Actually . . . the more you specialize people, the more power you can obtain over them, the more helpless and in consequence the more obedient they are. To shut people up in a watertight . . . occupational unit is like shutting them up on an island."

In this sense a class is a corral: it is a confining something, limiting a person to a certain pattern, giving to his character a restrictive definition, to his personality a strong and exclusive group color.—"Class" of course is here being used in the wider sense, as found in such expressions as "accountants, as a class, are very circumspect," or "clergymen, as a class, are very self-indulgent." I perhaps should have said this before.

A typical American, for instance, of the Babbitt order, is classifiable in a number of ways as a rule. About each of these departments of his being, by which his original ego is conditioned, he develops a good deal of fanaticism. First, he is a U.S. Citizen. That compels him from birth to a variety of conventional attitudes. Next he is, for instance, from the "Deep South," or a Westerner, or a Hoosier. Then a member of the "Grand Old Party," let us say: perhaps a Veteran of some kind. Add to that his religion—Catholic, or Jehovah's Witness, or Christian Scientist, and you have a man composed of intensely colored segments, as it were: classifiable as probably is no other national.

All of these sects, or clubs, or societies, or communions to which he belongs take each its toll of his independence: seeing that in each of these capacities he becomes terribly *typical*. That rather unreal thing (unless you have something to *do* with it) freedom, he has traded for something he likes better.—I have chosen the American rather than the Englishman because the latter is, in that sense, freer, and therefore less suitable. He has not gone so far along the path of social mechanization.

Men find their greatest happiness in type-life. Some strongly marked occupational type—the helmeted "Bobbie," the barrister with his wig, the schoolmaster with his mortarboard and cane; or pronounced national type—such as the strong silent Englishman, the "mad Irishman," the tough hustling American: out of being these types men derive infinite satisfaction. Sex provides similar joys: acting the "he-man," or the glamorous girl.

It is on account of this type-hypnotism that it is so difficult to persuade anyone of the great disadvantage of competitive nationalist emotions, and of the desirability of cosmopolis. Engaged as I am almost daily in desultory propaganda for world government, I find myself in collision all the time with the type-spirit.—Were one able suddenly to remove all the obsessive archetypes, conferring upon men's lives their mechanical patterns, everybody would be as miserable as are primitive peoples when White civilization interferes with their ritualistic practices. . . .

PART VI

from colony to cosmos

FROM the very start of his career, Lewis was an adamant and shrewdly original critic of nationalism in all of its forms. He thought that the standardization of customs brought about by the world-wide impact of technology and industrialism had both intensified the clinging to outworn tribal and national traits, now largely artificial, and had established an internationalism in fact which the nationalists could only deny by indulging in fantasies arising from a past that no longer existed.

In *Filibusters in Barbary*, the account of a trip to North Africa published in 1932, during the worst period of the world economic crisis, Lewis examined the effects of modern technique on one of the prime colonies of the Western world. Here there was much "local color" on display, but the paradoxical situations produced by the inroads of modern life was a perfect arena for his talents, and resulted in some of his wittiest and most perceptive pages.

After the Second World War, in 1948, Lewis wrote his most zestful and optimistic book, *America and Cosmic Man*. Once again, his concern with nationalism and war was the starting point for his reflections on American history and politics. "The destiny of America," he wrote, "is not to be just another 'grande nation': but to be the great big promiscuous grave into which tumble, and there disintegrate, all that was formerly race, class, or nationhood. . . . It is in all likelihood by such a process . . . that the universal society will come about." Cosmic Man, the antithesis of all that had produced wars and national rivalries, was being manufactured, quite appropriately, in the new land. ". . . occasionally in the air (of America) one thinks that one detects something so far not met with; the electric intoxication of the air breathed by prisoners set free. The American air is conditioned by these immigrant multitudes, hollow with the great *ouf* with which they have turned their back upon the European world. . . . I ought perhaps to say that our America, at the opening of what has been called the 'atomic age' is not any longer across seas. Instead it is a time, not a place; namely, the cosmic era which lies beyond the ruin and disintegration of atomic war."

That last, ironic touch is typical of Lewis' mind: even when elated by the prospect of possible universalism, he could not forego his realism, and insisted on the bare facts: atomic war might finally teach mankind to behave in a civilized fashion.

Tlemcen

TLEMCEN is a very important town in the history of Maghreb; it is geographically important; it is of first-class interest to the sightseer or student.

It is placed at one end of what the French call *la trouée de Taza*.[1] It faces Fez, at the opposite end of the long hole in the landscape in question. It is the first town, going west from Algeria and Tunis, where you get the Andalusian Civilization (the Hispano-Mauresque) and so it is the first Moroccan town.

But it is even the first *city*, that is, old-settled city—autochthonous and not one run up by the European overnight—between Tunis and Fez. "In Maghreb," says E. F. Gautier, "urbanism has only, in fact, developed at the two extremities of the country, around monster cities—Tunis at one end, Fez at the other. Algeria has no *citizens*, properly speaking, except at Tlemcen. The Algiers of 1830 was nothing more than a garrison and Turkish port, in spite of the presence of a few Andalusian immigrants, called by the French of 1830 *les Maures*.[2] One can only understand native Algeria (as distinguished from the Algiers of the French Occupation) by recalling that it is essentially rural."

So Tlemcen is in Algeria the only surviving city of the Middle Ages of Maghreb. The Bedouins, the Spaniards, Turks, Armenians etc., etc., destroyed all the rest. It is the only city of old standing at all. Of great cities like Tiaret, there is today not a trace. No one even knows where it was. So the well-informed traveler (and I was a very well-informed one, in-

1 pass or gap of Taza
2 the Moors

deed, as I have said) approaches Tlemcen with respect. Tlemcen, as a city, is not *le premier venu*.[3] Archir, La Kalaa,
Tiaret, Archgoul, El-Batha, all swallowed up in the destructive rage of the Arab, with others to help him—from Kurdish
archers to Norman chiefs. Only Tlemcen is left. *And* it is the
first Andalusian city, the beginning of Morocco: and a place
of great character and attractiveness. As I moved toward it in
the train from Oran across the Rio Salado (I suppose),
through the headquarters of the Foreign Legion, and at last
up into the mountain chain northwest of the Tell (definitely
continental, rather than coastal tracts at last) I knew, as well
as if I had been there, that in the Mellah a foreskin was
probably being tied up in flannel and hung over the mother's
bed as an amulet, whereas the Mauresques—why, *they* would
be on their way to their Marabout to burn incense, or *haoufi*:
while elsewhere a punctilious old Reb was bastinadoing a
Jewish corpse, preparatory to burying it, to spare it trouble
in the next world: all the cycle of birth and death, in short,
of Arab, Turk, Berber or Jew, all that the visitor ought to
know, to take an intelligent interest in—just as I knew that
it was the Zenata of "the second race" that had founded the
Abdenwadite dynasty: and the name of the first king, Yar-
morasen, I knew as well as I knew my own.

The dolomitic cliffs of this mighty *massif* [4] are more impressive than the Tarn, I discovered (though the wild country
immediately north of the Tarn is the only part of France that
is able to give you an idea of these African desert mountains, invaded by sand and salt, as is everything else in Maghreb, everywhere spotted with the flat nomad tent). The enormous, rufous battlements of nature thrown up about this entrance gallery to the Cherifian Empire are of course vaster
than the works of man, but, because they have a regularity
reclaiming chaos, these cliffs should be classed with the tremendous *kasbahs* [5] that the chieftains of the High Atlas have
built. For a traveler entering Morocco by this route the Massif
of Tlemcen is indeed a worthy gate to Barbary.

The city of Tlemcen is lost in an olive forest. The train,
after leaving the great red bastions of rock, where you have
been passing from Oranie into the dominions of the Maghzen,
goes to hunt for it in its cloud of olives: and when it finds it,

3 not just anybody
4 mountainous mass
5 Arab quarter

it is not the best approach, as it turns out afterward; you do not at once recognize why the position of this town is so much vaunted.—However, Tlemcen is on a rock itself—it was called Agadir to start with, which means "precipitous rock" (whereas Tlemcen means "source"). You may distinguish the distant sea-line from it upon a clear day. In winter, we are told, the almond blossoms are covered with snow. "The winter of Tlemcen occurs in the spring" is an Arab saying. How delightful when "winter" means snow, and "spring" the sun, with the most absurdly vivid, violent blossoming! With us these marriages of the seasons are deadly. They but result in worse mud. Winter wins. But that is not all: there is *no autumn* in Tlemcen, either—only three seasons. A sudden frost—and the summer is all over: except that the sun goes on shining, though not so hot. *To liquidate autumn*—what a good arrangement! Then to plant a spectacular winter in the midst of the flowers of spring! What happy climatic transformations!

"Well, if Tlemcen is all that you say, Mr. Guide," mutters the traveler, "it must be a premier city." But everything points to its being something of the sort. When its patron saint, an Andalusian mystic, Sidi Bou Mediene, first caught sight of it, he exclaimed, "What a jolly place to sleep one's last sleep in!" and died the same day. There are so many chances and accidents (I suppose he thought) that take us away for ever from these beautiful places! So he settled down once and for all, and put a stop to the destructive vagaries of Fate, as far at all events as he was concerned.

Tlemcen is in fact all that they say and more: but you must have a good smattering of the history of Morocco, or more properly of Maghreb, to be able to breathe its balmy citron-scented air intelligently—in addition to staring at its storks' nests at the top of all its minarets, and remaining open-mouthed in front of its fondouks and synagogues.

Often in the past I have stared stupidly at vast systems of machinery—in factories and powerhouses—for many minutes, until it got too hot or I was moved on, without having the least idea what these monstrous concatenations of steel might be for. A city and its history are the same as that. Wherever you get people you get this: it is all meaningless and really rather silly unless you know what it's all about.

There is an opposite difficulty of course: namely, when people know what a thing signifies *historically* (just as they might be informed of the uses of a complicated machine), often they see too much, and much that is not there at all. Thus nothing will persuade me that the Koutoubia (the celebrated mosque tower at Marrakech) is anything but a pleasantly arranged square tower. The lyrical flights of fancy regarding it are aberrations merely of the historically minded —a triumph of history over the eyes in the head.

For one popular authority upon Morocco, for instance, the Koutoubia possesses "the stern harmony of the noblest architecture": and this writer adds, "the Koutoubia would be magnificent anywhere: in this flat desert it is grand enough to face the Atlas." That, to my mind, is a pure exaggeration: the Koutoubia, the Giralda at Seville, and the Tower of Hasan at Rabat, are the three star pieces of Hispano-Mauresque. The ruined tower of Mansoura, outside Tlemcen, must have made a fourth, had it been left intact. But because, come to Marrakech, the traveler knows, or ought to, that "the Victorious," "the Golden," El Mansour, himself, built that tower, with the assistance of a million Christian slaves, to be a monument not easily demolished to the splendor of Arab arts and arms, that is not to say that the traveler should see it larger than it is—in its "severity" a match for great mountains, for instance: nor that, just by itself, it constitutes more than a good tower, of a certain style. Also there is a better one near it— that of the Mosque of the Kasbah, beside the Saadian Tombs. —The ruined tower of Mansoura (two kilometers from Tlemcen) is, I think, more impressive, in its ruined state: all these works would be better as ruins. It is useless to claim for the Hispano-Mauresque more than a relative interest. Hispano-Mauresque is Arab. The Berber idea is much grander than the Arab idea. It is best expressed in that rougher *genre*—in the giant Atlas kasbahs. And those you do not see till you reach the High Atlas. Nowhere north of that is there anything approaching them in interest.

It was at Tlemcen that I saw my first *souk*: and souk is "market," or, in this case, "bazaar." In a city like Tlemcen souk means bazaar, also the daily and weekly food and livestock markets. The souks, or the bazaars, a chaplet of fly-brown shops are, as elsewhere in the Orient, the main feature of Berber or Arab life.

Souk is an Arab word: the sound in Arabic is not "sook"— there is a complicated guttural tail to it. But the French have made this sound into "souk," as the nearest they could get to the original.

In English I have seen this monosyllable variously spelled.

On the analogy of "Sus" for the French *Sous*,[6] it is often spelled "Suk." Also I have seen it "Sok." The first looks much more like the sound of "suck" than the sound "sook," the second "sock." You miss the "oo" sound. Similarly if I spelled the French Sous as "Sus" (they sometimes spell it that way too, only with an accent on the u—"Sûs"), it would merely confuse the general reader, and make him think it was something to do with *Jew Süss*.—It is such considerations as these that have caused me throughout to stick to the French spelling, for these sounds often have no equivalent in a European tongue, and a conventionalized spelling is necessary.

The combination of lethargy and incessant movement is the first thing that strikes the traveler in these Moroccan bazaars, should he be as I was a novice in the Oriental picturesque. They are narrow cobbled lanes, often steep as well as winding, meandering in all directions, ending in covered markets; or they are open-air workshops doubling upon themselves within the lofty walls of private gardens. People swarm in them, and winged insects, especially where there are food stalls; mules, camels and asses, with sacks of salt or flour, pass up and down them, or sometimes a merchant on horseback, with the great peaked saddle of the Berber, so different from the Arab one (though the horse must be Syrian, and not a "Barbe," if the rider is to be pleased with himself).

The shops generally are cupboards in a mud wall. They start two or three feet from the ground. In these the merchant squats or crouches, often asleep or dropping to sleep, or if awake majestically resigned as regards the customer question. The customer question has been solved by Islam. That is left in the hands of Providence. The shopkeeper appears to have climbed up into his shop and sat down there, rather because it had been the Will of God that he should play his brief part upon life's scene as a merchant in a bazaar, than animated by any feverish desire to sell something. Even the Jews in the Mellah seem tarred with the same brush, and have the air of whiling listlessly away their time—though I dare say underneath they are aching to effect a sale, and live up to their reputation. But they do not show it, they act the same as the Arabs and as though Fate were their God as well.

On the other hand, the Producers (carpet makers, cobblers, potters and so forth) work very hard. Someone after all has to

6 penny

make the beastly article—Fate decides who it shall be. Only, once the thing is made, it passes into the hands of an indifferent guardian, rather than an eager salesman. It is expected to sell itself. It sells or it does not sell, at all events: if it sells, it sells; no one is in the least surprised when it sells, nor disturbed when it doesn't.

This great rule of massive mercantile indifference does not apply to the large establishments of the big rug and curio merchants. They, or their scouts, dart screaming out upon the visitor. Their emissaries lie all day long outside the European cafés, and when a new person drops in to drink they go in after him, and get him. Rug after rug is unrolled—some so large that they stretch right across the road to the opposite pavement. But these are people who have learned restlessness from the European, who is their main customer for such goods. Also their shops, at the heart of every Medina, are doubtless the cells, the small *succursales,*[7] of some well-organized Levantine concern, having its headquarters in Tangier, or perhaps in Alexandria. They probably stock anything from a miniature Pharaonic cartouche to a wax-inlaid *kiff* [8] pipe.

Fanning the flies with a palm fan then, a bearded personage sits impassibly, legs under stomach, behind a pair of scales, prepared to sell some *couscous,*[9] healing herbs, goat's meat, or what not, if asked—that is the rule of the bazaar. When no one arrives he may crawl out and put down his shutter, or else he may go to sleep upon the spot. When it gets cooler he wakes up, palm fan in hand. Meanwhile incessant swarms of silent and athletic tribesmen pass, occasionally saluting a friend, with the *Hush*-gesture of the finger to the lip, without looking otherwise to left or right. Up and down this tortuous and stinking lane, the rocky bed of a mountain torrent as Burton described it, the phenomenally silent inhabitants of the bled pass from morning till night.

That is, of course, "the Eastern bazaar," which has been so often described before. To see it is a first-class "Islamic sensation." As a sensation it is to be warmly recommended. I am told that the sensation is more truly Islamic in Morocco than even in Damascus, I dare say than even in Mecca.

It is naturally delightful to be in a place where industrialism has not put its squalid foot. Here it has not. You can see

7 branches
8 hashish
9 lamb dish

the ornate saddles and harness used by the rich merchants and notables cut out and sewn in a workshop open to the street. In the same way the shoe factory does not supply the *babouches* [10] as yet. All Berber footwear is made where you can stand and watch the phases of the workmanship, until there it is ready (if you are a Moroccan, or have gone native) for your foot.

Luxurious slippers, for great notables, their wives or well-paid prostitutes, have the traditional patterns being sewn into the flat sheet of Moroccan leather before it is attached to the silken welt. These consist of patterns as invariable as the tattoo spirals and constellations upon the skins of the Mauresques.

There are of course factories. I was taken through a dædalian labyrinth of passages and courts, and so into a large carpet factory. Upon three sides of a courtyard were ranked looms. The large wooden looms are like the upended frames of big English spring beds. At these upwards of a hundred girls, of thirteen or fourteen, in a profound hot hush, a stagnant studied gloom, manufacture rugs. They sat or stood before the looms as they worked. This was a very large workshop or factory, certainly: but none of the oppressive hustle and slickness was to be noticed of "the Works," when it is the Machine that is paramount. These fat brown children, the Fatmahs of tomorrow, occasionally whispering, made far less noise than a single gramophone, playing a waltz with a soft needle. One of the outstanding "Islamic sensations" of Maghreb is the absence of what the coster calls "loud-mouthed"-ness.

No argument is possible, I think, when these two modes of life are contrasted. At a period when man has not been powerful enough to transform the accidental dispositions of nature—with no dynamite to blast, or rock drills to disintegrate—and is compelled to build the streets of his cities in and out and up and down, inventing, as he goes along, untried architectural devices, delightful deformities and structural freaks, then, it is but too plain, the result is more agreeable and stimulating to the eye. By following the vast, non-human lines of nature, our human arts score their best successes. Projecting his tortuous, not yet oppressive, geometry out upon the chaotic superstructures—being methodic where he can, in the teeth of natural disorder—man is seen at his

10 slippers

best. He then produces something of intellectual as well as emotional value, which the unadulterated stark geometry of the Machine Age precludes. Without arguing pro or contra—whether some day the Machine will be put in its place—it is sufficient here to affirm that the labyrinths of these ancient souks are far more imaginatively pleasant places to be in than is, say, Hoboken, across the ferry from Manhattan, or (on a small scale) the Casa boulevards. . . .

Film Filibusters

BEFORE going south of the Atlas into "the mysterious" Sous—a land so pregnant with plots and so overrun with lawless outsiders as to make a mere tourist's hair stand on end—before rushing for four hundred miles up and down the sides of mountains in a mighty bus, and at last dropping with a dull roar into the ocean valley of Santa Cruz de Cap d'Ager, the very home soil and breeding ground of the essential filibuster (whose filibustering is the principal industry of the place), I will give some account of an important filibuster met with further north—not in the Sous—namely *the Film Filibuster*. I fell in with a huge caravan of them at Fez. And then (in more aristocratic surroundings and in a much grander form—juvenile-lead and magnate rolled into one) at Marrakech.

But if I take it upon myself to refer to the film pro or screen king as a "filibuster," it must be understood that I am casting no reflection upon his rectitude. At least, the ramp is elsewhere—the gulls are in the distant theaters, they are in such centers of civilization as Chicago or Glasgow, much more than among the natives of Barbary—among whom the Ufa and Pathé magnates send their troupes (not troops) merely to afford their sham sheiks a Hispano-Mauresque photographic setting. The whispering masses in the film palaces—it is for them that this description of filibuster filibusts—throwing up shoddy mirages, with his photographic sausage machine, of the desert life—so falsely

selected as to astonish into suspicion sometimes even the
tamest robot. As to the filmable populations—true, this mechanical Vandal degrades them as he does everything he
touches, but for the rest he puts many a lightly earned
peseta in their pockets, and is a pure benefactor as far as
that goes. And as to the Italian hotels of Barbary, it is
difficult to see what they would do at all if it were not for
those truckloads of queer fish brought from Paris and quartered on them by the gross. The touring film rabble make
up for the absent tourist—the latter a rarer bird every
minute, with every fresh oscillation of the world's exchanges
and every fresh currency ramp or tariff wall.

At Fez, the Hotel Transatlantic was closed—it is open
only for a few months in the cool season. Similarly all over
Morocco these huge hotels were shut down—they are the
"follies" as in other days they would have been called of a
steamship company, I believe. The Grand Hotel, when I
arrived, was open, but it was very large and it languished—
it had been conceived to meet the booming requirements of
a "Renaissance Marocaine" which has not materialized, and
for a volume of sightseers and filibusters far in excess of
what can now ever again be expected. The enormous dining
hall adjoining the café, with its numerous staff of white-
jacketed Algerian waiters, its Italian managers, was perhaps
a quarter full upon the first evening. Then upon the second
day the train from Casa came in with all its compartments
packed with a super sheik film company. Its fifty-odd personnel poured in for lunch, and immediately the winter
of our discontent was turned, at one blow, into glorious summer. These forty dumb characters in search of an author
dumb enough to concoct a plot and text for them (accompanied by the sharpshooters of the mechanical staff) swarmed
forward, vociferous and replete with a strident reality that
was so thin as to stamp them anywhere as screen folk—
creatures, that is, of an art at one remove from the shadow
picture. With all the prestige of this idiotic industry (as
practiced in our Western savagery) they gave the hotel staff
something to live for, and a scene of great animation was
the result.

They swung (if of the Mix class), danced, shuffled,
dashed, sidled, stalked or tottered in, each according to his
kind: noticeably *two-by-two* (as if picked out into sex pairs
by an official Cupid) like the animals entering the Ark—
for of course each of these stars, however impotent a one-

candlepower washout (even according to box office canons), must, off the screen, move in a triangle of bloodshot adultery—to satisfy the business end of the racket—in order to suggest the bombardment of an anguished fan mail—if to no one else, at least to their fellow actors. Only one or two dared to be solitary, for however brief a period.

This company had come to Fez to enact a rather elaborate arabesque of kiss-stuff-crime-and-contraband-of-arms, to be called *The Three Unlucky Travelers.* My informant was a half-caste waiter—pock-marked and with the scars of several other epidemics as well to underline his attractions. But he felt himself nearer to the great dynamic heart of the universe than ever before with these people—he told me that he had been remarked at once by the film boss. At sight he had been engaged for a minor part. What part? Oh that of a blind mendicant, not an important part! They had *wanted* him to take a more important part, but he hadn't time. He wished in a way he had! They had asked him to go off with them when they moved on, to make one of them. Yes, they desired him to become one of them. But he did not see his way to do that. He could not be squared just now—so must remain at Fez.—At that moment one of the Three Unlucky Travelers (the Polish one, the least lucky of the lot) clapped his hands impatiently in our direction, and shouted for a straw for his ice water. When the waiter returned to me (after watching for some minutes the star make use of the straw) he informed me that the one he had just obliged—who had just asked him to help him about a straw—was the first of the three to fall a victim to the spells of the magician's daughter (who was the leading lady) and to fall over a cliff. The cliff as it happened (by this time everything was shipshape—Fez had been ransacked scenically) was the other side of the Medina. It was a very big rocky lump, which the Fési has accounted for by attaching it to a local legend—it is supposed to be the colossal detritus of an indignant divinity, who was disgusted with the people of Fez, and took this rather objectionable way of showing it.

The Unlucky Traveler Number One was French, as was right and proper in a Parisian film. His was the almost matchlessly empty histrionic blend of attractions of the French Music Hall—those throaty troubadours of the Third Republic who mouth with a mealy sweetness the songs that are hawked in broadsheets afterwards by tenoro-guitarists in the provinces. Only I had been accustomed always to see that figure in a tuxedo. Therefore at first I was somewhat puzzled, for he considered an Aertex vest and canvas slacks sufficient clothing even for dinner in these sporting tropics, and in that form he was at once terribly familiar and yet absolutely strange. Of course so clothed his athletic proportions stood revealed, but they were pallid (as one would suppose the city songster's to be in spite of his cavemanly cawing and basso-profundo cooing). He looked in fact not unlike those half-naked bakers who occasionally emerge in pastrycooks' at the time the hot cottage loaves are brought up from the subterranean ovens.

When this clumsy Hearty, the first juvenile lead, entered the restaurant, he swung himself over to his place at table, as if in the atmosphere a system of massive ropes had been secreted—his torso, which was flat but very wide, swung in one direction, his arms (which were a clerk's and not a blacksmith's—but large-boned at least, if innocent of muscle) swung in the other direction. And he remained at all times a man-of-the-hour, although he would not be "released" for a twelvemonth. If he went over to the kiosk, which stood in front of the hotel, to buy a newspaper or packet of cigarettes, he inflated his chest beneath the porous fabric of the Aertex beforehand—*then* he started: he swung across the road (again as if ropes upon either side of him, suspended in a fluid medium, led direct from café to kiosk). Unfortunate Traveler for six weeks (the troupe was to remain there for at least as long as that, they said) he was a most melancholy gymnast, his existence a footlight one, overshadowed by an epic struggle on the other side of the Medina—on the Tarpeian Rock—then out in the pitiless bled with a bloodthirsty sheik—never off-duty, compelled to remain stripped (to his Aertex) for the fray, by the etiquette of his profession. Did the poor chap ever relax? Did he in his bedroom relax, and become the clumsy, slouching clerk of his early youth once more—or did he sleep bolt upright, even in his sleep an Unlucky Traveler, with his chest stuck out three inches beyond the norm of its recumbent silhouette?

These simple universal problems (for the onlooker) are provided in common by all those who live by impersonating "unlucky" characters, cast for abnormal episodes, of great physical violence. But it occurred to me as I watched these film cattle that the stage actor, whose work is done upon a stage, and the film actor, the backgrounds for whose work are the scenes of everyday, though they have much in common, must differ very widely in important particulars. The stage actor, for instance, could at all times be spotted out of the theater, in his nonpublic life. Likewise the film actor, but less so. For on the whole with the latter the actorishness must be of a more insidious sort. His artificiality has to be more intense, since the demands of the *real* everyday background are more exacting. In his professional displays the screen worker in the nature of things is the last word in *naturalism,* at the opposite pole to a formal art. His actorishness therefore (the stigmata of the trade of Make-believe stamped into his features and attitudes) must be a distortion of a very common-or-garden norm, rather than the reflections of a transcendent, an abnormal, existence. The film man will tend to be a very intense, very slightly heightened Everyman, whereas the Garricks and Irvings would carry about with them in private the impress of successions of great Individuals separated by all the arts of the formal stage play from that everyday nature of Everyman, which is the particular province of film photography.

The huge company that came to the Cherifian Capital to reproduce the great dime-dream of *The Three Unlucky Travelers* was conspicuously polyglot. One of the luckless heroes was a German, but every nationality was represented, even English. The spectacle of this cosmopolitan social organism taking shape beneath one's eyes was a mild diversion. They arrived in a mere chaos of personalities upon the scene of the Grand Hotel. But at the end of three or four days they had separated out into well-defined classes. The Leading Parts (irrespective of nationality, age, salary or looks) sat at a smaller table. This became a sort of High Table. There was a second table for those not quite so eminent. But from this second table people were occasionally promoted to the first. This was usually as a consequence of successful love passages with a male or female of the first rank. This necessarily brought them into the charmed circle of Stars (if the love passages lasted, that is). But upon the first day of one of these adventures the couple involved in the new intrigue would separate upon arrival in the restaurant, and would go to their respective tables, according to class. Sometimes after a day or two at the High Table a Second Classer would have to return to Table Number Two, upon being superseded in the affections of the Star in question. There was therefore a constant going and coming. It was an evolutionary pattern, supervised by Cupid, the *motif* divorce, of course.

After four or five days a new phenomenon was to be remarked. A pair of important stars would roughly break away from the central tables, and go off into a corner by themselves—to a table à deux. At the end of the sixth or seventh day most were back again where they had started, in their original groupment. Others had, meanwhile, broken away and were to be seen with their heads together alone at a table, even perhaps going so far as to order a half-bottle of rather better wine (say, two francs' worth of sauterne) than was supplied gratis with each meal, generally Algerian.

As two would come in—and, instead of going to their usual seats, according to class, at a common board, were observed to pass down the room and establish themselves in a distant spot—all the other tables would be in a fulsome momentary ferment—people would turn round and point, chatter and signal from one table to the other. In short, the attitude of all these people to their own actions—of "passionate" couplement and precipitate divorce, and then new couplement and further violent separation—was exactly the same as though they had been a crowd of *fans*, instead of a crowd of *pros*. They acted the fan for each other! Their shop was as much, or a great deal more, *publicity*, than it was the art of acting, that goes without saying. The good looker, not the good actor, would become the star. It may be regarded as certain that each morning a fan mail would come up with the principal's breakfast. It would be composed and dispatched overnight by lesser members of the flattersome company. And from the camera staff such attentions would come particularly well no doubt. All day long the individuals of this herd were showing off to each other, attempting to convince the rest that they were "coming" stars, or if already by way of being stars, that *this* show would give them a place in the center of the world spotlight, with semi-Garbo-like laurels—or recall the days of Valentino, when stars were stars indeed.

The quality of the female élite of the company I regret to say was exceedingly low according to any standards. They were all undersized, almost like another species, and their intense artificiality took the form of an odd degenerescence. In *forcing* the normal everyday reality, as it were—in compelling it to conform to what was certainly a vulgar average, but a particularly odd variety of the vulgarest commonplace—they suggested the exact opposite of the *heightening* said to characterize the finest art. Theirs was a *lowering*: but it was a descent so much below the average level as to be eccentric and extraordinary. Here were indeed the authentic *depressed* levels of the universe of the Untermensch,[1] in all their blatant pretentiousness. Seeing that their departure from the norm was in the direction of a dwarfishness, an eccentricity, an air of impaired health—with the demented self-assertiveness of the *asphalt* folk that they of course are, and the demented concentration upon *effect*—an impression (even necessarily) of a *degeneration*—from power, law, dignity and sense—was conveyed by their presence. It was as if some patently *inferior*—some less healthy, less excellently balanced, less beautiful—some half-mad midget people, were, father to son, film professionals. In Maghreb all the acrobats come from a particular tribe in the Sous—all the builders and masons come from a particular tribe in the Great Atlas; in the same way all the personnel of this film world might come from a certain district—say, in Galicia or in Czechoslovakia. One could imagine them as a diminutive, phthisic, gutter people, who had started in gutter theatricals, prospered, spread over the world (like the Berber tumblers of the Noun) caricaturing any eccentricity, or imitating any particularly brutal behavior on the part of the full-grown, "normal," master people by whom they were surrounded—falling in and out of love, to show that they were real and not just puppets, and even taking their desperate pretense of reality so far at times as to blow their papier-mâché brains out—a small vampire, or vampish—kohl-lidded, heterosexed clan—an important subdivision of the Untermensch—selecting for their imitations for preference Crime—some specializing in gangster parts, some in coke-addict parts, some in Lesbian roles —some partial to blackmail, some to arson, some sticking to "straight" Murder Club stuff, some having patient sidelines of fancy homicide—but *all* violent—*all* guaranteed to be intelligible to the least talented, to the most adenoid-stifled gutter infant, or to the lowest average level of city serfdom —always the crudest box office "appealed" to—everything imitated by them to be vulgar and violent *de rigueur*. So, restless and keyed up to jazz-concert pitch, this swarm moved about the hotel; to overhear a dialogue in the elevator was

[1] sub-man

to be let into a secret of the heart of a star. At the mere presence beside them of a stranger (a potential fan) they began talking feverishly, so that you should feel that when they passed out of sight a pistol would be fired—a pipe of opium resorted to—an illegal operation consummated—or (at the mildest and meekest) a fruity adultery be instantly forthcoming. This "atmosphere of climax" in this great hotel became somewhat oppressive at last. It blotted out the Arabs finally, and made the Berber a little dim—I was of course grateful for the eclipse of the Hispano-Mauresque Babs and Minarets, Medersas and Mosques! They certainly cast a spell over the "capital of the Islamic world" as the Sultan's good town of Fez is often called. They swarmed everywhere—they whispered in the passages, danced in the café, wrote masses of letters and cards (to languishing fans) in the writing rooms, monopolized the bars.

The three he-men and their three he-friends were the principal American bar guests—one in puggaree and pipe, two walking advertisements for underwear—and then the three understudies of course to match, though exaggerating the absurdities of their principals—dressed in an inferior quality of men's vests, and with even an inferior quality of skin—though the latter was in fact somewhat of a feat, in the way of subordination!

The younger officers of the Fez garrison mingled on terms of equality and patronage with the film folk—not of course sitting at their tables, but occasionally inviting one or two to theirs—or often a film man would come up and sit down with them unasked, and they suffered this with a good grace.

I take it that this big film troupe was a second-rate French one, dispatched to Fez on the cheap, on a Cook's Tour basis—probably "done" by the hotel at ten francs per day per head, for six weeks—everything found, the least choice Algerian wine thrown in and glad to get rid of it. Trade was at an abnormal ebb—the Economic Blizzard must have emptied every hotel from the Bermudas to Bombay—and this ill-favored herd certainly filled up the place and gave it a spurious air of prosperity. . . .

The Clubman Caesar

FRANKLIN DELANO ROOSEVELT was the third greatest American President. Jefferson, the originator of democratic America, the hero of the Bill of Rights; and Lincoln, who saved the Union, are the two who excel him.

No scarred and beetling figurehead for the ship of State, like Abraham Lincoln, almost a "city slicker" by comparison; beside Jefferson's intellectual endowment, a mediocre mind, however nimble. It does not even seem very certain that the late President was an extraordinary democrat, though I say this under correction. But his nonstop presidency effected great changes—almost, one felt once or twice, was going to slip over the invisible line dividing politics from something else. He remained, however, the politician: but so important a one that no other President except the two mentioned above (neither of whom were politicians to the same extent) deserved so high a place.

The great Party Machine . . . strained, and roared, and gave off dense clouds of steam, and at last it put this man, with his terrible physical handicap, into the White House. Then really remarkable things began to happen, and continued to do so up to the moment when he put his hand up to his forehead and said "I have a perfectly terrific headache!" and collapsed.

It was almost as if the strenuous, cunning, stupid Party junta, ignorant of the nature of their gift, had presented the nation with a Poltergeist for a President. Things began at once to fly about, at all events. And they had an uncanny habit of hitting the right people.

A radioactive something was secreted in the tall stately interior of this bland, calm, too generously chinned figure, perpetually seated: reaching up to pin medals upon people's bosoms, or to extend a dignified glad hand and a beautifully dentured welcome—who began in the most well-mannered and easygoing way possible to govern with a witchery that made the most violent measures appear much less out of the ordinary than they were. In the end he put a spell upon the Congress: there seemed to be nothing he could not do, and at last there was nothing they would not let him do.

A man hardly above the average in visible ability, what was the secret of his success? I make the suggestion that the answer is to be found mainly in his *receptivity*. To magnify (and exaggerate) for analytical purposes, he was a tactful medium, who knew his place. Add to this two assets: (1) his social position, and (2) that remarkable woman, his wife. And not to leave that out, though that alone would account for only a fraction, he was a very smart politician.

Belonging as he did to one of those not very numerous American families with an historic name, with the "backgrounds" of established wealth and, so, social position, Roosevelt brought to his great office the outlook of the "man of society." He was daring where less plushily backgrounded politicians would be cautious. He flung billions about lightheartedly, since he had no craven superstitions regarding money. His flippancy was proverbial. He was capable of frivolous decision: he loved to astonish: the more he confused people, his supporters as much as the public, the better pleased he was.

On this side of the picture there was more than a reminder of Frederick the Great, one of whose favorite pastimes (war of course being sport No. 1) was ragging or "hazing" his entourage. But Frederick had a very vicious streak, whereas F.D.R. seems to have been kind (in spite of Falla, which, of course, rouses one's suspicions, as did Lord Baldwin's pipe). It was only in that one particular he was like Frederick.

He was a typical modern American of the "clubman" species: extremely fond of the absurd, and getting a big kick out of all that was inconsequent and irrational. Out of nothing more mischievous than "mischief" he would stick a square peg in a round hole and observe its antics (for the peg of course was human). Often it was rumored he had lost his reason. The slander of enemies, doubtless, or else a conventional or provincial reaction to an "illogical" proceeding of his or some horseplay of his offstage satellites.

The country had never been so lively a place, and probably

never will be so lively again. Often he turned the United States up on its head, which is the best possible thing for any country. Most people forget that half of us living so eccentrically upon this spinning globe are walking upside down all the time, though which half it is who knows? Mr. Roosevelt never forgot that. Such was the kind of thing about him which makes him stand next to Lincoln, in the Presidential hierarchy, and above Jackson, who took great liberties, as did he, with the Constitution, but was not a sorcerer.

His ease and disinvolture were perfect. He conducted himself at times as would the stereotyped "cynical clubman" were that gentleman called upon suddenly—as the result perhaps of a bet—to desert momentarily his exclusive clubs, yachts, race courses, boxes at the Opera, and govern an enormous nation. Poker-faced, without the flicker of an eyelid, he would take the controls. As one would anticipate in such circumstances, the nation shot ahead, in the most sporting style. It would have reached the goal of an intelligent, American, socialism, had not—how shall I put it? the clubman been also a politician.

Mr. Roosevelt was a capital actor. He had one notable impersonation, namely that of his erstwhile master, Woodrow Wilson. It was uncommonly lifelike, even down to the austere Wilsonian mask. In some of his photographs at Big Three meetings it would be the "Presbyterian Priest" himself one is looking at; as also in his plagiarism of the Gettysburg Address, he walked in the footsteps of a hero of his youth.

In the interesting European groups (though I am afraid this will make it seem as if I were always ranking him *below* somebody else), it was Stalin, unassuming, matter-of-fact, without any theatricals, who makes the best impression. Mr. Roosevelt by any computation was what we call a great man. But he wanted too much to look it. For the Russian "greatness" would seem anyway a romantic superstition of Westerners.

When Franklin Roosevelt came to power he plunged in straight away, in approved Roosevelt style; declaring he was going to be either "the best or the worst President the United States had ever had." Actually he was one of the most dazzlingly successful. With him the United States moved forward a century or so. This was of course the work of many people: but, as impresario, he gave them every encouragement, up to a point. No one since Jefferson had given encouragement of that type.

First he had a "brain trust," and latterly what in Jackson's day was called a "kitchen cabinet." Hopkins, Judge Rosenman and the rest, the cabinet behind the scenes, were the true Administration, much more than the big foreground figures in the ministerial limelight, who came and went.

Often they went with a farcical suddenness, as they would in a Groucho Marx film—shooting out of sight unexpectedly down a trapdoor; or after a violent altercation before the footlights, to the amazement of the spectators, a *couple* of them would be hustled off, waving their arms and protesting, never to reappear. These noisy disturbances became quite frequent toward the end. Into the showmanship crept a note of nervous violence. His pathetic chuckling "I can take it" speech, during his last election campaign reminiscent of the final phase of Wilson's career, enlightened the audience as to the condition of the showman himself. By that time he was a dying man. And those who knew all that Roosevelt had meant for America held their breath. His disappearance would leave a dangerous vacuum.

Franklin Roosevelt undoubtedly became more frolicsome as he went on; for his appointments had a deliberately facetious look at times. Sometimes an angry frolicsomeness made itself felt: his jokes were of an insulting kind, now and then. No politician *loves* his public—or only during the honeymoon period. He of course carefully peruses every morning all the insults leveled at him in the Press, daily more bitter: it is but natural, after, say, ten years of it, that he should insult back. One could only wonder how the President was able to keep his patience as well as he did. And prior to this last period of his life his equanimity was one of his most striking attributes.

This is a largish thumbnail sketch. Its aim is to bring out certain specific things about the American system, that and nothing else: regarding that aim, the character of Mr. Roosevelt, the nature of his success, and of his endowments, is invaluable evidence.

No greater centralizer than he—in an age of centralizers, or would-be ones—existed. He almost succeeded in splitting the Constitution—that most obstinate of atoms. Of the famous check system of triune government of the United States there was not much left when he was through with it. The Supreme Court, packed with his appointees and stout Partymen, ate out of his hand. The Congress, which once had climbed up on top of the President, had never been so powerless.

No contemporary statesman was so confirmed an internationalist. He, more than any man, was in the secret of the peculiar destiny of his country.

All that he did, whether wittingly or not—and much he was personally responsible for—was *good*. He was, however, the archetype of the democratic autocrat—the "Czar" or "Caesar." Though—typically—not a New Dealer, he was firmly cemented into a Caesarian power by that remarkable organization—since Jefferson's democratic societies the greatest revolutionary phenomenon in the United States.

When, in retrospect, one considers what the New Deal accomplished, one is astonished that so great an event was not better understood in other countries. One reason was, no doubt, that it was obliged in its own country to conceal its real character, all the time. Publicists like Pegler (a first-class journalist) kept hammering away at it. From a selected batch of Pegler's articles anybody could see exactly what the New Deal was far better than from material favorable to it. These massive polemics, invariably amusing, sometimes scurrilous, you would receive, naturally, with a shovelful of salt. Some of this columnist's conclusions you would simply reverse. Pegler has always thought the Employer infallible. If a workman asked for more pay, he must be wrong: the Employer would give it him if he ought to have it. His feelings about the New Deal may be imagined. Mr. Roosevelt was for him something like a Leader of the underworld. But he had a sharp eye for a marxist tucked away in a Ministry.

The New Deal, however, did show a way how a civilized country could be ruled: not a new feudal world like Russia, or a military caesarism like a Hitler. It turned the U.S. on its head. F.D.R. lay back and laughed to see such sport. It sent troops into the offices of the dread lords of industrial capitalism, picked them bodily up, carried them outside and deposited them, speechless with rage, in the street. Within a decade this new bureaucratic power had put the big-business world under its spell. Could Roosevelt have lived a few years longer the New Deal might, for better or for worse, have effected a complete break in American tradition. They might have rewritten the Constitution—not of course torn it up—so that it harmonized with contemporary economic conditions.

The Party system might have been superseded by the New

Deal bureaucratic organization throughout the States. For it, like Party, was a strictly speaking illegal excrescence. And when two excrescences, both of which have usurped the functions of the legal government of the nation, come face to face, one disappears.

The greatest advertisement of Mr. Roosevelt is the New Deal: by that he will always be remembered. How could it be, then, that he was not a New Dealer? The answer is that the New Deal and the Constitution as it stands could not coexist. Mr. Roosevelt was, after all, President.

When Roosevelt became President, he probably had in mind a program of revolutionary window dressing on the Wilson model. He intended to go one better, of course. His aim was not a profound revolution or revaluation, but a demagogic power within the conservative fold. He and his wolves would not eat up all the sheep, because they would not be wolves but some other animal masquerading as such, in a more or less polite terrorism.

When Wilson came into power he started something he called the "New Freedom"—he christened his program that. Roosevelt, his admiring disciple, started the "New Deal." But it is unlikely that he had any idea of the energies his rallying cry would attract. Having opened the gates to all that was intelligently radical, a mob of young men rushed in, and thenceforth, smiling with a sardonic suavity, he was carried along to ends he could not have foreseen, since he did not know enough to be able to do that.

But he loved power as a schoolboy loves candy: he had behind him the vast and elaborate Machine of Party . . . but *that* might grow cold toward him. Why not build up another Machine of his own, or let these people build it up for him? He need not utterly commit himself to it. And that is what happened: and this new Machine—backed by the more serious labor organizations, aided still by the Party Machine— it became practically impossible to defeat, in the end, by democratic means. It was of course all highly "undemocratic," in the ordinary Party sense.

Conceived on the pattern of the Anti-Saloon League, the "Political Action Committee" (a near-marxist outfit), plus an army of Roosevelt-appointed federal agents in every state, formed a solid foundation. Millions literally of these federal agents, many more than there was any reason for, in most states exceeding in number those in the state service, were the President's private army: a great body of wolves. The power of appointment—what was the old "spoils system"—is recognized as the President's greatest source of power. He did not neglect to use it. In all the 48 states of the Union there were Roosevelt-appointed judges; so that in his disputes with outraged magnates, in the last phases of the world war, it was not easy to find a judge willing to adjudicate against the President. And the Supreme Court was as I described it just now: solid for its patron or its Party leader. Leagues of Woman Voters and suchlike agencies, in the great provincial cities, worked upon the electorate in the Roosevelt interest. There was superb radio support, and a majority of the Press were for him. All these and many other adjuncts of democratic power (as that functions in our mass civilization) proved irresistible at the ballot boxes.

This is a Caesarism of an oddly elaborate and round-about kind. It is a product of the famous "rigid Constitution" of the United States, when that instrument is sufficiently boldly interpreted. An elective kingship, it ensures enormous power to a skillful politician, with few scruples about "democracy," and not afraid of Wall Street.

Roosevelt had of course the best legal minds at his disposal, to tell him just how far he could go. It was as far as any ruler can go, short of open despotism, or totalitarian or Cromwellian "Protectorship" or Führership. But it is really more rule by a group than by an individual. Alexander Hamilton would have delighted in this "elective king," as a brilliant exponent of the principles of personal power, and consummate centralizer. But his economic escapades would have broken Hamilton's heart, could he have witnessed them.

This kind of ruler is a peg on which to hang power. When he is receptive and accommodating he can be a Trojan Horse for a democratic group, ruling collectively inside his hollow frame. Before proceeding to what I now am arriving at, let me put it in this way. F.D.R. it appears to me was a great frame, rather than a great picture. But much upon which we bestow that flattering epithet of "great" is just that. And to be a *great frame* is not so easy as it looks. It is extremely praiseworthy.

In the States it is regarded as bad form to be perfectly idle. They have to "work." But Roosevelt was born potentially one of this "idle rich" class of privileged "workers," and he possessed what is a marked characteristic of that class; he was no great scholar, passing his law exams, for instance, with considerable difficulty.

He did not however shy away from learning in another man, as do most of those conscious of limitations in themselves. On the contrary, he used brains wherever he found them and would even get these brainy fellows to write his speeches for him. (The public were always told, semi-officially, who had written such and such a speech of the President's.)

Perhaps the "man of society" came in here again. He was so well satisfied with being what he was that he despised, in true American fashion, all the things that make a man a "brain-truster": was that it? However that may be, beaming at them with his big animal chin and extending his hand in a welcoming sweep of "well-bred" patronage, he sucked in anything that displayed the glitter of vitality. He had a veritable genius for assimilation. In the end there he sat, a composite colossus, his presidential stature growing daily. His presidential throne was surrounded by human shells he had thrown away.

All are agreed that this glamorous Chief Executive was the reverse of unattractive. One of Mr. Truman's supporters, referring to his association with the late President, observed that being with him was like making a meal off nothing but caviar. For his part, he declared, he was glad to get back to ham and eggs. (This fare, of course, was Mr. Truman.)

Mayor La Guardia, one time, on leaving the White House, was reported to have shaken himself, inhaled a deep draft of fresh air, and exclaimed: "After spending a few hours like that with the President is like coming away from a necking party." His clubmanesque, his Rooseveltian charm was from all accounts overpowering.

He was a democrat in one sense, in contrast to Wilson. He worked readily with and through other people. He could never have performed what he (ostensibly) did without the daily and hourly cooperation of a staff of people often far more individually gifted than himself, as well as possessed of special knowledge he had never troubled to acquire. But it seemed to him that was just as it should be. A President of the United States is the creation of many minds and wills. He is a *collective* phenomenon. That was thoroughly understood by Roosevelt.

Few men so placed, however, would have picked assistants so self-effacingly (or so smilingly have allowed himself to be picked): with so fine an instinct for this queer collectivist game. His "buildup" of himself was slick and deft. Who would have picked, or let himself be picked by, the New Deal except F.D.R.? Though even he got frightened now and then by these dynamic associates.

Finally I arrive at that part of my Presidential portrait sketch where what seems to be a blemish must be dealt with. This blemish has a most obvious bearing upon his radicalism. It raises the question of his sincerity.

He and his predecessor and relative, "Teddy" Roosevelt, both started with a most valuable contempt for the rich. This was very rare even in F.D.R.'s generation, and was a first-class asset. In his autobiography the first Roosevelt wrote: "Of all forms of tyranny the least attractive and the most vulgar is the tyranny of a plutocracy." He was in some ways an even more extraordinary demagogue: I think that F.D.R. at no time referred to a capitalist he had gone after as a "fat spider." His exuberant relative did, however. "Why did you call Mr. Hill a fat spider, sir?" another spider demanded of the President. "That is *my* way of putting it," the President blandly answered. James Hill was the rail king, and hero of "the Bum Song."

This detachment from the world of wealth was perhaps Franklin Roosevelt's greatest asset. Without that—no New Deal! But of course history will recall—and here I am afraid objective criticism supervenes—that both he and his republican relative, Theodore, remained rich men; enjoyed all the advantages without stinting themselves of being rich, with the prestige that riches gave in a "plutocracy," while at the same time enjoying the advantages of being anti-riches.

You overawe people with your clubmanesque airs and graces, you live at "Hyde Park" (the name of his estate) in seigneurial style, *and* you derive great fame and personal advantage from denouncing the rich and all their works. That was no doubt to be wanting in entire honesty: the thoughtful historian of the future will conclude that, I am afraid. Again the late President liked rich men all right, to share his "old-fashioned" and enjoy some pleasant company; but for him there were *the right rich,* and *the wrong rich.* For Lenin, let us say, there was no such thing as *right rich.* All were wrong. But, of course, the statesman we are discussing was a demagogue, in a different universe to Lenin. He was a middle-class demagogue, a very recognizable product of the old Party system. The "forgotten man" got something out of him. But he got far more out of the "forgotten man."

One does decidedly have a rather disagreeable sense of snob appeal throughout the Roosevelt showmanship—even down to the naming of his property "Hyde Park." The "aristocrat" notion was played up, heavily, all along, it cannot be denied: and one would meet in America many a little re-actionary who, though he or she winced at the thought of the New Deal, and loathed most of his politics, spoke with a crooning deference, a complacent affection for this great gen-tleman in the White House, naughty radical though he was!

No picture of Mr. Roosevelt would be complete or truthful without some special stress on this—that he owed almost as much to the snob appeal as to the appeal to the underdog. One hesitates to say this, because he *was* of great use to the underdog.

The English reader, accustomed to aristocratic prime min-isters, will not see the full force of the above remarks unless he is made acquainted with a cardinal fact of American polit-ical life. I refer to the noticeable absence or scarcity of the rich class in politics. Leaving out of course the earliest days of the republic, the plutocracy, who have always ruled Amer-ica, do not go into politcs at all, which they regard as de-grading and "second-rate." They prefer to work behind the scenes. The Presidents have almost invariably been poor men—professional politicians. Whereas in England politics has traditionally been a playground of the rich, the aristo-cratic.

The same rule applies to the American Army or Navy. As there is no money to be made in either of these callings, they have always been despised, like the teaching profession. Un-der such circumstances it was a great novelty, in the case of both the Roosevelts, to have a rich man in the White House. The financial oligarchy must have greatly disliked Franklin Roosevelt's candidature: and it is most unlikely that the Re-publicans would have tolerated a second Roosevelt after all the trouble they had had with Teddy.

Let us at the last, however, forget this blemish. F.D.R.'s services to the United States were of such magnitude that this personal frailty is unimportant—if it was a frailty, for he may just have played up his "background" for all it was worth to outwit the snobbish element, and so camouflage his dark designs against them. The "First Lady" could have got away with murder in the Back Bay or in the snob troughs of the half-gilded end of the remoter cities. . . .

And how joyously he piloted his way, in the seething sea of unutterable nonsense in which all popular statecraft in America has to navigate, with a bump here, and a bump there, as his administration collided with some hoary absurdity. He understood as no other President had the really irreducible nature of those barnacled superstitions and crazy prejudices which clutter the waters athwart which the ship of State is obliged to direct its course. That ragtime thinking which, in one form or another, since the early days of this century, has been recognized as what is most essentially American in America (over against for instance the *bel canto* spirit of Italy, the proud Berber stamping, guitars and castanets of the Spanish world, or the martial crashing of Germanic orchestras which emotionally fastened upon the Teuton that heavy dream of Power) with that transatlantic philosophy this great American man of action was imbued.

Cosmic Society and Cosmic Man

THE logic of the geographical position and history of the United States leads only, I believe, to one conclusion: namely, the ultimate formation of a society that will not be as other societies, but an epitome of all societies. If a nation, then it must be a super-nation: so inclusive of all the various breeds of men, all the creeds, and fads, and philosophies, that its unity must be of quite a different character. It can only be something more universal than the Roman Empire, because its metropolitan area is conterminous with its imperial area. It has been built or is being built from outside, many different peoples and cultures converging on it—either, as that re-gards the people, as refugees, or as slaves or what not: people have moved in to make it, it has not moved out, like a spider constructing its web, to embrace all outside itself. Nor is it an endemic culture, moving out to modify other cultures, and subdue them to one standard, namely, its own. It has no original culture of its own (except for the Negro contribu-tion, which is African): it is eclectic.

Of course, all the peoples of the earth will not move into North America, but in the end there will be larger or smaller segments or pockets of all of them there. Now, if, like many Americans, you aver that all the different stocks present already are not in fact going to mix, thoroughly to merge into a homogeneous mass, but instead will remain, as in large measure they still are found, isolated from each other (in great cities, inhabiting separate wards or districts, or sprinkled over the country in discrete racial and religious settlements) then that is going to be a very odd kind of nation—if it is a nation that is intended, of the usual sort.

At present all these various stocks—and even religions—enjoy an anything but uniform social status. As I pointed out at an earlier stage, race has tended to be class in America. Economic disparity, even, is not more productive of class feeling than blood. In fact, to have a son-in-law of a racial stock not highly esteemed—say a Greek, or Peruvian—would be more embarrassing to parents than to have one of "poor boy" origin.

In Canada, for instance, there is the most impassable race barrier separating the English-Canadians and the French-Canadians: on the English side this is interpreted as indicative of a racial superiority, enjoyed by themselves *vis-à-vis* the "Peasoups." The fact that a majority of French-Canadians have Indian blood does not improve their chances of social equality with the Nordic Blonds; and catholicism is a peculiarly unpopular religion with the latter-day Puritans of this isolated and backward country.

The "Wop" in the States, as elsewhere I have indicated, is a much lower grade citizen than the Nordic (especially one with an English name). The Negro is naturally out of the picture altogether, from the standpoint of marriageability, as is also the "Chink." If either of these elements moves into a street, everybody else moves out. You have to be a remarkably poor White to take a colored mate, or to tolerate a colored neighbor.

The equilibrium is, however, highly precarious. Present conditions will not survive any major shock to the political and social system—such as a record slump, or a war which rocks America to its foundations, in the way the war that has just ended has shaken the British Empire. As to Negro and White, that situation at present approaches a bitter climax. If anyone believes that this huge population of Africans is going to remain as it is, an insoluble black lump, they will fairly soon be undeceived. The Negroes of the United States cannot be shipped out, as once they were shipped in, nor do even the most hostile suggest that. But they cannot remain there and continue to be treated as animals, whom you could no more marry than you could mate with a baboon.

That dark lump *will* melt, spread out and color the entire human contents of the States, until "American" will mean somebody with that dusky intermixture. As the traditional social supremacy of the "Nordic" dies out (and the instability of American family wealth, and the violence of economic change, accelerates the disappearance of this social advantage) all the other race barriers will rapidly dissolve.

Whether America has a Big Business Fascism, or some sort of change to a Socialist economy, will not alter the outcome, except that the latter would precipitate the process of miscegenation. If it were a Business-Fascist economy, with America's penetration of Asia greatly stepped up, that must result in the impoverishment of the white population. Cheap Asiatic labor—which would doubtless be used in America proper, as well as on the spot in Asia, in affecting disadvantageously the home labor market, and in reducing the living standards of the masses, would overcome snootiness of a racial order.

The policy of both the Socialist and his enemy the Capitalist would work out identically as regards the white and colored population. The former is committed to the non-recognition of race discrimination, the latter is the natural protector of all colored people, because they work for less money.

Why one takes any interest in this so-called Pot, and the problems of its melting, is very simple. We lock ourselves up aggressively, or are locked up, in that antiquated group-pen the "nation," and pretend to be a "race," and a mighty fine one too, as did par excellence the National Socialists. But in America you have a powerful country of great size which at least cannot call itself a "race." Like everybody else, it takes on the competitive attitudes, the Jingo emotionalism. But those devoutly hoping for an international order naturally see in America the thin end of the wedge. The requisite raw material is there, namely the great variety of races present—all that is needed for the manufacture of Cosmic Man.

But "cosmic man," as I have called him: would not the arrival of this hybrid be a bad thing? Should such creatures be encouraged? The answer is that in the event of a World Government (which man has been trying to bring about for so long, and there is good reason to suppose may now, with the help of nuclear energy—after a final conflagration—obtain) with a single government controlling all the affairs of the earth, a cosmic society would be a necessary corollary, as distinct from the mere Administration. It probably would not be very satisfactory for everybody stolidly to go on behaving as if nothing had happened: it would be better for man to unanchor, and circulate. In order permanently to banish the parochial or tribal spirit, that would be the best course.

The idea of a federative World Government—which is the most popular at present, because men so hate the prospect of rendering up their identity—might involve only a mechanical administrative change, a spiritual *status quo:* consequently it should be rejected. War out of the way (and let us hope its twin, the profit system with it) very little local government would be necessary. The latter serves to keep alive the ancient territorial rivalries.

It is not enough to have a central administration alone then. Some fresh approach to the problems of living in society should go with such a change. This is where the United States is so useful. It is not interesting only because it is a "melting pot." That might perfectly well be as dull as it sounds. What makes it so worthy of everybody's attention is the fact that in America there is, as nowhere else, the basis of a cosmic ethos. Even their gregariousness belongs to an, as it were, deep emotional fund, a sort of communal pooling of all the cordial reactions of man. . . .

For a World Government when first formed to have a genuinely cosmic society there already, practicing—and preaching—all the collective virtues appropriate in a world state, would be of great value. The example of a kind of universalized Everyman would prove infectious. And the new war-free, tolerant, nationless world society—arrived at last at the point reached by the forty-eight States of the Union—could do worse than take for its model American citizenship (purged of its nationalism, of course).

It is comprehensible that many people should be disinclined to accept the idea of a cosmic society, and so of a cosmic man. Human conservatism is fathomless, and when it comes to *roots,* habit is another name for those roots. But it is most difficult to see how any fairly intelligent man or woman could question the desirability of a World Government.

To take its minimum claim: a World Government could scarcely be as bad, however imperfect it might be, as a number of governments, or so-called "sovereign states." For the main incentive to be bad would be lacking. A large proportion of the crimes of governments arise from the existence of *other* governments. Just as a man all by himself, alone on the earth, would be debarred from committing most of the recognized crimes, which require the presence of two or more people (apart from ill-treating the animals, there is not much he could do), so if there were only one government in the world, it would have had removed from it the possibility of committing many major crimes. It could still, if so disposed, commit a great number of crimes against the people it governed. But at least it would have inter-governmental war removed from its repertoire of crime.

War is a major crime of government—there is none so great, where it is *total* war, *levée en masse*,[1] with all that that entails: paralysis of all the creative functions of the community for years on end; squandering of the nations' wealth, which otherwise employed would abolish poverty entirely; brutalization of millions of men; fearful catastrophes of every kind in the private lives of "unimportant" people, men, women and children; mental regimentation of communities; by appeals to the vanity, the causing everyone to have a stake in his own misfortune; the death in youth of multitudes, maiming, impairing of health, of opportunities in life—but I need not continue the catalogue.

A World Government appears to me the only imaginable solution for the chaos reigning at present throughout the world. Many would agree that it is desirable, but very unlikely, in their view, to materialize. Such is, and always has been, the logical goal of civilized mankind—though usually men have said, "We must give our law to the barbarian." It has been imperialist.

The Greeks had the notion of Cosmopolis, they were too power hungry and contentious to do anything about it. The Romans made the attempt: it was the Roman World and imperial, but became highly cosmopolitan. That fell to pieces, and in succession to it a theocratic universalism was attempted. But Christendom was the reverse of a reign of peace. Luckily, they had only battle-axes and bows and arrows, instead of the weapons of wholesale slaughter which we possess, or there would have been very little left, so remorselessly did the Sermon on the Mount impel those Christians

[1] mass mobilization

to homicide. Christianity, as a unifier, became a bad joke long ago.

With a start of surprise (followed by apathy) we find ourselves in the presence of the so-called Atom Bomb. Perhaps that will do what the Sermon on the Mount failed to accomplish. That this will come to pass *before long*—that the inhabitants of this planet have not only the chance, but the certainty, of again enjoying one government instead of a plurality—may, I believe, with complete confidence be predicted.

It has been suggested that probably the three governments capable of producing the Atom Bomb will agree not to use it, and go on as before, as if it did not exist. This is most unlikely. One of them would be sure to get so angry it would loose one at its enemy. Experience shows that once a weapon exists, the poor ape that man is cannot refrain from using it.

A corollary of such a merging of power in a world organization would be a society where the profit motive grew sanely domesticated: their attention no longer drawn away from domestic issues every few years by foreign wars, then all their energy absorbed in recovery from them, people would be unlikely to tolerate chronic racketeering at their expense, and licensed dishonesty under the name of "business." The ex-national frontiers again would be an invitation to leave your pen and fraternize with other peoples—trade, exchange ideas, and intermarry: they would no longer be a wall bristling with immigration and customs officials to keep you penned up, ready for the next visit of the Butcher.

To resume: the United States of America is a place where those conditions of fraternization and free intercourse, irrespective of race, class, or religion, already prevail, or enough at least for a start. Therefore it is a model for all other nations, still battened down within their national frontiers.

If it occurred to you to wonder how the Americans—without some beautiful old village at the foot of a down to love and cherish, that had been there perhaps since it was a Gesith, in the days of the eorls and ceorls—can without all that be so attached to their strange, rootless, restless, polyglot world, the answer is they like it that way. They only have a country to live in that is not much more *theirs* than the valleys and green meadows of the ocean. But the disdain of "rootlessness," they would declare, is a bluff or a supersitition. *Roots* are the last things they want. Released from all the stocks of Europe, Africa and Asia, they enjoy what is, in fact, a *cosmic* sensation. Their citizenship, about which they make so much fuss—and a justifiable fuss—is a kind of world-citizenship model A. For here is the beginning of the new world, which must one day be everywhere, when the term "American" would be as irrelevant as Polish, Irish, or Arab.

This is, I repeat, the only possible meaning of the U.S.A. —to be the place where a Cosmopolis, as the Greeks would call it, is being tried out. Either the United States is (1) a rather disorderly collection of people dumped there by other nations which did not want them—a sort of wastepaper basket or trash can; or (2) a splendid idea of Fate's to provide a human laboratory for the manufacture of Cosmic Man. It is, I feel, quite certainly the second of these alternatives.

Cosmic man is, however, not merely being manufactured in the flesh but also in the spirit. A cosmic society must have a cosmic culture: and that is being provided for it, at colossal expense and the deployment of a fantastic pedagogic apparatus. The cultural centralization in America, for so vast a place, is abnormal. New York, with its massed publishing houses, its swarm of art dealers (as headquarters of the book racket and picture racket) and control of theatrical reputations (both for playwright and player) is as much the cultural center of the United States as Washington is the political center. And it is a long way from New York to Texas or to Idaho.

New York's intellectual authority is feebly disputed at times by the Middle West. You will have heard the saying: "New York is not America." For a Texas Ranger, or a man growing potatoes in Idaho, it of course is not. In all cultural matters, however, it is that absolutely. It is the Mecca of all women, who play a so much more important role in America than elsewhere, it is the headquarters of Fashion, as Paris is in Europe, and its hotels are always full of visiting provincials.

That there is a cultural melting pot in America as well as a racial—that it melts a great deal more effectively than the latter: that it is part of a vaster melting operation, going on all over the world, not stopping at frontiers, so that the young man in Birmingham, Warwickshire, and in St. Louis, Missouri, is apt to be reading just the same books or literary reviews, and looking at photographs of the same pictures or buying the same musical records. . . . Science, naturally, is already internationalized, the pharmacologist or biochemist in Chicago or New York is in touch by letter with workers in the same field in India, South America, Europe. That is "culture," too, and it is enjoyed in common.

Naturally, there is nothing farther from the thoughts of most of those engaged in these cultural activities in America (most of them no doubt violently nationalistic) than a cosmic society of the future, or that they are in fact engaged in preparing the way for a "cosmic man"—a perfectly eclectic, nonnational, internationally-minded creature, whose blood is drawn—more or less—from all corners of the earth, with no more geographical or cultural roots than a chameleon. Yet it is to that end that their activities will imperceptibly lead. They cannot be a cultural center: they can only be a place that things blow through from the outside. But in the end, so conditioned, they will insensibly produce the sum of all assimilations, a cosmic fruit, indeed.

SELECTED BIBLIOGRAPHY

WORKS BY WYNDHAM LEWIS

Novels

Tarr, 1918
The Childermass, 1928
The Apes of God, 1930
Snooty Baronet, 1932
The Revenge for Love, 1937
The Vulgar Streak, 1941
Self-Condemned, 1954
The Human Age (Monstre Gai and Malign Fiesta), 1955

Short Stories

The Wild Body, 1928
Rotting Hill, 1951

Essays and Criticism

The Art of Being Ruled, 1925
The Lion and the Fox: A Study of the Role of
    Hero in the Plays of Shakespeare, 1926
Time and Western Man, 1927
The Paleface: The Philosophy of the Melting Pot, 1929
The Diabolical Principle and the Dithyrambic Spectator, 1931
The Doom of Youth, 1932
Filibusters in Barbary, 1932
Men Without Art, 1934
The Jews—Are They Human?, 1939
The Hitler Cult, 1939

America and Cosmic Man, 1948
The Writer and the Absolute, 1952

Autobiography

Blasting and Bombardiering, 1937
Wyndham Lewis, the Artist from "Blast" to Burlington House, 1939
Rude Assignment: A Narrative of My Career Up-to-Date, 1950

BOOKS ABOUT WYNDHAM LEWIS

Handley-Read, Charles. The Art of Wyndham Lewis.
Kenner, Hugh. Wyndham Lewis.
Porteus, Hugh Gordon. Wyndham Lewis . . . A Discursive Exposition.
Wagner, Geoffrey. Wyndham Lewis: Portrait of the Artist as Enemy.